NEW WRITING

New Writing 7 is the seventh volume of an annual anthology which promotes the best in contemporary literature. It brings together some of our most formidable talent, placing new names alongside more established ones, and includes poetry, essays, short stories and extracts from novels in progress. Distinctive, innovative and entertaining, it is essential reading for all those interested in British writing today. New Writing 7 is published by Vintage, in association with the British Council.

Carmen Callil is Australian but has lived in London since 1960. She founded Virago in 1972 and was its publisher and managing director until 1982, and chairman until 1995. From 1982 to 1993 she was managing director of Chatto & Windus and the Hogarth Press. The Modern Library: Fiction in English since 1850, written with Colm Tóibín, will be published by Picador in 1998; she is now writing Fireflies: Sex, Alcohol, Madness, Catholicism and Motherhood, an account of the lives of some women writers.

Craig Raine was born in Co. Durham in 1944, and was educated at Exeter College, Oxford. He has been books editor of the New Review, editor of Quarto and poetry editor of the New Statesman, and contributed to a wide variety of journals. He was poetry editor at Faber & Faber, and is now a Fellow of New College, Oxford. His books include The Onion, Memory (1978), A Martian Sends a Postcard Home (1979), A Free Translation (1981), Rich (1984), The Electrification of the Soviet Union (1986), 1953, a version of Racine's Andromaque (1990), History: The Home Movie (1994) and Clay. Whereabouts Unknown (1996). He has also published a collection of essays, Haydn and the Valve Trumpet (1990), and has edited a selection of Kipling's prose for Faber (1987).

NEW WRITING 7

edited by

CARMEN CALLIL

and

CRAIG RAINE

V I N T A G E

in association with
■■ The British Council

Published by Vintage 1998

2 4 6 8 10 9 7 5 3 1

Vintage
Random House, 20 Vauxhall Bridge Road, London SW1V 2SA

Random House Australia (Pty) Limited
20 Alfred Street, Milsons Point, Sydney,
New South Wales 2061, Australia

Random House New Zealand Limited
18 Poland Road, Glenfield
Auckland 10, New Zealand

Random House South Africa (Pty) Limited
Endulini, 5a Jubilee Road, Parktown 2193, South Africa

Random House UK Limited Reg. No. 954009

A CIP catalogue record for this book
is available from the British Library

ISBN 0 09 954571 3

Papers used by Random House UK Limited
are natural, recyclable products made from wood grown in
sustainable forests. The manufacturing processes conform to
the environmental regulations of the country of origin

Typeset by Deltatype Ltd, Birkenhead, Merseyside

Printed and bound in Great Britain by
Cox & Wyman Ltd, Reading, Berkshire

PREFACE

New Writing 7 is the seventh volume of an annual anthology founded in 1992 to provide an outlet for new short stories, work in progress, poetry and essays by established and new writers working in Britain or in the English language. The book is designed primarily as a forum for British writers, and the main object is to present a multi-faceted picture of modern Britain; contributions from English-language writers of non-British nationality will occasionally be accepted if they contribute to this aim. It was designed by the British Council's Literature Department to respond to the strong interest in the newest British writing overseas, where access to fresh developments is often difficult. It is hoped that, over the years, and under changing editors, it will provide a stimulating, varied and reasonably reliable guide to the cultural and especially the literary scene in Britain during the 1990s.

New Writing 8, edited by Tibor Fischer and Lawrence Norfolk, will appear in March 1999. Though some work is commissioned, submissions of unpublished material for consideration (stories, poetry, essays, literary interviews and sections from forthcoming works of fiction) are welcome. Two copies of submissions should be sent: they should be double-spaced, with page numbers (*no* staples), and accompanied by a stamped addressed envelope for the return of the material, if it cannot be used. They should be sent to *New Writing*, Literature Department, The British Council, 11 Portland Place, London W1N 4EJ. The deadline for *New Writing 8* is 17 April.

CONTENTS

Introduction *Carmen Callil* and *Craig Raine*　　　1

Short Stories
Big Things *Frances Stonor Saunders*　　　3
Love Letters *Lucy Ellmann*　　　11
The Revival *Julian Barnes*　　　30
V.O. *Jonathan Coe*　　　46
Carracks Off a Rocky Coast *Georgina Hammick*　　　66
The Gambler's Funeral *Earl Lovelace*　　　83
The Russian *Kirsty Seymour-Ure*　　　97
The Princess of the Pampa *Nicholas Shakespeare*　　　111
Mamacita's Treasure *Louis de Bernières*　　　149
Orphan *Peter Straughan*　　　163
Squirrel Man Mac *Matthew Singh-Toor*　　　247
Sawmill *Adam Thorpe*　　　272
Lover Pie *Michael Dibdin*　　　294
Four Reviews in Search of a Biography *Philip Kerr*　　　300
Deborah *Andrea Levy*　　　318
Natural Limits *Marina Warner*　　　327
Thirsting for a Worsting *Francis Wheen*　　　357
Blood Sugar *Charlotte Mendelson*　　　402

Extracts from novels in progress
English Passengers *Matthew Kneale*　　　18
Blind Solomon *Stevie White*　　　365

CONTENTS

Drama
Scenes from an Abandoned Play *Patrick Marber*   92
The Pleasure Dome *Ian McEwan*   170
Big Women (extract) *Fay Weldon*   346

Poetry
Halfway Head, Brother Peartree *and* The Coat *Ted
   Hughes*   15
Present, By the Round Pond, Idyll *and* How to Deal with
   the Press *Wendy Cope*   43
One White *and* The Morning After *Susan Wicks*   135
The Hopewell Haiku (extract) *Paul Muldoon*   161
Long Words *and* The Definition of Love
   Bernard O'Donoghue   245
Ramone *and* Jim *Ben Rice*   267
Sonnets for Helen *Oliver Reynolds*   291
Lewis Hollow Road *and* Night Train *Michael Hofmann* 297
Snow *Martin Turner*   354
A Night Out *Stephen Knight*   372
Staying with Friends *and* Elegy *Lachlan Mackinnon*   382
Suffenia the Poet *C. K. Stead*   394
Kerkenna *and* The Harbour *Cathal McCabe*   395

Essays
Penelope Fitzgerald: A Very English Genius *Hermione
   Lee*   137
A Day in a Swinging Londoner's Life *Kathy Lette*   315
Autobiographical Intents *Karl Miller*   374
Interview with Ian Hamilton *Gregory LeStage*   484

Biographical Notes   409

INTRODUCTION

T. S. ELIOT ended his lecture, 'Apology for the Countess of Pembroke', with this comment: 'the worst fault that poetry can commit is to be dull.' The same could be said of an anthology. This one, therefore, is deliberately miscellaneous. Not everything in it will be to everyone's taste. In fact, the editorial process itself occasionally – very occasionally – felt like a version of an Alison Lurie novel, *The War Between the Tates*. Nothing passionately opposed survived. Persuasive advocacy now and then overcame mild misgivings or a straightforward discrepancy in enthusiasm. Anyone over the age of twelve knows that co-editing isn't always an easy process whose outcome is unalloyed harmony. All the same, discussions have been friendly, robust, three-way, and we have agreed to disagree as well as agreed to agree. We believe the results are interesting, not dull.

Three-way? Yes. In all these British Council anthologies, there is the unsung but invaluable contribution of Harriet Harvey Wood, who co-ordinates, suggests, recommends, discusses, objects, concedes, objects – much like the two editors whose names are on the title page, and who would like to thank her for her patience, forbearance, tenacity and enthusiasm.

Our agreed guidelines were these: diversity, diversity and diversity. We wanted a healthy mixture of established names like Ted Hughes, Louis de Bernières and Jonathan Coe and relatively unknown or completely unknown writers whose work could sustain the comparison. We are pleased with how

1

immediately newcomers like Frances Stonor Saunders and Peter Straughan establish their own authority. We wanted interviews and essays. Increasingly, writers are pluralists. Georgina Hammick is a distinguished example of the ambidextrous – equally at home with the short story or the novel. Here we have a journalist, Francis Wheen, trying his hand at the short story. The poet may also be a novelist – like Adam Thorpe. Or a dramatist, or a screen-writer. Ian McEwan's film script, *The Pleasure Dome*, is an example of this general diversity and something which this anthology is uniquely fitted to bring to a larger public. It is long, but, then, some writing is long. As editors, we inclined to complete items rather than extracts. There are only two novel-extracts in the anthology, both of which chose themselves, so to speak, their merit outweighing editorial preconception.

There are, too, some lighter items here, not at all lightly chosen. Philip Larkin, asked by his *Paris Review* interviewer how he had chosen six of his own poems for *The Oxford Book of Twentieth-Century English Verse*, replied that they were 'representative': 'one pretty one, one funny one, one long one, and so on'. Elsewhere, Larkin claimed to organise his collections like a music hall bill of different turns. Variety, in other words. We were likewise determined to make room for the squib and the provocation. Great literature should include somewhere the perfect limerick. Anthologies are about access to excellence – excellence of all sorts and shapes.

Carmen Callil
Craig Raine

2

Frances Stonor Saunders

BIG THINGS

ALL BIG THINGS start small. And so it was with my father's illness. I first realised something was wrong when he left three identical messages on my answer-machine in quick succession. I sat down and cried, because I knew. This was a year before the doctor said he had got Alzheimer's, which Daddy wrote down on a yellow post-it and stuck in his diary, in case he forgot the name of the disease which makes you forget everything.

And so it was with my spot, which surfaced around the same time my father left those messages. Except I was now in New York, staring out of the window of a cramped, over-priced hotel room, the air-conditioning unit rattling like an asthmatic and dropping brown treacly tears on to the carpet. I found myself scratching a spot above my right eyebrow, and I decided it must be shingles, because I'd had it before, and it had presented itself with an identical spot in the same place.

Admittedly, things were a little out of hand when I found the spot. It was several days now since I had started crying freely in public places. And that morning, arriving early for a meeting, I had sat down in a brown leather armchair in a chintzy hotel and been instantly overcome with nausea. Next thing I knew, I was curled up like a kidney bean around the base of a loo, my cheek pressed against the cold marble floor, my body half protruding under the cubicle door. Thus installed, I lay very still, listening to other patrons' high heels clacking across the floor. In short, I was, by the time I found

3

the spot, a little bit unsteady.

I called a doctor (it was out of surgery hours), and, quicker than a home delivery of coronation chicken, he appeared at my door. His face was lined. His hands shook as he lifted my chin and tilted my head towards the light. He assured me my spot was nothing more than a simple spot, and wrote out a receipt for $150, which I paid in cash. On the receipt, he wrote his diagnosis as 'skin eruption!!' I only noticed the two exclamation marks after he had left. Daddy rarely used exclamation marks until he got ill. Then he began to use them like salt, shaking them all over the page. That was before he forgot how, and what, to write.

Now, I should perhaps have been able to sport the world's most expensive zit with pride. I should have embraced this case of *acne simplex* as a release from earlier anxiety. But the surge of adrenalin which had accompanied my panic discovery was refusing to diminish. I decided to still it with a cold bath. I winced as I lowered myself into the icy water, and for a long time I could only manage the sitting position. Whilst the bottom half of my body assumed the colour of old French linen, the top half, waist up, remained red and blotchy with the prickly New York heat. I sat very still, taut, so that my belly-button wouldn't descend below the water line. Finally, I took a series of short breaths, ha-ha-ha, felt a tightening of the heart muscles, and under I went, right under, waist, breasts, shoulders, head, whoosh! water curling in a single wave over the side of the bath and all over the floor. Bad bathroom husbandry, but good for the soul (and the only cure I know of for head-spin).

I reached for the soap and began, as the nuns at school had instructed, to wash from the face down (the other way, dear, is dirty). And then I made my second discovery. As I ran the soap over my right breast, I thought I felt it ride over a bump. I repeated the manoeuvre, and again I felt an irregularity. I put the soap down, and worked over the breast with my fingers. There it was, hard, a lump the size of a small door handle.

Aldous Huxley said death was the acropolis against which no dog dares to piss. But when Huxley was writing, the acropolis was probably still pure, still white, and not the pile of greying teeth which it has come to resemble today. Death is dirty. You shit yourself, you cough up your lungs. But perhaps there is a soul, and maybe this is clean and white, like a peeled chestnut.

The morning after that cold bath (which I remember like no other bath), I delivered myself into the trembling hands of the same doctor who had visited my spot the night before. As I lay on the trolley bed in his surgery on Central Park South, his hands roving across my breasts, I was curious to note there was nobody else in the room. What, no witnesses? In New York? How would I know if he was molesting me? I looked up at his mappa mundi face, and searched its geography for any signs of titillation. I looked down at my breasts, parted to left and right by their own weight, the gap in the middle wide enough for the Prussian army to march through.

'I'm going to send you for a mammogram.'

'What's that? What does that mean? Why do I have to do that? What have you found?'

Have I got cancer? Am I going to die? Don't speak to me in riddles, you old fuckwit.

'There's no need to be alarmed. It's quite standard, it's just a way of finding out what these lumps are.'

'Lumps? You mean there's more than one?'

My breasts are peppered with malignant growths. Why didn't he sit me down first? Where's the fucking counsellor?

'Yes, yes, there are many, all over. But this is a good sign. I would be more worried if there was just one.'

More worried? How fucking worried are you, then?

He was wrong about the mammogram. When we called whatever place it was that does them from his telephone, the woman at the other end shrieked, 'Ma-a-am, I cyan't give you a ma-a-amogra-a-am as you're under thirdee.' For extra reassurance, she added, 'Your doctor should know that.' Well, yes he should. I could see a court case looming, me, wan and hairless, conducting my own battle from a hospital bed in between bouts of surgery and chemotherapy. We settled on a sonogram, which was booked for the next morning. I thanked the doctor profusely for his help, paid the bill, and promised to let him know the results of the sonogram. I never contacted him again. Oddly, whenever I pass his surgery in New York, I'm tempted to go in and say hello, but somehow I never get round to it.

Is the knowledge more cumbersome than the disease? Daddy's illness seemed to become more aggressive once he knew he had it. Time was no longer tellable, distance no longer measurable, objects no longer recognisable. 'This is very good, I can recommend it. You cut it up and it's sort of hard and really quite delicious. What's it called?' 'A loaf of bread.' When he began to forget the names of his children, his face would contract, his eyes blinking rapidly, and he would begin to cry. But then he would remember he was ill, and he would rush off to look for his diary with the yellow post-it. He would reappear, triumphant, waving the magic word which gave his memory loss an official logic. As long as he could locate this word, he was comforted. Sometimes, he would lose the post-it, and then he would painstakingly write out a new one. Gradually, of course, he lost track of how the letters were organised, and the word began to fall to pieces:

A-L-Z-H-E-I-M-E-R-S
A-Z-H-I-E-M-E-R-S
A-H-Z-S-M-E-I-R-L-E-R

In the beginning was the Word. And in the end there was no word. Just his mouth, slightly open, with a little bit of bristle under his lower lip.

'Fascinating breasts, fascinating.' The Polish sonogram operator was happy. I lay on the bed, naked but for a paper slip which had been peeled down to my waist. My breasts, smeared with blue gel, looked like two enormous molluscs, a glistening catch. I had recruited a girl friend to accompany me, and she stood guard, arms folded, in front of the sonogram monitor. 'This is amazing! Your tits look like fruitcake,' she said cheerily. I smiled bravely. 'Fascinating,' repeated the Pole, in a voice loud enough to attract most of the hospital's traffic to divert itself into the room for a look. 'Hey, why don't we just sell tickets?' said my friend, in an attempt to stem the flow. 'And WHO are you?' she boomed at a man in a white coat who had come into the room and started washing his hands. Glib, unsmiling, he announced his title, which amounted to chief breast doctor, and proceeded to knead my breasts yet further. Half of Manhattan had done this already, and still I had no answers.

Sticky with gel, I left the hospital carrying a large manila envelope containing the negatives of my sonogram. These I was told to hand over to my GP in England. In the meantime, I was to get used to the fact that my breasts were brimful with fluid-bearing cysts. On the negatives, these appeared as numerous black holes, each with a measurement meticulously graphed in, like finds from an archaeological dig. But how did they get there?

There are no answers. When my father was dying, I wanted to know how long it was going to take. 'How long will it be?' I asked. The nurses said it was impossible to tell. They had put him on morphine, which was pumped into his scrawny arm from a small box with a battery. The box had a Laura Ashley-type quilted cover. They said you can get a strange smell from a patient on morphine, so we lit a scented candle and put it by his bed. He was turned, washed and shaved every day. On the last day, the nurse shaved half his face. She said he was too weak to turn, so she'd just do the one side.

'Darling, you've got such a good figure, why don't you show

it off a bit more?' My friend closed the lift doors and pressed the button for the third floor.

'Look, I don't feel like showing off my tits. I've told you, they're full of lumps. Someone might notice.'

'What do you mean? For God's sake, it's not like you can *see* them.'

I watched the first floor glide past through the glass doors of the lift. I wriggled out of half my clothes and released my right breast. 'Look, here, look closely, you can see one of them, the big one, my Koh-i-noor.'

'I can't see any . . . wait . . . you mean . . . that . . . that thing . . . Jesus, I had no idea. Have you had it looked at?'

Mid-inspection, as we passed the second floor, I saw the feet, shopping bag, hands, waist, bust, then expressionless face of a large matronly figure reveal themselves in sections and then recede.

'Looked at? Jesus, I've told you, I may as well bottle it in aspic and put it in a display case at the British fucking Museum for all the times I've had it looked at.' The lift jolted to a halt on the third floor.

It turns out the cysts are harmless. They just bob about in the sea of my mammary glands, but occasionally the odd one may begin to swell, expanding its fluid content until it's big enough to merit a mention on the shipping news. Then, as my breasts are now in the public domain, they are passed freely from hand to hand, as I lie again prostrate on a trolley bed, until finally a decision is made to have the offending lump aspirated. This entails the introduction of a long syringe, and then the fluid – which looks like brown ale – is extracted. Simple, really.

The first time this happened, I found myself sitting in the corridor of London's top breast diagnostic unit, housed in a portacabin. I was wearing the obligatory paper slip (the wrong way round). I stared at a notice on the wall called 'The Patient's Charter'. This included a series of promises which had been conspicuously broken: I had waited over an hour already, and no one had sat down next to me, taken my hand, and explained gently why there was a delay. I started to get snotty. A nurse appeared with a clipboard, and I asked whether she thought it was a good idea or not for me to insert a further four pounds into the parking meter, or maybe I'd be better off putting the car into an all-day parking lot? I looked around for moral support. The other victims stared silently at the wall.

When it came to my lancing, the nurse wielding the syringe was, of course, the same one I had been rude to. To add to my humiliation, she was kind and gentle, and even sent for another nurse to hold my hand when I said I couldn't possibly go through with this. Finally, between my pre-emptive shrieks and dramatic breathing exercises (ha'huuuhhh, ha'huuuhhh, ha'huuuhhh – I'd seen women in childbirth on television), she inserted the syringe deep into my breast, punctured the biggest cyst, and extracted the fluid. One hand over my eyes, the other squeezing the knuckles of the extra nurse, I continued my panic routine, unaware that the procedure was over (I hadn't felt a thing). 'Oh my God, oh my God, ha'huuuhhh, ha'huuuhhh, ha'huuuhhh.' 'It's all right, I've finished. You can stop now.' Everybody told me how brave I had been, and that I should go off and get myself a stiff drink.

Daddy took no fluid in the last days. His lips dried and peeled like old paint. The nurse moistened them with a cotton bud. He rattled all the time.

The distance between breaths.

You would lean close to his mouth, and count to ten, eleven, twelve, thirteen seconds, and still no breath. Just when you thought he must be dead, it came again, a long, hiccoughy gurgle, and you would jump back in surprise. More than once, this odd sport reduced us to paroxysms of laughter.

I went to the local Benedictine school to collect the old Abbot, who had agreed to come and give my father the last rites. It was a dank, slushy evening, and I had difficulty seeing out of the windscreen. When the Abbot got into the car, I could see he had bits of food on his cassock. He lit up a cigarette. I asked him if he knew my cousin, a famously eccentric monk who had died twenty years ago. The Abbot said yes, indeed, he had received a letter from him recently. I changed the subject. Could he refresh my memory, and tell me what the Seven Deadly Sins were? That was a good one. He could only name four, and the exercise took up the rest of the journey home. I opened the front door, and gestured for him to go in first. 'Gee, thanks,' he said. I got the giggles when he read the last rites.

Daddy died the next evening. We put a wild flower from the garden in his hands, and folded them on his chest. His fingers were the same colour as the yellow enamel of the Aga in the kitchen downstairs. We sat with him, and someone made a hot wine punch, which we drank, and then the undertakers came. There were people coming out of the pub next door, so they had to wait a bit before they could take him out of the house. I keep thinking of his fingers, of how he used to bite the nails down almost to the quick, leaving little crescents. And how, when we were little, he used to cup his hands so that we could drink from them.

Lucy Ellmann

LOVE LETTERS

MOMMY

Mommy. Mommy, before lunch, liked a glass of Punt è Mes with ice, and a bowl of crisps. At 5.30, she had a glass of malt whisky and soda, which she never finished. In her time, she had smoked Camels, Marlboros, Trues, Parliaments, Benson & Hedges, but she finally proved a faithful supporter of Silk Cuts.

She liked clam chowder, fried shrimp, onion rings, Won Ton soup, McDonald's cheeseburgers and Harrods' hand-made Belgian chocolates that have to be eaten up within ten days.

Mommy played Scrabble with convivial zest but preferred to play cards alone: Solitaire. She perfected a method of shuffling that perturbed the morally rigorous but did not seem to enable her to lose any less often. When she won, she and the four piles of cards would remain immobile until congratulated – another mild pleasure.

Mommy liked Jane Austen, Muriel Spark, David Lodge, Beryl Bainbridge, John Mortimer and Molly Keane. She was rather tired of James Joyce. She was also a great telly fan, cheered and disappointed by its offerings in about equal proportions. She liked John Cleese, Morecambe and Wise, Alan Bennett, 'Z Cars' and – so I've been told – Benny Hill. She was always game for a re-run of *Casablanca* or *Dr Zhivago* too, the theme tunes of which she would readily, if unsteadily, sing. She did *not* like 'Star Trek' or the News.

11

As for the animal kingdom: Mommy's taste centred on sheep, guinea-pigs, elephants, donkeys, parrots, red cardinals and penguins. Yet our two consecutive dogs, Pierre and Pepito, never doubted her preference for standard poodles. Little did they know how much they resembled sheep.

Mommy had a crush on her chemistry teacher in high school, and almost majored in chemistry at college as a result. She was in love with someone who died in the war. Later she was dumped by a playwright in favour of an elevator heiress. She realised she loved my father when she saw his legs lit by the headlights of his car.

She once saw a production of *Madame Butterfly* in which real fireflies were let loose on stage.

She used face powder and Nivea. She was addicted to reading car number plates in search of whole words. She was particularly fond of one on a little sports car often to be found parked near Marble Arch, which said, EGO. For the last twenty years of her life she wore the same shade of pink lipstick, and needed a nap in the afternoon.

Mommy objected to snobs, male chauvinists, anti-Semites, anti-smokers, New College dinners, Sci-Fi, the operas of Wagner, and Those Who Jog. She hated inane optimism – and its opposite in the form of distrustful physiotherapists who accused her of 'cheating'. But most of all, with unwavering disgust and dismay, she loathed the telephone.

EMILY

Emily, from birth, had eyes like a whale's. So thoughtful.

She travelled in a sling until she got too heavy and had to use a pushchair. She would never have learned to walk if she hadn't grown out of her self-propelled indoor wheely seat in which she zoomed around the kitchen. Once, she spun herself into a corner and stuck the plug of the electric kettle in her mouth. She sucked it until it gave her a shock. She cried for forty minutes. Another time, I let go of the shopping trolley in which she sat and it crashed against a kerb and tipped over, hurting her hand. Another time, I broke her favourite cup. (On purpose.)

For years she hated her hair to be brushed and I had to cut the tangles out with scissors. She also would not brush her teeth, until the reality of the dentist's chair took hold. She suffered terribly from ear trouble for many years. Her first real meal was avocado, but she grew up on noodles.

She liked Pound Puppies, My Little Pony, Puppies in my Pocket, Barbie dolls, Julip horses, Magpie models, and excessive numbers of stuffed animals. She was so thrilled to be given a rocking-horse one Christmas, she cried.

She read *Mallory Towers*, the *Saddle Club* and *Nancy Drew* books again and again, at great speed. She vehemently hated *Jane Eyre*.

Until the age of twelve, she slept in my bed for fear of burglars and alien abductions. She also has a slug phobia, a shark phobia, a fear of the dark and a fear of heights. She dislikes all my male friends, has always found my sister funny, and loved my mother.

She likes to watch American sit-coms, and longs to see more Hitchcock. She likes Latin, and plays the harp. She used to draw little people on every spare bit of paper. She has the will-power to brush her teeth twice a day, write a diary and learn to ride horses. She's resentful of change, careful with money, scathing about injustice to people or animals, and has yearned for years for a hamster.

She likes Start cereal or Weetabix, 'Dolly' noodle soup, Peking duck and pancakes with cucumber slices and Hoisin sauce, garlic and herb roulé cheese, asparagus and pepperami sausages; but hates pepper, oranges, aubergines, courgettes and fish.

We play Monopoly together or, more peaceably, a card game called 'Go-Go'. She is diligently developing a taste for pop music.

That night when I howled from grief Emily scraped up the pieces and put me back together again.

Curtains moving at an open window the way curtains wave in windows all over the world. Life is a long line of tragedies, disasters, peppered with tiny amusements: Morecambe and Wise, 'Dolly' noodles, the pretty pink clouds at dawn the day my mother died.

Ted Hughes

HALFWAY HEAD

He wanted to be here.
Toes guaranteed it. Fingers
Were ready for just this.

And ears. And eyes
Machined to the millionth.

Foretested at the limits.
A clone of triumphs.

So why does he stare as if blinded

Like a new ghost – blinded
By the sudden sun of afterlife?

Body, and its tongue, after all,
Cannot move an atom.

Time ruffles its wings, and preens.
Space looks clean through him.

He half stands, half hangs
Mirrored over the river of life:

A cenotaph, hacked in clay,
Worn with rains of unbeing.

BROTHER PEARTREE

Yellow and peach pink –
A translucence of late October
Thinner day by day
Reveals what's not there.

I send you fewer letters – fewer and thinner
Year by year. Can I really be thinking
It's just not worth it any more?
What was it I once hoped for?

Paradise. The whole bag of dream
That boyhood was made of
Heavy with rivers and forests. And the game
Quaking the earth like a drum.

Then I made do with a folktale tree
You planted in my orchard.
That's our shared life – that pear-tree.
We're that little in touch.

The year sticks leaves on it – they drop off.
I still stick sentences
On our plans for us –
They drop off.

Pretty yellow and flamey pink.
Till the boughs are an empty crate.
It has never brought me a single pear.
Is it too late?

Or the wrong side of the earth?
Your roots are here, as we say.
Drinking my thoughts. So those branches are roots.
And the real, the flourishing tree

Is on your lawn in Australia. Maybe

16

The one that ripened for you that gigantic,
Protected, solitary pear
Which you tied with a string to its branch

Just to make double sure –
But you never got it. He did –
Lounging in from your garden, slurping the core,
Your friend's awful kid.

THE COAT

No help that it was only dyed marmot
And not natural tiger. No help
That being draped idly over chairs in bars
To soak up the nicotine, it was not
Gripping him by the broken small of the back
And forcing him through brambles. It made no difference.
No good that it left his limbs
Watermarked not with the lickings
Of what had fed but with the perfume-dating
Of that summer, like the imprinting shock
Noon-stench of a discovered corpse. Nobody
Can deter what saunters
Up the ferny path between
The cool, well-ironed sheets, or what spoor
Smudges the signature of the contract.

No help that it was only the lining
The grass-shadow
Of eye-lashes and a hunger heedless as time
That ate faces. It was the bed horror
Of the Passover night. It lifted away
Screams that split bodies. It left
Roofs falling in, the morning empty.
The sun itself silenced. The face
Of after-shock that only dusty stones
Know how to wear.

17

Matthew Kneale

ENGLISH PASSENGERS

Extract from a novel in progress

TRULY, ONLY YOUR Englishmen could come with such a sweet notion as hanging a man by his neck. In most places it'd be enough just to snip off a body's life and do it cleanly, but your Englishman wants more. He wants proving some point, which means the poor so-and-so dancing and twisting at the end of a rope for all to watch, like a fish on his hook.

No, hanging has altogether too much of the knowing for my tastes. Get yourself shot by a firing squad and you'd hardly notice it's even happened – likewise with your guillotines and axes – but that length of rope won't be hurried. Even with a blindfold you'd not miss so much as a moment. First you'd feel that floor, all wobbling beneath your feet, as you're stood on the trap. Next you'd feel their steps, as the parson and your other new friends all stride quietly away. And then, quite the surprise, you'd feel that slipping and falling away into nothing, and your head's jerked back like it might come clean off, while that noose closes your throat down like a big soft hand. Not that this would be the worst. The worst would be just after. That's when you know yourself caught as caught can be, all dangling and kicking like a big fool, and not able to get yourself something as simple as a little sweet gulp of air, though it's the only single thing in all the world that you need. And your mind's still awake and knowing and watching it all happen.

But like I said, I'm here safe as that rabbit in his burrow. It's just the dark makes me wonder sometimes.

Besides, I'm straying off. Because not even your shiniest button Englishman would hang a man just for carrying a bit of contraband.

Well. Three long days we had the customs men doing their search, all sniffy and hardly saying a word. They weren't my favourites, those three days, all the while the terrible mad din of London – which hardly one of us had seen – spilling over that high guarded wall like a threat, as it was one of those new sealed docks they had put us in. And all of us thinking it only takes one find, or one fool of a body getting himself into a panic and . . .

Truly, there's no thoroughness like customs' thoroughness. First they had us move all the barrels on to the quayside and tip out the kippers. Next they checked all our stores, down to every cask of hard tack in the pantry. Then there were all the creatures: the chicken coop and the sheep pen and the sty where the pig had been. Also our possessions, including the prints of the royal family – which they took out of their frames – and even my uniform, feeling the cap just in case there were a few ounces of tobacco hidden inside. And when they'd done with that they started all over again, now tapping and banging their way round the vessel, now pulling up a floorboard, now making little fires to see where the smoke went.

Worse was the interviews. Every one of us was taken off alone to the dining cabin for his little chat. Given the whole treatment, too. Stories were checked, particularly my blurt about the boat Quayle was supposed to have bought his cheese off. Or they'd just go prodding and pushing for someone to go off like some rocket. 'We're going to find the stuff soon enough anyway. You may as well make it easier on yourself by telling us now.'

Three whole days. And what did they find after all this fuss?

Not a thing.

I could hardly believe it myself. I mean I knew we had a

wonder made of wood, and that the crew were every one of us picked, but still ... Was this not the very cream of Her Majesty's Royal English Spying and Conniving Customs Service, and in their own dread nest of London, too? And us just a shipload of poor, ignorant souls from Peel City? Not that I'm one to go talking wonder and miracles, but it did seem a little out of ordinary. I almost wondered if giving that Bishop Chalmers a ride might have brought us some joy after all.

That was a thing to celebrate. Not that I'm one for foolishness, but there was no stopping them after those three long days. Down the hold we went, where nobody could spy, and nobody speaking a word except Manx, just in case. Drinking? Well, there might have been. Singing? I dare say. Toasts? That there's no denying. 'Boiys da dooine as baase da eease,' which means in English 'Life to men and death to fish', and is about herring, as are all Manx toasts. Also 'Death to the head that never wore hair,' and 'Here's death to our best friend.' Meaning herring, of course.

Well, there is a price to be paid for that sort of thing. Though in this case I will say the price was rather higher than seemed fair. Stumbling out of my cabin with a sore head – the din of London outside making it worse, sounding as it did, like some great fight with wheel carts – what did I find waiting on the deck but a stranger. A leaning sort of stranger he was at that, all propped up against a coil of rope with a pipe. He got up when he saw me, but even this was in an altogether gradual sort of way, like I wasn't worth a hurry. 'Captain Kewley? My name's Hooper.' With that he handed over a piece of paper that I saw at once had that mean, interfering scribble which was the mark of the Customs. Well, it was worse even than it looked.

The Board of Customs, the letter announced, had decided on the evidence of the foreign goods discovered aboard the *Sincerity* – this being Quayle's cheese – that the ship had clearly broken her journey in a foreign port, without this being duly reported. Consequently her master – which was me – was to pay a statutory fine of two hundred pounds.

Two hundred pounds. That was as much as some men would hope to earn in ten years. Two hundred pounds, that we didn't have. Plus port fees, which were high, being London – where we hadn't wanted to go – and were increasing with each day we stayed. And not forgetting ninepence duty for the cheese. Of course this wasn't your real law. This was just raw revenge for their being beaten. Forget all their talk: there's never a bad loser like an Englishman, especially an Englishman in a uniform. No wonder all those Indian Hindoos had mutinied, with the like of this going on. I felt like joining them.

'I'm to stay here till it's paid,' added Hooper, in a leaning, watching sort of way. 'Just to see how you're doing, you know.'

I knew all right. He was there to spy. Having failed to find a thing through all their searching, the Customs were now hoping to smoke us out with fines and watching.

We sold all we could, to agents in the dock, or to other vessels. First the kippers went, though these got little enough, as they had been seen all laid out on the quay, out of their barrels. Next any spare ship's stores, down to the sheep and the last of the chickens. I even tried to get some shillings for the prints of Queen Victoria and her eight babes, though without much luck. When all was done, and I counted out all we had, still we were almost eighty pounds short. More, in fact, by the time we had done with the port officer, who came round snarling overdue payment and threatening confiscation of the ship.

We needed a loan. I sent Kinvig with a telegram to Dan Gawne, the Castletown brewer. I had hopes of that telegram. Gawne had already lent us some, and so might be scared into giving more. Besides we seemed a fair enough risk. If we could just get free of this port and away to Maldon, we'd have money enough for anyone. His reply came just two days later.

'Sell the ship and pay me what you owe.'

That was no reply. That was nothing more than long distance malice. As if I would sell the *Sincerity*. As if I even

21

could, considering what her new owners would surely find in her. We called Gawne some names that morning, I can tell you. That scrapy old sleetch, with his little sharp spiddagh of a wife, sitting on their shillings like they were somebody. That big fat hibernator. That cretchy old crab. The scrissag. Scrawly Castletown snot, all stink and thinking himself the high one.

Not that it made much difference, of course.

In fact within the hour we were in more trouble than ever. That was when two of the starboard watch – Tom Hudson and Rob Kneale – jumped ship clean in front of the whole crew, springing over the side with their sea chests. 'No thanks,' they taunted, when I ordered them back. 'We'd rather find a boat that can pay.'

Well, I couldn't be doing with much more of that, I can tell you. With other vessels this wouldn't have mattered, and would even have had its uses, as their wages would be kept, but the *Sincerity* wasn't the kind of ship that could take on any old crewmen. They had to be Manxmen from Peel. All in all, it was getting to the time when we had to take a chance, even though it was a long one. It's no good betting pennies, as the wise man says, when the dice have snatched your horse and your house.

Now if you go knocking around ships you do hear things, including gossip about places you've never seen and never expect to, and I had heard talk about London. Including the name of a particular inn near these docks, where certain people might be found, and certain arrangements made. Surely, I reasoned, it should be possible to get ourselves a loan out of someone. Once we were free, they could have our cargo at the most reasonable of prices. There were dangers, of course, as we would not know who to trust, and might find ourselves negotiating with a customs officer himself. But it had to be tried.

First I needed samples. As a precaution I sent Kinvig up to distract that Hooper with a bit of talk, and had Kelly set the men working at something noisy. Then I went to the pantry. Above the rim of the door frame I reached to that certain piece of cord that Captain Clarke had so narrowly missed, and I gave it a good tug. The answering click didn't come from nearby, of course, but across in the dining cabin. Not that you would have known what it was that had clicked there, unless you happened to go crawling beneath the dining table and pick at a floorboard that was suddenly a little bit loose. Which I did. And there beneath was a piece of cable just asking to be pulled. Which I did too. And what did we have now but another click, this time from my own cabin. In fact from the wooden panel with the print of Queen Victoria herself. Now there's a surprise, the whole thing swings open on a hinge, nice as nip, leaving a space big enough for a man to climb through.

I'll tell you why all those serious-faced Customs men never found a thing. It was because the *Sincerity* wasn't just some piece of cheap faked-up carpentry, the *Sincerity* was two ships, one inside the other. The inner hull was from a boat that was being broken up and sold as timber. I'd had it thinned out a little, of course, but it was still solid enough not to sound hollow if you gave it a thump. And it was weathered and damp, just like it should be. As for the gap between the hulls, this was no more than eighteen inches – more and the cabins and hold would have looked too curious – but eighteen inches round a side of a ship holds an awful lot of bales of tobacco and flasks of brandy. Not to mention certain pieces of French painted glass that I had taken at the same time. Yes, quite a sight it was just to look upon it all, stretching into the dark, all tidy and valuable, with that rich smell of wood and leaf and spirit to sweeten your nostrils.

I only needed enough to show. A few ounces of tobacco in a tin. A small flask of brandy. One of those certain pieces of painted glass. Even the piece of glass was small, and it all fitted neatly enough in a discreet inside pocket in the lining of my coat. All I wanted now was a little luck.

Luck there seemed to be. Hooper was still talking with Kinvig as I stepped on to the deck, and hardly seemed to pay any interest as I gave the nod to Kelly and China Clucas. Nor were the guards at the gate any more curious, waving us through with hardly a glance.

And so we were in London. I can't say I much liked the place. We decided to walk – just in case the cabs were spying for the customs – and as we went London seemed to be watching like some great mangy dog sniffing for fear. I don't know what it is with your beggary Londoners – it's almost like they teach them at some special school – but there we were, three fellows walking quietly down the street, ordinary as seawater, and yet it was as if they could smell we were strangers. It was there in their looks: half amused, half licking their lips for a good feed.

'You stay close,' I told Clucas, just in case he got curious at something. The fact was, China was a bit on the simple side. I suppose if you're as strong as he was there's hardly much call for cleverness.

'I think we're being followed.' It was Kelly came up with this. He didn't miss much, did Kelly. He may have looked slow and dozy, with those big pale eyes and his mouth that never seemed quite closed, but he was shrewd enough. The body he pointed out was just a lad. Hardly that, even, being mostly a ball of dirt and rags and little sharp eyes. 'He was after us three streets back.'

It was hard to believe a thing like that could be in the pay of Her Majesty's Customs Service. But you never did know. Just as I was wondering what to do next, off he vanished.

It seemed as well, besides, as only a few streets further on we came to the inn we wanted. The Waterman's Arms. Certainly it looked right, being a leaning, shifting sort of place, with little windows like squinting eyes. So we got ourselves ready, putting on hard looks, and China holding up his shoulders high like he could cause a good bit of wounding if he felt in the mood. And in we went.

There was only one problem. It was all but deserted. Instead of a raucous, smoke-filled place full of knowing faces making deals, the room we stepped into was about as lively as a tomb. Aside from the barman polishing glasses, there was not a soul there except a little old fellow getting drunk by himself in a corner.

'Perhaps we're too early,' suggested Kelly.

It wasn't yet lunch-time, true enough. But there was another possibility occurred to me. 'What if it isn't this place at all?' That was the trouble with London having grown so big. In Peel you always can rely on there being just one of everything.

It was the little drunk I went to, as barmen can get huffish if you ask them about other pubs. He giggled, as if it was quite the funniest question he had ever been asked. 'For sure, there's more than one.'

In the end, of course, we never did find out whether we were in the right Waterman's Arms. When we stepped out into the street to look for another, we found ourselves curiously confronted. 'Oi.' It was the little bag of rags that had been following us earlier. Now he was standing before us almost like a sentry, with 'oi' as his challenge. 'Oi, where's my three guineas?'

It seemed funny enough, this bit of dirt coming up with this strange demand. I think we all had ourselves a little laugh. China Clucas, being soft-hearted as well as a little simple, stooped down so he was more on a level with the creature. 'Sorry, my lad. We haven't got your guineas. I might have a penny for you.'

'Give me my guineas,' the boy insisted. 'You stole them off me.'

I don't know where the old man came from. He just seemed to appear like some genie out of the dirt and brick: a little crazed body with mad hair, and eyes that didn't look at you, leaning himself on a long black stick. 'You give my boy his money.'

This should have been funny too, I dare say. For a start he was old enough to be the boy's grandfather. Yet it wasn't quite funny any more. 'We haven't got . . .' I started saying. But then the lad drowned me out.

'Thieves,' he yelled, almost like he was one big whistle.

Suddenly they were everywhere. His 'mother', who looked

younger than he did. His 'brother', who looked older than the mother. Uncles and aunts. And some more who weren't specified. A very close family they seemed, too. Their one wish, as they straggled towards us, was that we should give their relative back his four, no five, guineas. Well, I may not know London, but I knew what this was about. 'Let's get out of here.'

For a moment I thought we might get away nice and stately. Most of them were no bigger than the lad himself, after all. Slow, we started, going mostly backwards, with China holding the line. But there were just too many. All at once one of the smallest sank his teeth into China's leg, and while China was distracted with that, the little old man belted him one with his stick. At that we just ran, taking the street at a full gallop, with a sort of howl rising up behind to hurry us on, dodging past loiterers – especially the ones with out-stretched arms – and on. Till I caught sight of a big plain building that could only be a chapel. The door was open and someone was going inside. 'Over there.'

A moment later there I was, huffing and panting at the back of a sermon. A popular one, too, and full to standing. Sober people in poor clothes, they were, some giving me dirty looks for being so out of breath when the preacher was talking. China was just behind me, squeezing into the congregation as best he could. But of Kelly there was no sign. 'Did you see what happened to him?' I whispered, catching myself a 'shhhh'.

China shrugged, then rubbed his leg where he had been bitten. Then we looked at each other, wondering if we should go back out and have a search. But then they might all still be there. 'We'll go a bit later,' I suggested, which China seemed happy enough with.

'You must know,' expounded the preacher, 'that this grave crisis in India is nothing other than the first step on the road to the battle that shall end all battles.'

So he was an Armageddon man. Not that he looked it, being a neat little fellow with spectacles. Well, I didn't mind a bit of fire and brimstone, though I didn't much believe in it.

Manx, you should know, are generally not too pure over their scriptures, often going to two or three different churches on the same Sunday, especially if there isn't much else to do. It seems a shame to keep just to one, when it's the Anglicans who have the best singing, your Romans who have all the smoke and smells, and for a bit of theatre you couldn't beat a fellow like this one.

Armageddon was just two years down the road, it seemed. Gog of Rosh, Mezhek and Thuval was none other than the Tsar of Russia, Muscovy and Siberia, and the final battle, which would be followed by all the great pestilences and apocalypses and such, was to be fought between Russians and the Englishmen's army.

'So who shall be swept away by this mighty tide of destruction?' He had quite a list, pausing between each, for full effect. 'Fornicators. Drunkards. Breakers of the holy sabbath. All those backward peoples who have not acknowledged the glory of Christ, though they have surely had time enough. Papists and the followers of Dr Pusey . . .'

This was the part the congregation had come for: that tingle of fear at the thought that they will likely be burned to ashes, followed by that sweet relief that it may not be them after all, with the extra spice of knowing that those troublesome bodies who seem to have all the luck are well beyond redemption, and can be pitied their terrible fate.

But it was strong stuff. Though no end-of-the-world man myself, just hearing it predicted with such certainty did pull at me a little, throwing little doubts and wonderings. As for poor China, he was quite struck, his eyes wide and frowning. In fact it was the sight of him decided me that it was time to go.

'Come on then.'

But China didn't want to go. He sort of flapped his arms to say so.

'First you must confess your sins before God,' explained the preacher, who had reached that stern but reassuring part where he handed out a little hope after all.

Of course with most ships' crews discipline is a fierce thing, especially on those American boats, where you can get yourself beaten almost for sneezing. But Mann Island is too small for the formal, and accordingly Manx ships – and especially ones like the *Sincerity* – generally don't go in for flogging and such. Right now I almost wished they did. 'Able seaman Clucas, did you hear me?'

He only went and turned his back on me. I suppose escaping eternal burning seemed more important. The trouble was, China was one of those large bodies that hardly seems to know the scale of themselves. Instead of just turning his back, he had to do it in a shoving, walloping sort of way. That's what caused the trouble. At once there was a kind of sharp click from inside my jacket, followed by a tearing sound as the lining ripped. And a ringing clatter as three little items dropped on to the stone floor.

If there's one sound that will carry nicely it is breaking glass. Even the good preacher went quiet. Likewise there's no smell like brandy to catch the nostrils. All who were close enough peered round to see. And there at my feet was a fine little sight for them. Next to the smashed bottle was the tin with the tobacco spilled out, and next to that was the remains of the glass plate. This was broken but it still wasn't hard to make out the subject of the photograph on it, as this was very neatly done. It was of a young miss – of no small dimensions – sat in a comfortable chair holding a kitten. As for clothes, well, she had a neat little bonnet, and a fine pair of ankle boots. And the kitten. But that was about as far as it went. The detail was very fine.

'Drunkard,' hissed a voice.

'Fornicator,' spat another.

At least it got Clucas moving. In fact you couldn't have got him out of there quick enough.

The only other good thing was that, as we stepped outside, there was no sign of the lad and his extended family. The street was quiet now, while just a few yards down, sunning himself on a wall, was that sly one Chief mate Paddraig Kelly.

'D'you think it's true though?' Clucas had got himself in a proper blather. 'Is Armageddon coming?'

My thoughts were more for those samples the big walloping gorm had gone and broke. 'For you, certainly.' The fact was, it was no small disaster. There was little point in trying to find the right Waterman's Arms now, as we had nothing to show.

To my surprise Kelly seemed hardly bothered by the news of what had happened. 'Captain, I've had an idea,' he announced from his comfortable wall. 'Why don't we offer up the *Sincerity* for charter. That'd get us the money for the fine. Take ourselves a few passengers.'

Well, there was an idea. And it seemed harmless enough, besides. But then, as I have already related, giving a free ride to that Bishop of Mann *seemed* harmless enough.

Julian Barnes

THE REVIVAL

1. PETERSBURG

IT WAS AN old play of his, written in France back in 1849.
The censor had banned it the following year, and licensed it
for publication only in 1855. It finally reached the stage
seventeen years later, when it ran for a pitiful five nights in
Moscow. Now, thirty years after its conception, she had
telegraphed asking permission to abridge it for Petersburg.
He agreed, while gently protesting that this juvenile invention
had been meant for the page, not the stage. He added that the
play was unworthy of her talent. This was a typical gallantry;
he had never seen her act.

Like most of his life's writing, the play was concerned with
love. And, as in his life, so in his writing: love did not work.
Love might or might not provoke kindness, gratify vanity,
and clear the skin, but it did not lead to happiness; there was
always an inequality of feeling or intention present. Such was
love's nature. Of course, it 'worked' in the sense that it caused
life's profoundest emotions, made him fresh as spring's linden
blossom, and broke him like a traitor on the wheel. It stirred
him from well-mannered timidity to relative boldness –
though a rather theoretical boldness, one tragicomically
incapable of action. It taught him the gulping folly of
anticipation, the wretchedness of failure, the whine of regret,
and the silly fondness of remembrance. He knew love well.
He also knew himself well. Thirty years earlier, he had
written himself into the part of Rakitin, who offers the

30

audience his conclusions about love: 'In my opinion, Alexei Nikolaevich, every love, happy as well as unhappy, is a real disaster when you give yourself over to it entirely.' These views were deleted by the censor.

He had assumed that she would play the female lead, Natalya Petrovna, the married woman who falls in love with her son's tutor. Instead, she chose to be Natalya's ward, Verochka, who, in the way of plays, also falls in love with the tutor. The production opened; he came to Petersburg; she called on him in his rooms at the Hotel de l'Europe. She had expected to be intimidated, but found herself charmed by the 'elegant and likeable grandpa' that she discovered. He treated her like a child. Was this so surprising? She was twenty-five, he was sixty.

On March 27th, he went to a performance of his play. Despite hiding in the depths of the director's box, he was recognised, and at the end of the second act the audience started calling his name. She came to take him onstage, but he refused, and took his bow from the box. After the third act, he visited her dressing room, where he grasped her hands and led her to the gaslight. 'Verochka,' he said. 'Have I really written this Verochka? I didn't even pay attention to her when I was writing . . . The focal point of the play is Natalya Petrovna . . . Your Verochka is alive.'

2. THE REAL JOURNEY

So did he fall in love with his own creation? Verochka onstage beneath the floodlight, Verochka offstage beneath the gaslight – his Verochka, prized now the more for having been overlooked in his own text thirty years earlier? If love, as some assert, is a purely self-referring business, if the object of love is finally unimportant because what the lover values is the emotions aroused, then what more appropriate circularity than for a dramatist to fall in love with his own creation? Who needs the interference of the real person, the real *her* beneath the sunlight, the lamplight, the heartlight? Here is a photo of Verochka, dressed as if for the schoolroom: timid and appealing, with ardour in her eyes and an open palm denoting trust.

But, if this confusion occurred, she incited it. Years later, she wrote in her memoirs, 'I did not *play* Verochka, I performed a sacred rite ... I felt quite distinctly that Verochka and I were the same person.' So let us be forgiving if the Verochka who was so 'alive' was what first moved him; what first moved her was perhaps something else that didn't exist – the author of the play, now himself long gone, thirty years away. And let's also remember that he knew this would be his last love. He was an old man now. He was applauded wherever he went as an institution, the representative of an era, someone whose work was done. Abroad, they hung gowns and ribbons on him. He was sixty, old by choice as well as by fact. A year or two earlier, he had written, 'After the age of forty there is only one word to sum up the basis of life: "renunciation."' Now he was half as old again as that defining anniversary. He was sixty, she was twenty-five.

In letters, he kissed her hands, he kissed her feet. He sent a gold bracelet with their two names engraved inside. 'I feel now,' he wrote, 'that I love you sincerely. I feel that you have become something in my life from which I shall never be parted.' The phrasing is conventional. Were they lovers? It seems not. For him, it was a love predicated upon renunciation, whose excitements were called if-only and what-might-have-been. And just as, before the age of renunciation, physical vigour naturally appears as proof, or, at least, corroborating evidence, of professed emotion – the erection to the witness box! – so in the slower, later years the debility of the flesh confirms the heart's decline.

But all love needs a journey. All love symbolically is a journey, and that symbol needs bodying forth. *Their* journey took place on May 28, 1880. He was staying on his country estate; he pressed her to visit him there. She couldn't; she was an actress, at work, on tour; even she, at twenty-six, had things that must be renounced. But she would be travelling from Petersburg to Odessa; her route could take her through

Mtsensk and Oryol. He consulted the timetable for her. Three trains left from Moscow along the Kursk line. The twelve-thirty, the four o'clock, and the eight-thirty: the express, the mail, and the slow train. Respective arrivals at Mtsensk: ten in the evening, four-thirty in the morning, and nine-forty-five in the morning. There was the practicality of romance to be considered. Should the beloved arrive with the post, or on the railway's equivalent of the red-eye? He urged her to take the twelve-thirty, redefining its arrival more exactly, to 9.55 p.m.

There is an ironic side to this precision. He was himself notoriously unpunctual. At one time he made an affectation of carrying a dozen watches on his person; even so, he would be hours late for a rendezvous. But on May 28th, trembling like a youth, he met the nine-fifty-five express at the little station of Mtsensk. Night had fallen. He boarded the train. It was thirty miles from Mtsensk to Oryol.

He sat in her compartment for those thirty miles. He gazed at her, he kissed her hands. He did not dare to kiss her lips: renunciation. Or, he tried to kiss her lips and she turned her face away: shame, humiliation. The banality, too, at his age. Or, he kissed her and she kissed him back as ardently: surprise, and leaping fear. We do not know; his diary was later burned, her letters have not survived. All we have are his subsequent letters, whose gauge of reliability is that they date this May journey to the month of June. We know that she had a travelling companion, Raisa Alexeyevna. What did she do? Feign sleep, pretend to have sudden night vision for the darkened landscape, retreat behind a volume of Tolstoy? Thirty miles passed. He got off the train at Oryol. She sat at her window, waving her handkerchief to him as the express took her on towards Odessa.

No, even that handkerchief is invented. But the point is, they had had their journey. Now it could be remembered, improved, turned into the embodiment, the actuality, of the if-only. He continued to invoke it until his death. It was, in a sense, his last journey, the last journey of the heart. 'My life is behind me,' he wrote, 'and that hour spent in the railway compartment, when I almost felt like a twenty-year-old youth, was the last burst of flame.'

Does he mean he almost got an erection? Our century rebukes its predecessor for its platitudes and evasions, its sparks, its flames, its fires, its imprecise scorchings. Love isn't a bonfire, for God's sake – it's a hard cock and a wet cunt, we growl at these swooning, renouncing people. Get on with it! Why on earth didn't you? Cock-scared, cunt-bolted tribe of people! *Hand*-kissing! It's perfectly obvious what you really wanted to kiss. So why not? And on a train, too. You'd just have to hold your tongue in place and let the movement of the train do the work for you. Clackety-clack, clackety-clack!

When did you last have your hands kissed? And, if you did, how do you know he was any good at it? (Better, when did anyone last *write* to you about kissing your hand?) Here is the argument for the world of renunciation. If we know more about consummation, they knew more about desire. If we know more about numbers, they knew more about despair. If we know more about boasting, they knew more about memory. They had foot-kissing, we have toe-sucking. You still prefer our side of the equation? You may well be right. Then try a simpler formulation: If we know more about sex, they knew more about love.

Or perhaps this is quite wrong, and we mistake the gradations of courtly style for realism. Perhaps foot-kissing always meant toe-sucking. He also wrote to her, 'I kiss your little hands, your little feet, kiss everything you will allow me to kiss, and even that which you will not.' Isn't this clear enough, to both writer and recipient? And if so, then perhaps the converse is also true: that heart-reading was just as coarsely practised then as it is now.

But, as we mock these genteel fumblers of a previous era, we should prepare ourselves for the jeers of the next century. How come we never think of this? We believe in evolution, but only in the sense of evolution culminating in us. We forget that this entails evolution beyond our solipsistic selves. Those old Russians were good at dreaming a better time, and we take their dreams as our applause. But we are the more complacent.

While her train continued towards Odessa, he spent the night at a hotel in Oryol. A bipolar night, splendid because he thought only of her, miserable because this prevented him from sleeping. The voluptuousness of renunciation was now upon him: 'I find my lips murmuring, "What a night we should have spent together."' To which our practical and irritated century replies, 'Take another train then! Try kissing her wherever it was you didn't!'

Such action would be far too dangerous. He must preserve the impossibility of love. So he offers her an extravagant if-only. He confesses that as her train was about to leave he was suddenly tempted to the 'madness' of abducting her. It was a temptation he naturally renounced: 'The bell rang, and *ciao*, as the Italians say.' But think of the newspaper headlines if he had carried out his momentary plan. 'SCANDAL AT ORYOL RAILWAY STATION,' he delightedly imagines. If only. 'An extraordinary event took place here yesterday: the author T—, an elderly man, was accompanying the celebrated actress S—, who was travelling to Odessa for a brilliant season in the theatre there, when, just as the train was about to pull out, he, as though possessed by the Devil in person, extracted Mme S— through the window of her compartment and, overcoming the artiste's desperate efforts, etc. etc.' If only. The real moment – the possible handkerchief being waved at the window, the probable station gaslight falling on the whitened crest of an old man – is rewritten into farce and melodrama, into journalese and 'madness'. The alluring if-only does not refer to the future; it is safely lodged in the past. The bell rang, and *ciao*, as the Italians say.

He also had another tactic: that of hurrying on into the future in order to confirm the impossibility of love in the present. Already, and without 'anything' having happened, he is looking back on this would-be something: 'If we meet again in another two or three years, I shall be an old, old man. As for you, you will have entered definitively upon the normal course of your life and nothing will remain of our past . . .'

Two years, he thought, would turn an old man into an old, old one; while 'normal' life is already waiting for her in the banal shape of an officer of hussars, clanking his spurs offstage and snorting like a horse. N. N. Vsevolozhsky. How useful the thunderous uniform was to the gauntly bent civilian.

We should not, by this stage, still be thinking of Verochka, the naïve, unfortunate ward. The actress who embodied her was robust, temperamental, bohemian. She was married, and already seeking a divorce; she would marry three times in all. Her letters have not survived. Did she lead him on? Was she a little in love with him? Was she, perhaps, more than a little in love with him, yet dismayed by his expectation of failure, his voluptuous renunciations? Did she, perhaps, feel just as trapped by his past as he did? If for him love had always meant defeat, why should it be any different with her? If you marry a foot fetishist, you should not be surprised to find him curled up in your shoe cupboard.

When he recalled that journey in letters to her, he made oblique references to the word 'bolt'. Was this the lock on the compartment, on her lips, on her heart? Or the lock on his flesh? 'You know what the predicament of Tantalus was?' he wrote. The predicament of Tantalus was to be tortured in the infernal regions by endless thirst; he was up to his neck in water, but whenever he bent his head to drink the river would run away from him. Are we to conclude from this that he tried to kiss her, but that whenever he advanced she retreated, withdrawing her wet mouth?

On the other hand, a year later, when everything is safe and stylised, he writes this: 'You say, at the end your letter, "I kiss you warmly." How? Do you mean as you did then, on that June night, in the railway compartment? If I live a hundred years I will never forget those kisses.' May has become June, the timid suitor has become the recipient of myriad kisses, the bolt has been slid back a little. Is this the truth, or is that the truth? We, now, would like it to be neat then, but it is never neat: either the heart drags in sex or sex drags in the heart.

3. The Dream Journey

He travelled. She travelled. But they did not travel; never again. She visited him at his estate, she swam in his pond – 'the Undine of St Petersburg' – and when she left he named the room in which she had slept after her. He kissed her hands, he kissed her feet. They met, they corresponded until his death, after which she protected his memory from vulgar interpretation. But thirty miles was all they travelled together.

They could have travelled. If only . . . if only. But he was a connoisseur of the if-only, and so they did travel. They travelled in the past conditional.

She married for the second time. N. N. Vsevolozhsky, officer of hussars, clank, clank. When she asked his opinion of her choice, he declined to play. 'It is too late to ask for my opinion. *Le vin est tiré – il faut le boire.*' Was she asking him, artist to artist, for his view of the conventional marriage she was about to make to a man with whom she had little in common? Or was it more than this? Was she proposing her own if-only, asking him to sanction the jilting of her fiancé, or, at least, inviting him to muse on the possibility that she might?

But Grandpa, who himself had never married, declines either to sanction or to applaud. *Le vin est tiré – il faut le boire.* Does he have a habit of lapsing into foreign phrases at key emotional moments? Do French and Italian provide the suave euphemism that helps him evade?

Of course, if he had sanctioned a late withdrawal from her second marriage, that would have let in too much reality, let in the present tense. He closes it off: drink the wine. This instruction given, fantasy can resume. In his next letter, twenty days later, he writes, 'For my part, I am dreaming about how good it would be to travel about – just the two of us – for at least a month, and in such a way that no one would know who or where we were.'

It is a normal dream of escape. Alone together, anonymous, time on one's hands. It is also, of course, a honeymoon. And where would the sophisticated artistic class go for their honeymoon if not to Italy? 'Just imagine the following picture,' he teases. 'Venice (perhaps in October, the best month in Italy) or Rome. Two foreigners in travelling clothes: one tall, clumsy, white-haired, long-legged, but very contented; the other a slender lady with remarkable dark eyes and black hair. Let us suppose her contented as well. They walk about the town, ride in gondolas. They visit galleries, churches, and so on; they dine together in the evening; they are at the theatre together – and then? There my imagination stops respectfully. Is it in order to conceal something, or because there is nothing to conceal?'

Did his imagination stop respectfully? Ours doesn't. It seems pretty plain to us in our subsequent century. A crumbling gentleman in a crumbling city on a surrogate honeymoon with a young actress. The gondoliers are splish-sploshing them back to their hotel after an intimate supper, the soundtrack is operetta, and we need to be told what happens next? We are not talking about reality, so the feebleness of elderly, alcohol-weakened flesh is not an issue; we are very safely in the conditional tense, with the travelling rug tucked round us. So . . . if only . . . if only . . . then you would have fucked her, wouldn't you? No denying it.

Elaborating the Venice-honeymoon fantasy while she is still between husbands has its dangers. Of course, you have again renounced her, so there is small risk that by exciting her imagination you might find her outside your front door one morning, perched on a travelling trunk and coyly fanning herself with her passport. No; the more real danger is of pain. Renunciation means the avoidance of love, and hence of pain, but even in this avoidance there are traps. There is pain to be had, for instance, in the comparison between the Venetian capriccio of your respectful imagination and the impending reality of her getting disrespectfully fucked on her actual honeymoon by an officer of hussars, N. N. Vsevolozhsky, who is as unfamiliar with the Accademia as he is with the unreliabilities of the flesh.

What heals pain? Time, the old wiseacres respond. You know better. You are wise enough to know that time does not always heal pain. Your image of the amatory bonfire, the eyeball-drying flame that dies to sad ashes, needs adjusting. Try instead the hissing gas jet that scorches, if you will, but also does worse: it gives light – jaundicing, flat-shadowed, and remorseless, the sort of light that catches an old man on a provincial platform as the train pulls out, a valetudinarian who watches a yellow window and a twitching hand withdraw from his life, who walks after the train a few paces as it curves into invisibility, who fixes his eye upon the red lamp of the guard's wagon, holds on that until it is less than a ruby planet in the night sky, then turns away and finds himself still beneath a platform lamp, alone, with nothing to do except wait out the hours in a musty hotel, pretending he has gained when truly he has lost, filling his sleeplessness with cosy if-onlys, and who then returns to the station and once more stands alone, in a kinder light but to make a crueller journey, back along those thirty miles he had travelled with her the previous night. The journey from Mtsensk to Oryol, which he will fetishize for the rest of his life, is always shadowed by that unrecorded return from Oryol to Mtsensk.

So he proposes a second dream journey, again to Italy. By now she is married, a change of status which is not an interesting subject for discussion. Drink the wine. She is going to Italy, perhaps with her husband, though travelling companions are not inquired after. He approves the journey, if only because it lets him offer her an alternative; not a rivalrous honeymoon this time but a trip safely in the painless past conditional. 'I spent ten of the most delightful days in Florence, many, many years ago.' This use of time anaesthetises pain. It was so many, many years ago that he was then 'still under forty' – before the basis for life became renunciation. 'Florence left on me the most fascinating and poetic impression – even though I was there alone. What it would have been like, had I been in the company of a woman who was understanding, good, and beautiful – that above all!'

This is safe. The fantasy is manageable, his gift a false memory. Later, in our century, the political leaders of his country would specialise in airbrushing people from history, removing their photographic traces. Now here he is, bent over his album of memories, meticulously inserting the figure of a previous companion. Paste it in, that photograph of the timid, appealing Verochka, while the Florentine light rejuvenates your white hair into black shadow.

4. AT YASNAYA POLYANA

Shortly after meeting her, he had gone to stay with Tolstoy, who took him out shooting. He was put in the best hide, over which snipe habitually passed. But that day, for him, the sky remained empty. Every so often, a shot would ring out from Tolstoy's hide; then another; then another. All the snipe were flying to Tolstoy's gun. It seemed typical. He himself shot a single bird, which the dogs failed to find.

Tolstoy despised him from the start; thought him ineffectual, vacillating, unmanly, a frivolous socialiser and a despicable Westerniser; hugged him, loathed him, spent a week in Dijon with him, quarrelled with him, forgave him, valued him, visited him, challenged him to a duel, hugged him, despised him. This is how Tolstoy expressed sympathy when he lay dying in France: 'The news of your illness has caused me much sorrow, especially when I was assured it was serious. I realised how much I cared for you. I felt that I should be much grieved if you were to die before me.'

Tolstoy at this time would have despised his taste for renunciation. Later, Tolstoy himself became a renunciator, railing at the lusts of the flesh and seeking to hug a Christian peasant simplicity. It didn't work; he wasn't much good at it. Some might think him a fraud, a fake renunciator; but it was more that he lacked the skills. His flesh declined renunciation. Three decades later, he died at a railway station. His last words were not 'The bell rang, and *ciao*, as the Italians say.' Does the successful renunciator envy his unsuccessful counterpart? There are ex-smokers who decline the offered cigarette but say, 'Blow the smoke in my direction.'

She was travelling; she was working; she was married. He

asked her to send him a plaster cast of her hand. He had kissed the real thing so many times; had kissed an imagined version of the real thing in almost every letter he wrote her. Now he could lay his lips on a plaster version. Is plaster nearer to flesh than air? Or did the plaster turn his love and her flesh into a memorial? There is an irony in this request: normally it is the writer whose creative hand is cast in plaster; and normally by the time this is done he is dead.

So he proceeded deeper into old age, knowing that she was – had already been – his last love. And, since form was his business, did he at this time remember his first love? He was a specialist in the matter. Did he reflect that first love fixes a life for ever? Either it impels you to repeat the same kind of love and fetishizes some of its components or else it is there as warning, trap, counter-example.

His own first love had taken place fifty years before. She had been a certain Princess Shakhovskaya. He was fourteen, she was in her twenties; he adored her, she treated him like a child. This puzzled him until the day he found out why. She was already his father's mistress.

The year after he shot snipe with Tolstoy, he visited Yasnaya Polyana again. It was Sonya Tolstoy's birthday, and the house was full of guests. He proposed that they should all recount the happiest moment of their lives. When his own turn in his own game arrived, he announced, with an exalted air and a familiar melancholy smile, that the happiest moment of his life was the moment of love, that instant when the eyes met. This has happened to me once, perhaps twice. Tolstoy found this answer irritating.

Later, when the young people insisted upon dancing, he demonstrated what was new in Paris. He took off his jacket, stuck his thumbs in his armpits, and capered about, legs kicking, head waggling, white hair flopping, as the household clapped and cheered; he panted, capered, panted, capered, then fell over and collapsed into an armchair. It was a great success. Tolstoy wrote in his journal, 'Turgenev – cancan. Sad.'

'Once, perhaps twice.' Was she the 'perhaps twice'?

Perhaps. In his penultimate letter, he kisses her hands. In his last letter, written in failing pencil, he does not offer kisses. He writes instead, 'I do not change in my affections – and I shall keep exactly the same feeling for you until the end.'

This end came six months later. The plaster cast of her hand is now in the Theatre Museum of St Petersburg, the city where he had first kissed the original.

Wendy Cope

PRESENT

On the flyleaf
of my confirmation present:
'To Wendy with love
from Nanna. Psalm 98.'

I looked it up, eventually –
Cantate Domino.
I knew the first two verses
and skimmed the rest.

Thirty-five years afterwards,
at evensong on Day 19
the choir sings Nanna's psalm.
At last, I pay attention

to the words she chose.
O *sing unto the Lord*
a new song. Nanna,
it is just what I wanted.

BY THE ROUND POND

You watch yourself. You watch the watcher too –
A ghostly figure on the garden wall.
And one of you is her, and one is you,
If either one of you exists at all.

How strange to be the one behind a face,
To have a name and know that it is yours,
To be in this particular green place,
To see a snail advance, to see it pause.

You sit quite still and wonder when you'll go.
It could be now. Or now. Or now. You stay.
Who's making up the plot? You'll never know.
Minute after minute swims away.

IDYLL

(after U. A. Fanthorpe)

We'll be in our garden on a summer evening,
Eating pasta, drinking white wine.

We won't talk all the time. I'll sit back,
Contemplating shadows on the red-brick path,

And marvel at the way it all turned out.
That yellow begonia. Our gabled house.

Later we'll stroll through Kingsgate Park.
My leg won't hurt, and we'll go home the long way.

Asked to imagine heaven, I see us there,
The way we have been, the way we sometimes are.

HOW TO DEAL WITH THE PRESS

She'll urge you to confide. Resist.
Be careful, courteous, and cool.
Never trust a journalist.

'We're off the record,' she'll insist.
If you believe her, you're a fool.
She'll urge you to confide. Resist.

Should you tell her who you've kissed,
You'll see it all in print, and you'll
Never trust a journalist

Again. The words are hers to twist,
And yours the risk of ridicule.
She'll urge you to confide. Resist.

'But X is *nice*,' the publicist
Will tell you. 'We were friends at school.'
Never trust a journalist,

Hostile, friendly, sober, pissed,
Male or female – that's the rule.
When tempted to confide, resist.
Never trust a journalist.

45

Jonathan Coe

V.O.

THERE CAME A point where it stopped being an interview and turned into a conversation. And there came another point, some time later, where it stopped being a conversation and turned into a flirtation. William could not have said when either of these things happened, with any certainty.

He did notice, however, that Pascale had laid aside her notebook, and was no longer writing down everything he said. And he noticed that they were no longer talking about his forthcoming film project, or his last CD, but had begun to discuss the unsatisfactory progress of her own career in journalism.

'Even now,' she was saying, 'I can't be sure that they will publish this article. And you know, that's annoying for you – because you have taken the trouble to talk to me – but also for myself, because it's a lot of work, to transcribe all of this and to write it up and then to be told that they don't want to use it after all.'

William smiled the self-deprecating smile at which he was so practised, and said: 'You make me wish that I was more famous. I'm sure if you were interviewing Jerry Goldsmith, or Michael Nyman . . .'

'No, not at all,' said Pascale. 'I can assure you that your film scores are very well known in France. They are very popular. It's just that – I don't know . . .' She shook her head, and stared ruefully into space. 'They are so unreliable, these people. They say one thing and they mean another.'

46

'I'd enjoy talking to you,' said William, after a pause, 'whether you were going to write about me or not.'

Pascale turned. For a moment he was convinced that the remark had sounded too crass, too forward. Her eyes were screened: all he could see in her Raybans, dimly, was his own reflection. But the smile that now flickered onto her face was pleased rather than mocking.

Instead of responding directly to his compliment, she said: 'Are you enjoying the festival, so far?'

'Yes,' said William. 'Yes, I am.'

'It's not exactly Cannes. Not many celebrities, not many famous names.'

'Well, there's Claudia Remotti: wouldn't you say that she's one of Italy's biggest movie stars, these days? It's not often I get to spend so much time with a woman like that.'

Pascale pouted. 'So the jury spend a lot of time together?'

'Absolutely. We watch the films together, we eat together, drink together . . .' But William was irritated, even as he said this, by the thought that he didn't know where the other jury members were at that moment. Were they socialising, somewhere, without having invited him – without even noticing that he wasn't there? Was some other man – that self-assured Spanish director, perhaps – sitting next to Claudia and plying her with alcohol? He felt a bitter pang of jealousy and poured more beer into Pascale's glass.

They were drinking at a seafront bar on a small promontory which jutted out from the shore, so that the ocean glimmered, turquoise and opalescent, on three sides. William's eyes were smarting from the white sunlight. He had forgotten to bring his sunglasses to France; had been on his way to buy some, in fact, when he had stopped at the bar for a drink and been waylaid by this charming journalist. She had asked him if they could meet for a short interview some time during the week, and he had said that now was as good a time as any; relieved, as it happened, for the distraction it afforded, the chance to empty his mind of the telephone call he had made five minutes earlier. He had attempted to phone home, only to be greeted by a new message on the answering machine; a message from which Alice, as threatened, had removed his own name. This was bluff, he told himself: surely this was bluff. Just before William left for the festival, she had indeed told him that she never wanted him to come back, but he had assumed this was a fleeting, impetuous over-reaction. There was no way she would throw him out. Not over something as silly as that letter . . .

'I'm sorry?' he said now, conscious that he had not been listening to Pascale as she addressed a direct question to him.

'I said, Are you a fan of this kind of film? Horror films. Fantasy films. I wondered if you felt an affinity with this particular genre.'

William considered his answer carefully. His concern, as always, was not to express any firmly-held opinion of his own, but to make sure that he did not give offence, or provoke disagreement: and since he had not yet learned Pascale's views on the subject, this was difficult.

'I think that serious artistic statements,' he said, pompously, 'can be made within any kind of generic restrictions. It doesn't do to be snobbish about these things. Horror films don't tend to be taken seriously by critics but if you look at many of the entries at this festival, you'll find that they are very finely-crafted works of art – the works of real *auteurs*, real visionaries.'

'I'm sure you're right,' said Pascale, smiling at him with a furrowed intensity he already found endearing. 'And what film do you have to see this afternoon?'

William consulted his festival programme. '*Mutant Autopsy 3*,' he said, and signalled to the waiter for two more beers.

The 14th Annual Festival of Horror and Fantasy Cinema was based in a large, modern, impersonal hotel about two kilometres from the centre of town. Although it housed a massive cinema auditorium, which would often be filled to capacity even for the most unpromising-sounding films, William soon realised that the hub of the festival was not here but in the bar on the ground floor. This bar was open to members of the public, of course, as well as to the filmmakers and critics, so there was always a fair smattering of Goths, Trekkies, slasher fans and gorehounds spread around the tables in a sea of black clothing and grey, pallid, bloodless complexions. But mainly it was a place where the festival insiders could exchange gossip and do deals. William soon got into the habit of going down there every evening at around 7.30, in the hope of seeing Claudia Remotti for a drink before dinner.

On the fourth night of the festival, just before leaving his room on this errand, William sat on his balcony and flicked idly through the programme to see what delights awaited the jury members during the rest of the week. He was getting tired of rapes, mutilations, ritual slayings, decapitations and chainsaw massacres. Apart from anything else, as the only composer on the jury he was supposed to be looking out for a potential winner of the best soundtrack award, and had been finding it hard to concentrate on the music that tended to accompany such scenes. He was ready, now, to see something a little more original, a little more sophisticated.

He held out little hope for tomorrow's offering, a Spanish movie billed as a 'hilarious necrophiliac comedy' called *One Corpse at a Time, Please!*; nor for the American film they would be seeing the day after that, *Vampire Brainsuckers Get Naked*. The last entry in the festival, however, looked marginally more interesting. It was a German film, a supernatural love story involving ghosts and out-of-body experiences, whose title translated as *The Haunted Heart*. He looked down the credits to see who had written the music, and found a name that he didn't recognise. Then he looked at the other credits and suddenly saw, in a spasm of wild astonishment, a name that he knew only too well.

Gertrud. Gertrud Keller. It was her screenplay. She had written this film.

William snapped the programme shut. He wasn't ready for this information yet. Coming so soon after his latest domestic crisis, and the stirrings of attraction he had already begun to feel for Pascale – not to mention the rush of excitement that always came over him whenever he found himself near Claudia – it was more than he could handle. There was only so much pressure that the human heart could withstand at once.

So she had made it, anyway. She had written something for the movies, just as she always said that she would.

He reflected on this as he rode down towards the bar in the futuristic, glass-bottomed lift, and the thought cheered him; cheered him, to his surprise, almost as much as the sight of Claudia sitting at a corner table in the bar, sipping champagne with no more serious rival for his attentions than Michel, the festival administrator. Michel was a small, dapper man, his hair slicked neatly into place, his body giving off a permanent and overpowering aroma of sweet Cologne. He was pleased to see William, having some important information to convey to all of the jury members.

'Tomorrow's film is from Spain,' he said, 'and as you will be aware from the programme, it is being shown in its V.O. format, or "Version Originale". This means that the print will be in the Spanish language, with French subtitles. So, naturally, we have had to make an arrangement for our non-French-speaking judges.'

This arrangement, it transpired, involved assigning to each of the judges their own personal translator, who would sit beside them in the dark and whisper a rough and ready English version of the French subtitles into their ears, while trying not to disturb the members of the paying public seated throughout the rest of the auditorium. It didn't sound the most satisfactory solution, and Claudia was, as usual, full of complaints as soon as Michel had left.

'Really,' she said, 'this festival is the most badly organised I have ever attended. I don't think I have ever been treated like this in my life. They put us up in this dreadful hotel, and make us watch these terrible movies all day. The food is shocking, quite shocking. And now they are even going to show us these crappy movies in a language we don't understand!'

William let her talk on, nodding in a sweet and conciliatory way every so often but in reality paying little attention to her words. Not for the first time that week, he was rendered almost senseless by the thought that he was sitting, actually sitting and drinking, in the company of one of the most beautiful and sought-after women in Europe: a woman about whom most male filmgoers would only ever fantasise. Not for the first time, too, he found himself thinking of the spectacular nude scene in her most recent film, and imagined himself taking the place of the statuesque Italian actor who had been her lucky collaborator in that marathon, acrobatic sexual encounter.

'Who is that man?' Claudia asked.

William's gaze came back into focus. 'What man?'

'That man who has been staring at you for the last five minutes.'

A muscular, overtanned figure with shoulder-length blond hair, who looked a little like a high-class male stripper, did indeed seem to be watching them from the bar.

'I'm sure it's you he's staring at, actually,' said William.

'No, I don't think so. In any case, we'll soon find out. It looks like he's coming over.'

When the man came closer, William suddenly recognised him: it was Stephen Manners, with whom he had once, many years ago, shared a hall of residence during his days as a student at Leeds University. Stephen had been a drama student of very limited talent who had left the country after graduation, disappeared from view and then, much to everyone's amazement, surfaced in the early 1990s as the token British actor in a popular American sitcom. Since then the only significant development in his career had been a transition to low-budget, straight-to-video horror movies, which presumably accounted for his presence at this festival.

'It *is* William, isn't it?' he asked, standing over their table. '"Little Bill", the keyboard maestro?'

William winced to hear his student nickname being revived in this company, but nodded and shook Stephen by the hand.

'Hi, Steve. It's good to see you again.'

'Wow. I mean, this is freaky. Times have changed, right?'

'They certainly have.'

Not wishing to intrude upon an old friends' reunion, and having business of her own to attend to, Claudia soon excused herself and left them to catch up on the stories of their recent lives.

'After Leeds, I went down to live in London for a while,' William explained. 'Big mistake. I joined this terrible band – The Alaska Factory, they were called – and got mixed up with some pretty dodgy people, and had a love affair that turned into a complete disaster. So then I went back up to Yorkshire. Started hanging around the university again, wrote some music for student plays and got friendly with this lecturer who was making short films on the side. He was shooting experimental stuff on Super-8 – home movies, practically – but then someone at Channel 4 spotted him and put up the money for a feature. So he turned out this rather arty post-modern thriller, and against all the odds it crossed over and became a hit. I got a BAFTA nomination for the music, and the next thing I knew, everybody wanted to work with me. So that was the start of it: I've been doing film music ever since.'

'But that's fantastic, Bill. And is that why you're here – you've got a film in competition?'

'No, I'm on the jury, actually. What about you?'

'I'm in this thing they're showing on Thursday.'

'The *Vampire Brainsuckers* thing?'

'That's right. I thought I'd better show willing and come out here, do a few interviews.'

'Is it a good movie?'

Stephen frowned. 'Well, you know, these things are relative. We're quite proud of it, as it happens, but I don't think Eisenstein would have counted it among his finest.'

'What's the music like?'

'It's not bad. We got this sort of garage, thrash-metal soundtrack from a band called Anal Prolapse. You should meet them sometime, actually. They're nice guys. A bit threatening, but nice.' Then he leaned forward and said,

excitedly: 'Tell me about Claudia, though. I mean, are you
. . . hitting it off with her? She's just the most amazing-
looking woman. Totally stunning.'

'We get on fine. She seems very nice.'

'I mean, did you see that scene in her last film? With the ice
cubes, and the zucchini?'

William nodded, his mouth suddenly dry.

'Listen, man,' said Stephen, 'I'm not going to step on your
territory, or anything, but if you hadn't got there first . . .'

'Got there first? What do you mean?'

'Come on – I was watching the two of you. I saw the way
you were talking to her. You were coming on pretty strong.
And she was enjoying it, too.'

'Look, Stephen, you've got this completely wrong. I wasn't
coming on to her. I'm married, you know.'

'You are?'

'Sure. I've got a wife back in Leeds. Alice. She's a lawyer.'

'Any kids?'

'No.'

Stephen was curious. 'So how does it work? Do you have
one of those open marriage things?'

'No, of course not. I'm faithful to her. We're faithful to
each other.' (Though he wondered, even as he said it, whether
it could strictly be described as true.)

'How long have you been married?'

'Six years.'

'You mean – you've only slept with *one* woman, in the last
six years?'

'Yes,' said William: trying to inflect the word with pride,
rather than the sense of defeat and desolation that was
beginning to steal over him.

Stephen regarded him admiringly. 'You know, I envy you,
William,' he said; then thought for a moment. 'Shall I tell you
what I hate most about being an actor? An actor in American
movies, on American TV?' He ran distraught fingers through
his mane of hair. 'It's the girls. The young girls. They just
won't leave you alone. They won't take no for an answer.'

'Girls?' said William, lowering his voice to a conspiratorial whisper. 'What girls?'

'The fans, William. The groupies. They just go wild for anybody they've seen on the screen.'

'When you say go wild . . .'

'They hang around the studios, they follow you around on tour, they turn up outside your hotel room . . . I'm telling you, William, I can barely take it any more.'

'Take what?'

'The sex, of course. The hours and hours of draining, joyless sex. Night after night.'

'Night after night?' repeated William, faintly. His throat was drier than ever, and he drank off the last of his warm, flat champagne. 'With – with young girls, you say?'

'The seventeen- and eighteen-year-olds: they're the worst. The . . . just the *stamina* of these women is incredible, you know? The things they demand of you – the *positions*, the different locations, the group sessions . . .'

'Group sessions?'

'Three in a bed, four in a bathtub . . . You know, I'm getting *old*, William. I'm not sure how much longer I can cope with this sort of thing.' He sat back and exhaled deeply. 'That's why I said that I envied you. A steady, monogamous relationship: just the one person, nice and low-key . . . It sounds great.'

'Yes,' said William, staring ahead and feeling his eyes mist and glaze over again. 'That's the . . . that's the ticket, all right.'

Stephen still seemed to find his story incredible. 'Haven't you *ever* been unfaithful in all that time?

'Not physically,' he answered. 'Not physically, no. There have been . . . you know, incidents. Situations have arisen.'

'What kind of situations?'

'Well, at the moment, for instance: there's this woman back in Leeds. A few months ago I did a CD of some chamber pieces I'd written, and she played the cello on it. So we got friendly, while we were doing the recording, and then we started going out for coffee, we had a few drinks together, and . . . Well, you know where that gets you.'

'Sure. You bang her and then you move on.'

William was horrified. 'I did nothing of the sort.'

'Well, why the hell not?'

'Because it's not that sort of relationship. There are feelings involved.' He sighed. 'Anyway, now Alice has found out about it. She saw a letter that she'd written me, and . . . well, we're in trouble, actually. Alice is saying that she doesn't want me to come back.'

'That's being a bit over the top, isn't it?'

'No, but the thing is . . .' William scratched his head vigorously, newly puzzled that he had managed to find himself in this predicament. 'The thing is that it's happened before. Something very similar.'

And so he told Stephen the story of Gertrud. The story of his trip to Berlin, four years ago, when he had been asked to write the incidental music for a new stage production. He and the playwright, Gertrud Keller, had developed an immediate attraction for each other, and had struck up an intense, intimate friendship which continued, by letter and phone, for several months after William's return to England. He had been so flattered by her attentions, his self-esteem so enhanced by the thought that this beautiful, stimulating and intelligent woman should take an interest in him, that he completely failed to see where the relationship was leading: failed to notice that he had allowed Gertrud – even encouraged her – to fall in love with him. By the time that he did notice, it was too late. Their final letters crossed in the post: his suggesting that they should break off contact, hers announcing that she had left her husband, Jakob, and was ready to start a new life with him either in Germany or England. William had not replied; and they had not seen, spoken or written to each other since.

William did not tell Stephen the strange postscript to this narrative: that Gertrud had since written the screenplay for a film which had been entered in competition at this very festival, and which he was going to have to watch on Friday morning. In any case, he suspected that Stephen would not have seen the irony of it. There seemed, as usual, to be only one aspect of the story that fascinated him.

'And you never even slept with this woman? Not once?'

'What's so weird about that?'

'It's not the weirdness of it, William. It just makes me . . . sad, somehow. I mean, sex without love can be an empty experience: I should know that better than anyone. But love without sex' – he shook his head wonderingly – 'that just strikes me as being a complete fucking waste of time.'

At the bar the next day, shortly before the screening of *One Corpse at a Time, Please!*, Michel introduced William to Henri, his personal translator.

'Pleased to meet you,' said William.

'What ho, old chap,' said Henri. 'Ripping weather we're having today, what?'

Henri, it seemed, was a local translator who was busily engaged upon an as yet unpublished French edition of the complete works of P. G. Wodehouse. While everyone else at the festival sported shorts, plimsolls and brightly-coloured T-shirts, he was wearing a three-piece, double-breasted tweed suit and was smoking a shockingly pungent meerschaum pipe. He shook William warmly by the hand and said: 'Tell me, old bean, what news from Blighty?' His diction was flawless, his vowels perfectly rounded. Henri's accent would once have guaranteed him a lifetime's employment on the BBC Home Service.

The air-conditioning in the cinema auditorium had some difficulty, at the best of times, in coping with the Riviera temperatures. Today it was hotter than ever, and it soon became apparent that Henri was sweating profusely through his numerous layers of clothing. There was nothing William could do about this, unfortunately. His need to follow every line of the film's dialogue gave him no option but to sit in close proximity to his translator.

'By Jove, sir!' said Henri. 'It's a bit bally warm in here, wouldn't you say?'

The film turned out to be a black comedy in the amoral, nihilistic mould popularised by Quentin Tarantino and his followers, and concerned a gang of necrophiliac bank robbers with a penchant not simply for killing their victims but for having sex with them afterwards. Most of the dialogue was not really germane to the plot at all, but consisted of cynical wisecracks which the characters would trade while indulging absent-mindedly in the most grotesque and appalling acts of violence. During an early scene, for instance, there was an argument over the distribution of some loot, prompting one of the crooks to shove a pistol into his colleague's mouth and snarl a few words in rasping Spanish. William could catch little of what he was saying even from the French subtitles, and it was left to Henri to furnish him with an adequate translation.

'The gentleman with the scar,' he explained, in his plummy English drawl, 'says, "Suck on this, you tight-arsed mother-fucker." Then he adds, "I don't know how the fuck you got involved in this shit-brained scheme, but the closest you're ever going to get to that fucking money is when I shove it up your bony fucking arse."' He sighed at the infelicities of this version. 'I'm giving you the merest gist of it, I'm afraid. Do forgive me, old fellow. It's a jolly poor show on my part.'

As the week went by, William became more and more aware of the presence of Pascale. She had developed an unerring knack for turning up at his elbow when he was least expecting it: at the bar, at the hotel's buffet lunches, on his daily promenades through the town and along the seafront. She told him about a small, little-visited beach she had discovered, ten minutes' walk from the hotel along a rocky cliff path, and for the last three mornings they had gone there together for a swim before breakfast. He liked her, there was no denying that. He liked her solemn eyes and her almost comical earnestness; he liked (of course) the fact that she considered him famous, and was so clearly in awe of him; he liked her doleful eyebrows and thick black hair; and he liked her body, or what he had seen of it on their swimming trips. They had got to know each other well, by now. He knew all about her feckless boyfriend in Paris, who had been seeing her for more than five years but still refused to move into her apartment; and she knew all about William's current difficulties at home, his latest rift with Alice, the string of unanswered messages he had been leaving on her machine all week. They found it easy – very easy – to confide in one another.

On Thursday night, the penultimate night of the festival, William decided to eat away from the hotel at a small restaurant down by the marina, and found himself leading a party which also included Henri, Stephen, Pascale and Claudia Remotti. Stephen was in high spirits after the afternoon screening of *Vampire Brainsuckers Get Naked*, which had been greeted with a standing ovation by the largely teenage audience, and his exhilaration soon infected the other diners. But a slight pall was cast over the meal when Henri hastily excused himself, just before dessert, and disappeared off to the toilets clutching his stomach. He had been the only person to order mussels, and when he returned to the table his face was pale and sweaty.

'Frightfully sorry,' he explained. 'A spot of bother with the old tummy, wouldn't you know. Don't want to put a damper on the high jinks, so I think I'd better be popping off to beddy-byes. Best place for me, eh what? Toodle-pip, old beans.'

Not long after he'd gone, Stephen also looked at his watch and started to yawn ostentatiously.

'Press conference first thing in the morning,' he said. 'Perhaps I'd better be turning in.'

'Oh, is that the time?' said Claudia. 'I didn't realise it was so late already.'

It was half past nine.

'I'll walk you back to the hotel if you like,' said Stephen.

'Thank you,' said Claudia; whereupon they wished the

others goodnight and set off together, the white of his shirt and the cream of her dress finally blurring into one bobbing dot of light, far in the distance.

'I suppose,' said William thoughtfully, 'that people who work in films must get used to going to bed early. All those make-up calls at five in the morning.'

'That must be it,' said Pascale, smiling at him as she sipped her coffee.

William tried to meet her eyes for a few seconds, then looked away. He found the steadiness of her gaze unnerving.

'And then there were two,' he murmured, half to himself.

The night was alive with a delicate soundtrack of creaks and tinkles from the huddle of yachts moored at the marina, while the ocean itself lapped gently at the seaboard only a few yards from their table. Otherwise, all was quiet. William's thoughts were fuzzy with alcohol. At the back of his mind was the notion that he ought to phone Alice again. There had been a small breakthrough earlier in the evening, when she had actually picked up the telephone and they had made the first, halting steps towards a reconciliation. She had said that she was prepared – for the very last time – to overlook his latest piece of stupidity, and he had apologised brokenly, profusely, with a contrition that was not affected. At which point Alice had started to cry, and then hung up, suggesting that he call again later.

'What are you thinking?' Pascale now asked; and when William told her about this conversation, she said, 'Good; I'm glad,' and seemed to mean it.

'Perhaps we should be getting back as well,' said William. But Stephen and Claudia had left them with a full bottle of white wine, and they could not let it go to waste.

It was almost midnight when they returned to the hotel. They skirted the bar – still throbbing with activity at this hour – and rode up to the third floor together in the glass-bottomed lift. When the doors hissed open, they turned right and walked together towards William's room, even though Pascale's room lay in the opposite direction. Outside the door, they paused.

'Well,' said William, fumbling hopelessly for words. 'Here we are.'

'Yes,' said Pascale. 'Here we are.'

The silence weighed down on them, as heavy as the damp midnight air.

'It's been a lovely evening,' William stumbled. 'I've enjoyed . . . I've very much enjoyed knowing you this week.'

Pascale said nothing at first. She was staring at him again, evenly, searchingly, as if trying to read his thoughts.

'At this moment,' she said. 'At this precise moment, William, what is it that you want?'

William wanted several things, in fact. He wanted to go to sleep; he wanted to speak to Alice on the telephone; he wanted to make love to Pascale. But he mentioned none of them.

'I want . . .' he began. 'I'd like to know . . .' Wearily, he said: 'I'd like to know that I shall see you again, after all this is over.'

'That's not going to be easy,' said Pascale, 'with me living in Paris, and you living in Leeds.'

'That's true. But—'

'And what about your wife?'

William rubbed his eyes. He had been drinking all night, and a headache was starting to develop. 'I'm sure we could . . . sort something out,' he said. 'We could write to each other, or—'

He tailed off. Pascale smiled: but tightly this time, without warmth.

'I'm sure we could,' she said. Then they kissed each other goodnight, and she walked back down the corridor as William groped in his pocket for the room key.

Michel seemed more than usually agitated when William joined him at breakfast the next morning. It seemed that the final day of the festival was already plagued by hitches.

'First of all, your friend Mr Stephen Manners fails to show up for his nine o'clock press conference,' he complained. 'And we cannot get any answer from his room. And then we get a call from your translator, Henri, to say that he is sick in bed with food poisoning and will not be able to attend the screening of today's film – which, as you know, is in German. So! I haven't the faintest idea what to do.' He looked at William hopefully. 'I don't suppose you speak German, by any chance?'

'I'm afraid not.'

'And your French is really not good enough even to read the subtitles?'

'Sorry.'

Michel shrugged. 'Well, we are screening it at ten o'clock this morning, which gives me precisely' – he consulted his watch, and tutted – 'twelve minutes to find another translator.' Before leaving on this errand, he looked around the breakfast room and was pleased to see that all the jury members were present: all except one. 'Have you seen Miss Remotti this morning?'

'Not so far,' William admitted. 'Usually she's one of the first to arrive.'

Michel pursed his lips. 'I hope she is not also unwell. That would be a disaster.'

'Well, I have to go up to my room before the film starts,' said William. 'I'll knock on her door, if you like – check that she's OK.'

When he did so, the door was opened after a few seconds by Claudia herself, looking tousled and sleepy, wearing a summery, pale green sleeveless dress and only one earring and one shoe.

'I am nearly ready,' she said. 'Tell Michel not to worry. I shall be there when it starts.'

In the time it took Claudia to mumble these words, William glanced towards the back of her room and saw, sitting on the sunlit balcony, a familiar figure reading the newspaper. He was draped in a white towel dressing gown and his mane of flaxen hair was still wet from a recent shower. Claudia smiled at William sheepishly, and came two steps closer. She touched him lightly on the chest.

'You know, one of the problems with a festival like this,' she said, 'is the way that everybody gossips all the time. I hope I can count on your . . . English discretion?'

'Of course,' said William stiffly, and hurried on to his own room without even waiting for Claudia's whispered 'Thank you'. He did not pause to examine the feelings of envy and betrayal by which he was for some reason assaulted, or to ask himself why he found this latest development, on the whole, so unsurprising. Instead he went through the mechanical routines of brushing his teeth and going to the toilet, then tore out a page from one of his notebooks, wrote his name, address and telephone number on it, and stuffed the folded paper into his trouser pocket. He was resolved to pass it on to Pascale sometime today, before they went their separate ways.

As it turned out, he did not have to wait long to see her again. At the entrance to the cinema Michel was looking out for him, and Pascale was standing by his side. They both welcomed him with a smile: hers enigmatic, his pleased and self-congratulatory.

'So,' said Michel. 'I have found you a translator. This delightful young lady – who tells me that you are already well acquainted – has kindly volunteered to step into the breach.'

'That's very good of her,' said William, and shook the hand which Pascale, rather dumbfoundingly, held out to him.

They took their seats together in the half-empty auditorium: it seemed that if anything could keep the festival's horror enthusiasts at bay, it was the prospect of a romantic German ghost story, shown in its original language, shot partly in black-and-white and targeted firmly at an art-house audience. William was disappointed, and hoped that this didn't provide an omen for the commercial fortunes of Gertrud's first venture into the cinema.

Then the lights went down, and the film began.

The following ninety minutes were among the strangest and most disconcerting in William's life.

The Haunted Heart told the story of a love triangle. A married couple – both working in the theatre – enjoy a quarrelsome but stable home life, until one day, a young painter encounters the woman in a café, and becomes her lover. Their affair, which consumes the woman entirely, only comes to an end when the painter dies in a boating accident while on holiday with his own wife and daughter. After a period of intense, almost unbearable mourning, the woman returns to her forgiving husband; and finally, having lived through months of terrible distress, she discovers that she is, at heart, relieved that her lover is gone. The affair had brought much unhappiness in its wake, and she now realises that she is married to a kind and understanding man. All is well, until one day the painter's ghost appears at her home, and she realises that even now, the relationship is not quite over . . .

In many ways it was a clumsy and humourless film, and most of the audience did not appear to be impressed. Often they would laugh at scenes which were clearly intended to be viewed with the utmost seriousness. But William was blind to both its merits and its defects. A myriad of tiny details – from the exterior shots of the Berlin theatre to the private language of jokes and catchphrases which the lovers invented for themselves – instantly stirred up his memories of Gertrud, bringing her vividly to life before his eyes. Every aspect of the film seemed to hold some special significance for him. Even the musical score (which would eventually, at his instigation, win the best soundtrack award) had sprung from their shared vocabulary, being based upon themes by Francis Poulenc – most notably the Clarinet Sonata, a recording of which he had once sent her as a gift. William sat through the film in a kind of hypnotic trance, numb with shock. He would not have believed that any film, any narrative, any work of art, could have transported him so suddenly and irresistibly into the past.

But that was not all. This film may have reawakened him to the past, but it also never allowed him to forget the present. It never allowed him to forget for a moment that

Pascale was sitting beside him, closer than ever before but at the same time more distant, with a new tone in her voice and a new meaning in her actions: teasing, now, and reproachful. She faithfully translated every word of the screenplay. All the endearments he had once exchanged with Gertrud were now replayed, and given back to him. All the messages she had encoded for him in this film now reached him through Pascale's voice. There were a number of sex scenes, and here it seemed that Pascale took an even greater satisfaction in the fullness and literalism of her translation. She repeated every word, every gasp, every broken phrase, her lips almost brushing against his ear but then pulling back, in a mocking parody of physical contact. She leaned into him, her leg against his thigh. He could feel the rise and fall of her breathing. He could smell her body in the pressing heat of the auditorium.

In the very last scene of the film, he could no longer be sure whether it was Gertrud or Pascale that was speaking to him.

Du hast mir nichts zu bieten, said the women to her ghostly lover. *Das sehe ich nun. Es wäre freundlicher, wenn du mich in Ruhe ließt.*

The French subtitles said: *Tu n'as rien à m'offrir. Je peux le voir maintenant. Ce serait plus gentil de me laisser seule.*

And Pascale whispered in his ear: 'You have nothing to offer me. I see that now. It would be kinder if you left me alone.'

Für dich ist vorsichtiges Benehmen zugleich ein Freundliches. Du glaubst, daß du dich harmlos benimmst. Aber, meiner Meinung nach, bist du ein gefährlicher Mensch.

Pour toi, être prudent et être bon, c'est la même chose. Tu crois que ce que tu fais ne porte pas à conséquence. Mais je crois que tu es dangereux.

'You think that by being cautious, you are being kind. You believe that what you do is safe. But I think you are a dangerous person.'

Damals hast du mir beinahe das Herz gebrochen.

Tu as failli me briser le coeur.

'You came close to breaking my heart.'

*Bitte, kehr in deine Heimat zurück. Dort wirst du
glücklicher sein. Manfred, kehr zurück.*

*S'il te plaît, retournes d'ou tu viens. Tu y seras plus
heureux. Retournes-y, Manfred.*

'Please go back to where you belong. You will be happier
there. Go back, William.'

He turned towards her sharply, and said: 'The character's
name is Manfred, isn't it?' But Pascale did not answer. All he
could see were her eyes, shining in the dark.

William sat alone in the cinema for some time after the
audience had left. He could not collect himself, or will himself
into motion. When he was at last able to leave, he drifted
around the hotel in a daze, not noticing the people around
him, not responding when they spoke to him.

He felt better after some lunch and a siesta. In the middle
of the afternoon he went down to the reception desk and
asked if he could leave a note for Pascale. He was told that
she had checked out shortly after one o'clock. His fingers
closed on the scrap of notepaper in his pocket, and he
crumpled it tightly into a ball. Then he walked into town, to
look once again for the sunglasses he had been meaning to
buy all week.

(With thanks to Ralph and Louis.)

in "New writing 7:
an anthology", Vintage '98
Ed. Carmen Callil + Craig Raine

Georgina Hammick

CARRACKS OFF A ROCKY COAST

HE WALKS, ON the right-hand side of her very long road,
scanning the gates and the front gardens. Then he walks
back. The return journey, uphill, against the wind, and with
the two bottles in an off-licence carrier weighing against his
leg, feels longer, less hopeful. More dispiriting. 'Look out for
a holly bush,' she said on the telephone. 'On the right-hand
side, by the gatepost. It's important because most of the
gateposts haven't got numbers. The numbers on the doors are
so small you have to go up the path, up the steps even, before
you can read them. When you've found the holly bush you've
found me.'

(At once a vision of her in tiny white briefs came to him. A
not quite opaque white, so that a shaded area, the hint of a
triangular – soft, but springy and prickly – cushion, was
detectable.)

Another thing she said on the phone: 'I could give you a
disgusting supper if you like.'

'Disgusting?'

'Because I can't cook. Because I'm a lousy cook.' But of
course he didn't believe her.

Another extraordinary thing she said: 'No tape recorder if
you don't mind. And no photographs.'

Tape recorder? Photographs? He nearly dropped the
receiver. Then he burst out laughing. What did she take him
for?

(Afterwards he wondered if she'd really said it. Or perhaps
it was her idea of a joke? Or maybe he'd heard her wrong.)

66

Another unsettling thing she said: 'If you drive here, don't park your car outside my gate. Park on the other side of the road – if you can find a space.'

The more he thought about this last instruction, the more furtive and peculiar it seemed. Unnecessary, too, because in the pub, where they'd landed up the evening of their first and only meeting, he'd confessed – no, boasted, giving environmental reasons – that he didn't own a car. His journey in any case was already planned and, in his mind, rehearsed: tube from Gunnersbury; change at Hammersmith and Green Park; sit – or, more likely, stand – through five stations; walk – or run – for twenty minutes; stop. Calm down; calm fucking down. Start search, calmly, coolly, for holly bush.

There are bushes of various kinds in these front gardens. There's dogwood, cotoneaster, viburnum, laurel, a white-splashed, large-leafed shrub he doesn't know the name of. There are rose bushes also, whipped to a rattle of twigs on this windy March evening, their pale leaf-buds not broken yet; and, on either side of the road, bursts of noisy yellow – forsythia – and quiet red – flowering currant. Most of the gardens have at least one of those.

Whenever he's pictured the holly, it's been something really noticeable and impressive. Once, on the edge of sleep, it transformed itself from a bush into a tree. He saw a grey-green trunk smooth and thick as a sapling stake, and over it, shading it, a dark and spiky umbrella. But bush, tree, whatever, the thing has to be unmissable. Why mention it otherwise?

The holly, when he finally recognises it, is a spindly shrub, dwarfed by a stone gate pillar and half hidden behind a wall. Its pointy, but limp and unprickly, leaves are striped yellow-and-white on emerald green. Is this a test? Has she set him some kind of fucking test? He stares up at her house. (No, not her house, he remembers; it's only the right-hand top-floor flat that's hers.) Like all the other houses this side of the road, it has a porticoed entrance above a flight of crumbling steps, and a stuccoed face painted, a long time ago, some sort of cream or white or grey. The right-hand top-floor window, her window, is open at the bottom, and a tail-end of curtain billows in and out, sweeping the sill.

She's up there now. The thought terrifies him. *She's in there somewhere. Waiting for me.*

He crosses to the other side of the road, dodging the cars and the purposeful home-going pedestrians, and props himself against a tree. (His hands are damp; his legs feel loose and out of control; a new and urgent pain in his gut can mean only one thing.) I don't have to keep this appointment, he reminds himself. Who says I do? I can go home now if I want. I can go anywhere. I can go to the nearest, or furthest, bar and get pissed out of my mind. I can get rat-arsed, if I feel like it.

But after a minute or two he wipes his sweat-slick hands on his jeans, and dials her number on his borrowed mobile phone. ('Don't phone if the window's shut,' she instructed him. 'And don't come near the house without phoning first.' She never asked if he owned a mobile.)

'Are you a spy or something?' he remembers asking (this was yesterday, which now seems a year ago), smiling into the receiver, not meaning it. And her reply – 'No. That's you. It's you who's the spy' – he remembers that.

The first thing she says when the door shuts behind him in her tiny hallway, is: 'You smell of office. You smell of work.'

He can't answer straight away; he's out of breath from the stairs which, the higher he climbed, turned him ever more tightly round on himself. And he needs a lavatory.

'No,' he says, wounded. 'No. No I don't. I can't do.' For he left work early. He rushed home, tore off his suit, showered, shaved the parts of his face that needed shaving, put on clean everything, pants, socks, jeans, T-shirt, overshirt, leather jacket. He has a picture of himself, after his shower, splashing his neck and shoulders with Toy Boy (a hahaha Christmas present from Jimmy); he can see himself unpinning the pink cleaners' ticket from the inside of his jacket, taking his boots to the sink, taking a kitchen knife to the hard mud on their heels and then vigorously, viciously, polishing the boots. 'Robert! was that my best chopping knife?' His mother, not angry, watched him from the stove. He fixed his leather saddle-bag crossways over one shoulder. 'Doubt I'll be home tonight. I'll probably take a bed off Jimmy.' She didn't question him. He and Jimmy, and Brian if he was free, usually went drinking on Friday evenings.

Now, in a foreign kitchen, a passageway so narrow that there's barely room for two adults to stand abreast between the sink and the cooker, the carrier of wine bottles is taken from him and stood upright on the counter. Next, a wall-telephone receiver is removed from its hook. 'So we don't get interrupted.' Next, his hands are imprisoned in hers, and lifted, and sniffed. 'Money, then. That's what you smell of. Are you made of money?'

'No. It's iron handrails you can smell. You know, on the tube steps.'

'I thought you were coming by car?'

'No.'

'Do you always say No?' Her tone is interested and curious. 'Do you answer No to everything?'

'No. Can you show me where to wash my hands please.'

From the bathroom window there's a far-off, vertiginous view of trampled back garden. 'I've got to get out of here.' He says it aloud to the ball of violet soap playing catch-if-you-can round the basin. 'She's a loony. She's not even attractive.' He cranks the flush handle for the third time. Still no joy. (The first time he tried, the cistern did empty in a half-hearted way. The lav gargled unpleasantly for a while; swallowed hard; choked – and spewed everything in the pipe back up into the bowl.) Cranking again, holding his nose, desperate, he spots a spray canister on the windowsill and fires it at the ceiling. A poisonous mist hovers for a second; descends. Not air-freshener; not odour-banisher; FLY and wasp KILLER. *For use only as an insecticide. Kills Bugs Dead.*

He sits, in her smoke-scented living room, where he was instructed to sit. On a hard two-seater couch affair draped with a patterned tablecloth, with his back to the window he saw from the road. When they entered, the room was lit only from outside, by twilight and a tangerine haze, and he perched, holding the saddle-bag on his knees like a passenger on a train, while she criss-crossed the room switching on lamps – and then, as an afterthought, walked round behind him, and fought with the window till it dropped shut; and drew the curtains.

'What are you going to have?' To drink, she means. There are bottles and glasses on a tray on a low chest of drawers, and he leans forwards and sideways to see what's on offer.

'What are you having?'

'I've already got a drink. Over there. Whisky.'

'I'll have a vodka, please.'

'Like that?' She holds up a tumbler.

'Great.'

'Tonic? Ice? Lemon?'

'Yeah.' Then he changes his mind. Not a brilliant idea to go along with all her suggestions. 'No lemon.'

Receiving an object, a full, cold, slippery, glass tumbler, from someone else's hand is an awkward business. Dangerous, it can be. It feels so to him. One moment the tumbler is circled by her fingers and thumb; the next, his own fingers and thumb are round it. His and hers, on the slippery glass together. Of course the two sets of fingers are bound to touch – the small circumference of the tumbler ensures it. But it's only for a second. An awkward, dangerous second – during which her brain and hand decide the precise, safe moment to relinquish the tumbler, and his brain and hand agree the precise, safe moment to take it.

(All those occasions in his life when he's received an object – a book, a hammer, a glass – from someone, or handed one over, and this the first time he's been conscious of it: the awkwardness; the potential danger; the unconscious co-ordination required; the miraculous speed of the brain messages that make the action possible.)

The tumbler is his now.

'Would you rather sit here?' She pats an armchair on the back. 'Some say the sofa's not that comfortable.'

'OK then.'

And now they're opposite each other, either side of her empty fireplace, in front of her bookshelves, in identical yellow armchairs. A married couple, it occurs to him, at the pipe and slippers stage. There's a miniature table beside the left arm of his chair, and after one icy and delicious swallow he puts his drink on it.

'Is it OK to sit in this chair? I mean, isn't it somebody's special chair?' He hopes that by asking he'll learn if there's a husband in the background somewhere, or a live-in lover who's out for the evening or away for the week. He forgot, or did not think it proper, to ask about her status when they met.

'No, it's anyone's chair. Your chair. Are you warm enough? Just a minute –' She's on her feet again, plucking a postcard from the mixed art show of postcards lined up on the mantelpiece. With one hand she lifts his glass, with the other she places the postcard, picture side up, on his table. She wipes the bottom of his glass on her sleeve and replaces it on top of a seascape. He peers to read the title: *Portuguese Carracks Off a Rocky Coast*.

'Just a precaution. No offence meant.' She smiles down at him.

But he is offended. 'Why me?' he says. 'Where's your postcard? You haven't got a postcard under your glass.'

'Only because that table doesn't matter. I painted it myself. It's just a bit of old junk.'

He looks away from her, anywhere, at the walls, at the ceiling, at the heavy curtains and delicate furniture. It's a very yellow room. The walls are a strong sunflower, the velvet curtains a brownish gold – except in the places where sunlight

71

has bleached them cream. In addition to the yellow arm-chairs, there are black-and-yellow cushions in a sharper, lemon shade. The lampshades, with one purple exception, are yellow. The patterned kelims on the floor all have some yellow in them – yellow stripes, or zigzags, or lozenges. Yellow leaps out at him from pictures on the walls and from the spines of books in the bookshelves. On a half-moon wall table, yellow tulips, past their best, twist and lean out of a blue glass jug.

'This is a very yellow room,' he says at last.

'A very yellow room – I like that, I like the sound of that. You could say something like that, couldn't you? Hers is a very yellow room. She lives in a very yellow room.' She sips her whisky. 'Perhaps I should have a copy of *The Yellow Book* lying around, or *Novel on Yellow Paper*, or something. What other yellow books are there?' (But she's asking herself, not him.) '*The Yellow Wallpaper*. Oh, and *Crome Yellow*. Have you read *Crome Yellow*?'

'No.'

'I wanted a feeling of sunshine in here because the room faces north. Are you warm enough?' She's in her chair once more, shrugging herself into the cushion at its back. She picks up her glass. 'The heating is on.'

'Yeah, fine.' But the fact is, he's too warm.

'Don't you want to take your jacket off?'

'Oh, OK. Sure.' But sitting in the chair, he can't get any purchase on the ringpull of his undulating zip; and eventually he has to stand, and tug his jacket straight. 'Where should I put it?'

'Anywhere. Back of your chair? Nice jacket.'

'Yeah.' He sits down. He picks up his drink.

'That satchel of yours is making me nervous.' She points to his saddle-bag, on the floor at his feet. 'What horrors does it contain? Notebook? Pencil? Scalpel? Probe?'

'Sorry?' His satchel, his saddle-bag, contains the following: change of pants and socks; T-shirt – in case modesty should require it – for sleeping in; clean shirt for tomorrow; razor, toothbrush and toothpaste in a plastic bag; a variety of condoms, one lot strawberry-flavoured. And his wallet. And his keys. And a paperback, to read on the tube.

'Well, I shall soon find out. Cheers, then, Peter.' She's looking straight at him, smiling, raising her glass. 'Bottoms up. Mud in your eye. Chin chin.'

'Not Peter, Robert.' He frowns. 'Cheers,' he says, frowning into his glass.

'D'you mind if I smoke?' There are cigarettes and a lighter on the blue-painted table at her elbow and she sweeps them into her lap. Her hands are tiny. He remembers the last time they were together, looking at her hands and thinking: They're a kid's hands – and then trying to work out what age kid. Seven? Ten?

'It's your place,' he says, 'you don't have to ask me. Anyway, I know you're a smoker, don't I?'

He does know. Because six weeks ago, at his company's annual Sponsorship bash – where he, as a junior, was on empty-glass awareness and chatting-up duty, and she was a guest – she said, 'Look, if you want to carry on this conversation, you'll have to come outside because I need a fag NOW.' He followed her, carrying their full wine glasses, out of the Board Room, down the wide and shallow and slippery stairs, across the marble wastes of Reception, out of the mahogany architraved-and-pedimented double doors, on to the pavement. A gang of shivering, sheepish or defiant smokers loitered at either side of the entrance. 'Come and join the élite,' somebody called, 'this is where it's at; it's all happening here.' He tried to light her cigarette for her, but the wind wouldn't let him. 'I'm not supposed to be out here, you know,' he reminded her back view, hunched over the lighter, 'I'll get shot, it's my job to look after the VIPs.' 'I'm a VIP,' she turned, triumphant with the lit cigarette; and removed her glass from his hand, 'it's your job to look after me.' Two or three drinks later, when he was back on duty in the Board Room, there was a tap on his elbow, followed by a whisper in his ear: 'I've had enough of these wankers, haven't you? Isn't there a pub round here we could go to?'

He watches her, over the top of his tumbler, sip her whisky, draw on her cigarette. Quick, nervous movements. Is she nervous? Can she be? Watching her, he finds to his annoyance that she is attractive after all. More than attractive, beautiful. Desirable. She wasn't when he arrived, she wasn't any of these things earlier, but she is now. There was a girl in the year above him at school who'd had this same power to confuse. The angel he thought and dreamed about, the memory of whose eyes and mouth devastated his home life, would at next sighting be unrecognisable, would be nothing at all. And then, suddenly and unaccountably – at dinnertime, say, in the canteen – her loveliness, her, what was the word, allure, would be back in place. Restored? Or – a positive action of their own – reasserted? Not being able to solve the puzzle had driven him crazy. He began to doubt his judgement and his eyesight. He came to believe that a malicious trick had been played on him.

'Well, Robert-not-Peter, I'm sorry I got your name wrong. I really am. Forgive me.' She hesitates. 'How about a top-up?'

'Thanks.'

His refilled glass has a slice of lemon in it. He sips. There's more vodka, less tonic, in this drink than last time.

'I did forget your name. But I haven't forgotten where you come from. So that's something.'

'Where's that then?'

'Norwich. Aha. I bet you didn't think I'd remember that.'

He smiles in spite of himself. A big wide disbelieving smile.

'I don't come from Norwich.' He waits a moment. (Is this a game? Is she trying to wind him up?) 'Gunnersbury. Gunnersbury's where I come from.'

'Oh I know that. I know you told me that.' She sounds impatient or, it could be, flustered. 'But I don't mean your flat, of course I don't, I mean your roots. Where your family live.'

'I haven't got a flat. I live at home, in my mother's semi. In Gunnersbury. I told you. I've always lived there.'

He had told her, because she'd asked him. They were

sitting in the pub, side by side on a banquette in a dark alcove (he'd wanted to sit opposite her, but the pub was full, there were no other seats anywhere), and she said: 'Tell me about yourself.' So he did. He told her about his father's dying, the months and months it had taken. How his older brother Steven had left home, without explanation, the day after the funeral – and gone to Adelaide, and never come back. He told her some embarrassing stuff, such as his father's habit of addressing him as 'Bob, old son'; he confided a lot of quite personal and difficult stuff, because she asked him. Quizzed him.

Nothing about Norwich. Norwich hadn't come into it.

'Well, where do I get Norwich from?' She frowns. She stubs out her cigarette and fishes in the packet for another. She's still frowning, pursing her mouth, trying to work it out.

I want you, he decides. (Or the vodka decides.) *I want to kiss your mouth. I want to kiss it now.*

If he could move, if his brain would send the required message to his legs, if he were another person altogether, he would get up, and cross the four-foot divide between his chair and hers, and kiss her mouth. Now.

'I know—' she waves an arm to get his attention, punching the air repeatedly with her fist – 'I've got it. The man in the moon came down too soon and asked his way to Norwich – you're not going to tell me you've forgotten that? You have to remember reciting that.

'Don't shake your head, Robert. Think. We had an argument about the porridge part, remember? You said plum, and I said no, it was pease. It was cold pease porridge the man in the moon burnt his mouth on. You were adamant – and I laughed at you because I knew I was right.'

He has to shake his head. Because although she had laughed – that was true, he remembers her laughing – her laughter hadn't been at him. She'd laughed at, or about, the other people in the pub. She said they were evil, they all looked evil; and she put her face in her hands (to shut the evil people out?). Eventually, she looked up and laughed. A spooky laugh, he remembers thinking. He remembers wondering if she did this often – took strange guys, young guys, to pubs or wherever.

'Well I dunno. I'll have one more try. Does Knickers Off Ready When I Come Home ring a bell with you?'

'Pardon?' A burning, unstoppable blush is spreading from his chest to his neck, is engulfing his ears, his cheeks, his forehead. Within seconds his whole head is on fire.

She sighs. She looks at her watch. 'Look, if you haven't changed your mind – and I assure you I shan't mind if you have – I think it's time we got started. It's ten past eight already, you know. I think it's time we got it over with.'

Started. Over with.

He picks up his tumbler, almost empty, and swallows. He peers deep into the glass. There are shards of ice at the bottom, and two lemon pips, and a slice of lemon. He examines them carefully. He inspects them minutely. The lemon peel is brownish, too tired, you'd think, to use.

'Well, it is on the late side for this sort of thing. You were late arriving, remember. That meant I had a couple of drinks before you even got here. I promised myself I wouldn't, and then I did. Nerves, I expect. I don't really know why I agreed to this – I hate being interviewed. Put on the spot, I can never think of anything interesting or illuminating to say. But if I don't make sense it'll be your fault. You said six-thirty.'

He turns his tumbler round while he thinks about this. The ice and lemon and lemon pips slide and re-form into new patterns. 'I'm sorry, I don't follow,' he says at last. 'I didn't come here to interview you. Why would I want to do that?'

Silence.

'Oh I see.' For suddenly he does see . . . 'Oh I get it. You think I'm someone else. You've muddled me up with someone else. Peter,' he says, 'you were expecting Peter.'

'Peter?'

'Well, not me anyway. You weren't expecting me.'

'I was. I thought I was. Look, some young man wanted to interview me. Someone at that function asked if he could. I thought it was you. I told him I was going to be away for a month, hoping that he would forget, that it would all go away. And then as soon as I got back from the States the phone rang. Remember me? the voice said. From the Archer & Thomson do? We've got a date, remember? I'd forgotten about the interview, naturally. And then when I did remember, I tried to put a face to the voice on the phone and I came up with yours. It was your face I saw. I thought it was your voice. There've been four calls from that voice, I think, since I got home. Yes, it must be at least four.'

He's made two calls. There've been two calls only from him. He phoned her ten days ago to make this date, and then he phoned her last night to check that it was still OK. To see if it was still on. 'I phoned you twice,' he says, 'we've talked to each other twice.'

'Robert,' she says. 'Look, Robert, if you didn't come here to interview me, why did you come? Why are you here?'

Sex. That's why I'm here. That's what I've come for. Sex.

But he can't say that. Obviously not. 'Because you asked me.' He can say that because it's true – she did ask him.

'Remind me, when, where, did I ask you?' She pushes herself out of her chair and then, with her back to him, goes to the chest of drawers where the drinks tray is. She pulls open the top drawer. 'I know there's a packet of fags in here somewhere.' He can hear her rummaging in the drawer, moving heavy things and papery things. On an impulse, he picks up the postcard from the miniature table and slips it into his saddle-bag. (Something of hers to keep. Something – the message on the back – to examine later, which might betray her. Something to prove he was here, in this yellow room, in this yellow chair.)

'Ah, thank God for that.' She's waving a cigarette packet. 'My lifesaver. Whew.'

I'm a thief, he tells her silently – and his secret makes him feel better. He feels stronger suddenly and more sure of himself. More confident and in charge. He waits till she's facing him. 'When we were in the pub,' he says, 'that's when you invited me here. You know – after you kissed me.'

Silence.

77

'You've got an empty glass,' she says eventually. 'Would you like a drink? Shall we both have another drink?'

She has no memory of kissing him, she is sorry to say. She confesses this when they're in their yellow chairs with a full glass in their hands. So he decides to tell her the circumstances of the kiss (Why not? he thinks. Why the fuck shouldn't I?), the simple facts of it. No details, though. He will not remind her how long the kiss went on – for ever – and he will not describe the – indescribable, anyway – effect the kiss had on him. She is not going to learn (why should he flatter her?) that what stays in his head is the subtle and insistent way she nudged his mouth open; and the, at first teasing, then curious, then desperate, way her tongue explored his tongue. (His teeth; his gums; his entire mouth.) Likewise the expectations and fantasies and aching desire her kiss triggered, the hellish days and nights he's endured – he won't say a word about those.

They were in the pub, he explains. They'd been there for a couple of hours, having a quiet drink and, you know, talking – when without warning she leant towards him, took his face in her hands, and kissed him. On the mouth. When it was over, she said, 'We must do this again.' He asked if he could take her home – so that they could do it again – and she said No. ('No, not tonight, Josephine', were the exact words she used.) She said she had to pack because she was going away in the morning. 'Give me a call in six weeks' time,' she said. She wrote her phone number down for him on a beer mat. She said, 'Find me a taxi, babe.' He found her a taxi. She kissed him again through the open taxi window. 'Come up and see me,' she said, in a Mae West drawl. 'Don't forget me, sugar.'

'What can I say?' She shrugs; she spreads her hands – a gesture of hopelessness or helplessness. Of appeal. 'I was pissed, you realise. We'd been drinking for hours, hadn't we – wine at the party, then beer, then shorts, no doubt. I don't remember anything. I must have been completely out of it.'

He sits watching her, sipping his vodka from time to time, relaxed. What stunning eyes, he thinks, huge and violet – like, like? That fifties movie star. Like Elizabeth Taylor's. What a beautiful, curvy mouth. All the better to kiss me with, my dear.

'You remembered you had to pack.' That's quite cruel, he tells himself, that's quite a cruel thing to say, Bob old son. But he can't stop himself. He has the power now, he's in charge and he senses victory, however long it takes, in the shape of her double bed. (She owes him. She owes him that, at least.) 'You remembered you were going away and had to pack,' he says. 'You can't have been entirely out of it. I didn't think so. It didn't strike me you were. You weren't too pissed to write your phone number on the beer mat.'

'That thing, that expression you used, something about Knickers off – what did that mean? What's that signify?'

She refills his wine glass, taking a lot of care, he notices, not to spill wine on the tablecloth. But she spills it anyway. 'Dear dear.' She refills her own glass. They've drunk nearly a full bottle of the wine he brought. Or she has. They're eating the disgusting supper she promised him.

'Norwich. But really it's the other way round.'

'Norwich?'

'Knickers Off Ready When I Come Home equals Norwich. It's made out of the letters in Norwich. It's an acronym – no, not acronym, what then? There must be a word for it. Anyway, it's a sort of code, a jokey code. People, servicemen, used to put Norwich on letters home to their wives or girl-friends. On the back of the envelope always, in capitals. NORWICH, you know, like SWALK. I thought everybody knew that. Have another slice of ham?'

The ham is ready-sliced. The slices are pink and shiny and slippery, rectangular in shape. The rectangles have rounded ends. They lie on the plate, half in, half out of, their plastic Safeway container.

'No. Thanks.' Norwich. He repeats the word in his head. Something not right somewhere.

'Another radish? Mnemonic. Mnemonic's the word I was looking for. I think. Or is it?'

The radishes must be several days old. There's no crack when you bite them, there's nothing remotely hot about them. 'No really, I'm fine. No' – he covers his wine glass with his hand – 'I'm doing fine.'

'D'you know something, Robert – there, I've got it right, *Rob*ert – I thought you were gay. I was convinced you were gay.' She tops up her glass. 'Whoops. Messy – are you gay?'

'No.' She's drunk, he realises. (He's drunk too, he knows that, but not that drunk. Not arseholed. Like she is, like she's just about to be.) I've got to stop her, he thinks. If this is going to work, if we're ever going to have sex, I've got to get her sober.

'I think it was your boots – your very very highly polished boots. Yes. And your leathers – that butch leather coat. And your bag. And your very very very short hair.'

'My hair isn't short.' He runs a hand over it to check. 'I was thinking only yesterday it needed a cut. Everyone wears leather, you know. It's fashion.'

'Ah well, yes, well. Maybe.'

'The gay guys I know are into long hair at the moment. A lot of them are.'

'Cheers then, Robert.' She raises her empty glass. Her eyes, in the candlelight, have a glassy and empty look. Her smile's not quite right either – lopsided? Yes, that's it, lopsided.

He gets up from the table and steadies himself, balancing his weight evenly on both feet. 'I'm going to make some coffee. OK? I could murder a cup. I expect you could.'

'Fine.' She smiles and nods. 'Fine. Anything you want, anything you like. It's fine by me.' She goes on nodding at him, up and down, up and down, like a car toy in a back window.

'Knickers is spelt with a K,' he says. Supper is over. He's on his knees at her feet, leaning his head against her knee. She's stroking his head, rhythmically but vaguely, with the tips of her fingers. 'I knew there was something wrong. Your Norwich thing doesn't work. Norwich begins with an N.'

'Doesn't matter. 'Snot important.' She goes on stroking. 'It's like a brush, your hair, a prickly old brush.'

The rhythm of her fingers is beginning to get on his nerves. He would like to get up off the floor. He would like to take her to bed now, he's been dying to fuck her for hours, but she keeps putting him off. 'What's the hurry?' she keeps saying, and 'We've got all night, remember,' and 'Le's have another drink.' (At one point he took the bottle away – this was the second bottle of the stuff he brought – but she wove her way to the kitchen and came back with a different bottle altogether, one of her own. 'Abracadabra,' she said. He took the bottle from her hand and put it on the mantelpiece; they didn't need any more of that, he told her. Neither of them needed any more. He gripped her by the shoulders and tried to kiss her, but the moment their lips touched she pushed him off. 'Later,' she whispered, reaching for the mantelpiece. 'Later. Don' be a spoil-sport, Peter ol' son.')

'It's bedtime.' He says it loudly and firmly. (Be masterful, Jimmy warned him yesterday, you gotta let her know who's in charge. They like it when you take charge. How old is she? Thirty-five? Forty? Those older bitches can get up to all sorts of tricks. You gotta go for it right away. The minute you're inside her door, OK?)

'Up you get.' He disentangles himself and gets up. He stands over her and holds out his hand. 'Come on. On your feet.'

'Anything you like, sugar. Anything you want.' She stares up at him, not seeing him, ignoring his hand. Not moving.

He lies in her bed, on her pillows, under her duvet, staring into the tangerine-tinted dark. If he turns his head a fraction he can make out her face. Heavy lids, child's nose, vulnerable mouth (open at this moment, and emitting a powerful ashtray-and-rotten-fruit smell). She stirs from time to time, she shudders, she snores a sudden grunting snore, she groans. Her eyelids flutter, she mumbles, she flings out an arm – but she doesn't wake.

He didn't make love to her before she slept; they didn't have sex. When he finally managed – half carrying her, his arm round her waist, her lifeless arm round his neck – to get her into the bedroom, she passed out on the bed. In her clothes.

He keeps away from her in the bed (his body still wants her), as far away as he can. He remains on his back, with his eyes open, his hands tight by his sides, going over the evening in his head. There's always the morning, he thinks, it might be OK in the morning, she'll want me in the morning. *She lives in a very yellow room.* The phrase slips into his head and he says it out loud, and repeats it – as though there were something to be done with the words. As if the words had the power to help in some way, or change anything, or explain, or solve, anything.

Earl Lovelace

THE GAMBLER'S FUNERAL

CHRISTMAS IS MY time. As soon as the night breeze in this valley begin to blow chilly and the chaconia leaves turn red, I tune up my cuatro and I gone: Mamoral, Tabaquite, Arima, San Raphael, all those places in the island where people come to lose themselves in the music and merriment of parang. Leave my brothers to run our undertaking business for a change, sure that they not going to miss me, because in this season people too busy enjoying themselves to worry to dead.

But the day before the day before Christmas Eve, I find myself with a glass in my hand in front a flask of rum, with Leroy and Archer, on the narrow veranda of Independence Recreation Club, waiting for Felix who gone to the store to get some new strings for his guitar to come back before we head for the big parang party in Arima. I there looking out at the road for Boodram taxi, when Clarence come in with a bag with a ham and two bottles of rum and straight away call for another nip. Right behind him Smithy and Jazzy arrive, dressed up, both of them, Smithy in a maroon silk shirt and a polkadot scarf, and Jazzy in a black bow-tie and a black suit.

They had come from the second funeral of Dorlene Cruikshank who twenty-seven years earlier opened her eyes in a coffin at her own funeral; and who, but for the alertness of her grandson, would have been buried alive. The family was about to put the lid on her coffin when the little boy thought he saw her eyelids flutter and before anyone could stop him, he reached into the coffin and began to shake her. To the shock and fright of all in the church at the burial

83

service, she began to cough and splutter, then she jumped up cursing, blaming her family for trying to kill her.

After she revived, she never spoke a word to any of her family except to the grandson who had saved her. And from that day to the end of her life she had nothing whatever to do with anyone who called himself a doctor. She cut out meat from her diet and, together with a young Shouters leader who used to be goalkeeper for Cosmos Football Club, opened her own church, set up as a fortune-teller, and had a rich life that gave gossips in the The Guaya plenty to talk about. She had already put herself up to run as an independent candidate for the County Council elections when she got a vision that directed her to go to the villages and towns around the island and warn people about the calamity that was to overtake the nation if we didn't take better care of one another. She had spent seven years on that mission and had just returned from walking forty miles from Pinto Road in Arima, through Valencia, Matura, Sangre Grande and the villages along the Manzanilla Road when she took in with a pain in her side. They rushed her to the hospital but she refused to let a doctor touch her and she died. This time the death was followed by a post-mortem.

It was Miss Dorlene we talked about as we sat around the table. We were going on and on, recalling the juicy episodes of her second life, when Smithy picked up the cards and motioned to Jazzy:

'Enough talk. Sit down, Jazzy. Jazzy, sit down!' So Jazzy sit down, and the four-hand rummy start: Clarence and Leroy against Jazzy and Smithy.

'You all, don't go yet. We cooking,' Cap called out from the kitchen. But I couldn't stay. Felix came back with the guitar strings and we leave to go Arima. So I wasn't there to see for myself what happen; so, I selling the story just as I buy it.

Maybe for half an hour, the four of them sit there playing rummy, then, after a while more, fellows come and the poker start. As the game going on, Cap bringing food, Cap bringing rum, he bringing chicken, he bringing ham. Everybody eating and having a good time. Clarence, with an early run of luck, eating and drinking, cracking jokes, laughing hard and taking delight in sucking out the marrow from the bones of the chicken. Then his luck change. When the game finish, Leroy have all the money. Clarence pocket empty, Clarence look for his bag. He find the bag with his two bottles of rum, but no ham.

'Where the ham I had in this bag?' he asking everybody.

At last Smithy who is kind of the resident comedian in the club say, 'Put the man out of his misery, Jazzy. Tell him about his ham.'

And Jazzy – with that sorrowful surrendering look on his face that he uses when he want to tell a man who want to borrow money from him that he don't have none – spread open his hands and say, 'Clarence, boy, you eat your own ham. The ham you was eating was your own ham.'

Christmas morning was the next time I see Clarence. He left a message that he wanted to see me, but that whole week I had it real busy. I reach home sometimes two, three, four in the morning, sometimes I don't reach home at all. Anyhow, late Christmas morning, I land up with my band by Clarence where he living there in The Guaya.

We play two tunes outside his door and he come out with his estate constable uniform on and a face that fighting to look happy. But in his voice, you could hear the misery. Still, he call us inside and he put a bottle on the table. Rum is not what we after; 'tis the brotherhood, really, in this short time we have here. We play two more tunes and we take a drink, not big shots to damage the bottle, but good enough, and then we look to leave.

'Where Pauline? Where the mistress of the house?' Smithy ask, talking hard so that Pauline, if she inside, would hear. 'We can't come to your house and have the lady stay inside. Pauline!'

'She gone by her mother.' And when Clarence hear the silence, he add: 'To bake.' Nobody believe him, but not even Smithy had the heart to ask him for any further explanation.

'I hear you want to see me,' I said.

'Yes, but it too late for that now,' making me think it musta been about money. Clarence see right through me. 'No, this is about another matter. But we can't talk now. I have to go and take up duty.'

'Later, then,' I tell him.

But my band get itself into the finals of the parang competition and suddenly we in demand. Everywhere people want us to come and play. So is after New Year that I will see Clarence.

He walk through the parlour and he come into the office of the funeral agency and sit down like he have the world on his shoulders. On his face is the knot of a smile, and in his eyes the glimmer of a wisdom that make me a little uneasy.

'I want you to arrange a funeral for me,' he tell me.

'Who you burying?'

'Me.'

'You?'

And then he tell me the story. Pauline leave him. 'She find out about Rosey.'

'Rosey? You's a madman or what? You couldn't find a woman who not living next door to you?'

'Is not what you think. Nothing happen.'

'And you killing yourself for this nothing?'

'I didn't say burial,' he tell me. 'I say funeral. Like Norlene Cruikshank,' the knot of his smile tightening and his wise eyes watching me.

'Oh, I see.'

Clarence is always tempting fate. He do things without thinking. He find himself in the middle of something that he never intended to be in and instead of standing still, he go and do something else more foolish that sink him deeper in calamity. I see it with him in gambling and it happen with him with women. The marvel is that even in the deepest hole, he believe there is a way out just for him alone.

Sometimes I think is because he know he lucky and that people like him. Just so women does fall for him. So he take the world for granted, doing all kinda stupidness and expecting things to fall back into place. And what make it so hard to write him off is because he have this repentant side to him. He try to make up. I suppose that is why Pauline stay so long with him. But Pauline is a young woman; Pauline have feelings. Six months ago in order to make up for some stupidness to her, he decide to send her by her brother in New York for the holiday she had always wanted. He put himself on his best behaviour. He not going to the club, he going home straight from work, he stopping at the bakery to buy bread to carry home, he carrying home plants, he taking her to wrestling, he washing clothes and in full view of the neighbours hanging them out on lines to dry.

When you see him like that, you feel so sorry. You feel that the world has turned upside down. And you actually feel relief when Clarence break away again and go back to his old ways, gambling his money, drinking, staying out days, slipping off somewhere with some woman, Pauline take plenty.

The last straw for her was the Christmas Eve morning when he reach home without the ham. Pauline ain't tell him a thing. She merry and singing and cleaning like nothing ain't happen. Then Christmas Day he come back from work. Pauline not there; but he meet the table set. Flowers in the vase, fern and anthurium and chaconia, the place well put away, the best tablecloth on the table, making him feel he is forgiven. Clarence sit down to eat. When Clarence lift up the plate turned down on the table in front of him, it was to see a jack of spades.

When he uncover the bowls, there was a playing card in every one.

When I look at Clarence face I couldn't even laugh, it was so pitiful.

'Harold, you have to organise the funeral for me.'

'Why you don't just go and talk to her?'

'You don't think I try?'

I got the picture. I guess he run out of making excuses and this funeral business is the only way back to her.

'Suppose she don't come to the funeral?'

'She will come.'

'This thing going to cost, you know. You will have to have a casket and everything as if it is a real funeral.'

'Harold, you can't believe I want you to do this for free. I will pay you. Just total everything.'

'And if you want people at your funeral, this is not a good time. January month everybody broken. You turn around twice and the Carnival season upon you. And, Carnival, well, no matter how much people like you, death is the last thing people want to think about in that season. Everybody going to fete, they going to hear steelbands, they going to get their costumes make. And Pauline? You don't think she might want to play mas? You don't want her to feel that you die just to spite her, just to put her in mourning and prevent her from feting and enjoying the Carnival?'

'So when you think is a good time, then? I have to do it before she go New York, the trip I promise her. I buy the ticket for her already. Right now the only thing keeping her here is her visa.'

'It going to have to be Easter. If you want people to turn out, the best time for your funeral is Easter.'

'OK,' he say.

So we settle on Easter.

'You sure you want to go through with this thing? Look, man,' I tell him, 'even if I organise everything, it will still look fishy. You can't die just so. You not sick. People will get suspicious. Everybody will want to know what happen, inquest and everything.'

'Harold, people could die anytime. Just last week I read about a doctor who drop down jogging. Healthy like a fiddle one day, next day you gone. Every day it happens, healthy people collapsing.'

'But you have to remember this is something you staging. It have to be truer than the real truth.'

'You right.' So Clarence put on a short pants and he started jogging.

Everybody in The Guaya notice Clarence in this activity, because, since Clarence leave school, he ain't hold a bat, he ain't kick a ball. Now, suddenly, he is an athlete.

'With your lifestyle, at your age, you could get a stroke,' Poliah, the other estate constable, tell him.

'Madman!' was all Smithy say, not knowing that Clarence playing a part.

I thought it would have been harder to pull it off; but I forget how afraid people are of death and anything to do with dying. When you in the coffin, your best friend don't even want to look at your face. And if people do look down, it is their own face, not yours, they see. So in the end it was easy. I arrange everything, first to tell people that the body in the mortuary, and second to make a mask that will look like Clarence face for people to see in the coffin.

The wake surprise me. People come out from all about, not only from The Guaya but from Rio and Mayaro where he worked as a painter before he got the job as estate constable with the County Council. Gamblers from all parts of the island come. Fellars from far. Women in their numbers. When the sun come up next morning, in the house it had people singing hymns, and outside under the shed in the yard, three different gambling games still going and it had plentiful rum and coffee.

And then the funeral. It was a real nice funeral. All the fellars from the club was there, Jazzy and Smithy, Leroy and Archer. Poliah, bursting out of his uniform, his belly hanging over his belt, saying, 'I tell him not to jog. You see me? Exercise will never kill me.'

But the person I looking for is Pauline.

I am standing by the graveside when I hear this rustling noise behind me and when I look around it was to face the solid weightiness of this woman, fabulous, perfumed, all in black with a black veil falling from her hat over half of her face, about her this rubbery, exhausted, wordless, almost triumphing grief. Her two sisters, one on either side of her, holding her up. She loosened herself from them and went alone to the graveside. She reached the coffin and all she said was, 'Why you do it, Clarence? Why?' and I wasn't sure if she was talking about what she thought was his dying or something else.

I know that Clarence was somewhere nearby hearing her. And I was waiting for him to show himself and tell her he not really dead. But then I begin to wonder how he will tell her, with what words. What he will say. All while they tumbling earth into the coffin that is what I wondering.

After the funeral, we all gather by his house, everybody chatting, drinking rum and laughing, remembering him, consoling one another, people holding up each other as if now they needed each other more than ever. I listened to them talking about this man, the good of him, the foolishness he did, the chances he took, the jokes he give, the money he lose, the money he win, the women he had, his love for Pauline, the number of times they break up, the number of times they make back up again. Smithy tell the story about the time when he come in the club and every bet he make he say, 'This is for the money to send Pauline to New York', and when he lose the bet saying, 'Fellars, have a heart. Pauline have to go to New York.'

In the end nobody had a bad word to say about him. People understand him. His whole life story had come out, things I sure he didn't know that people know. His whole life was out in the open. He didn't have anything to hide any more. I up and down pacing the floor, waiting for him to come through the door.

I kept waiting for him to show. I was uneasy. People took it for grief. People come consoling me: 'What to do, Harold, boy,' like at a real funeral.

'Yes, what to do?' like if Clarence really dead in truth.

And then the thought hit me that maybe he not going to show, and I start to think about what my brothers will say about the money I spend on this whole affair. Still, I wait.

We remained, a hard core of us there with Pauline well into the night. Clarence didn't turn up. I don't know if he was waiting for us to leave so he could face Pauline by herself. I don't know if the things people say about him was too much, too good, make him realise that he couldn't compete with the Clarence who was dead. And then just so it hit me, Clarence not coming back, like a pain, like the cold staggering terror that you get at the glimpse of your own death. I spend all this money on this funeral for this man. And what in it for me?

'Harold,' I tell myself, 'you get trapped. You get trap.' And I know my brothers not going to find it funny. I say goodnight to everybody and I walk the mile and a half home alone. In the yard, my own yard, I stand up and watch the bed of flowers, the croton and the ginger lilies and the chaconia and heliconia. I needed a knife to cut them from the stems. I break off a small branch from the ixora with the red needles of two flowers. And I open the door.

Inside, Ivy was waiting up for me. I give her the branch with the flowers. She took it at first without really looking at me. Maybe it was something in the way I remained standing, or maybe in the way I was looking at her. Or in the soft, kinda sad way I said, 'Here,' when I gave her the branch with the flowers.

'Hey, what happen?' she ask me.

Together we sit down on the sofa and I take her two hands into my own and I begin to smooth out each finger, one by one.

'What happen?' she asked again in a voice filled with suspicion, looking into my face this time, her eyes brightening, then chuckling with wisdom and a mischievous tenderness as if she knew what I was after.

'Nothing.' I just held her.

Patrick Marber

SCENES FROM AN ABANDONED PLAY

OFFICE

Blake is on the phone. There is a large revolving chair in front of his desk.

BLAKE: This is a deal breaker. You just broke the deal. No my friend, *you* go fuck yourself. No it's the line . . . I said go fuck yourself. What? No . . . you . . . Y-O-U . . . go . . . G-O . . . F-U-C-K . . . yourself. Uh-huh. That's what I said. I know exactly who you are. Absolutely. Go fuck yourself, you queer plastic-faced fuck.

He puts the phone down. Marcia enters.

Fuck off.

MARCIA: I'm –

BLAKE: The new PA, I know. Fuck off.

MARCIA: I –

BLAKE: And get me forty Rothmans. (*Sweetly*) Please.

Marcia exits. The phone rings. Blake waits and then picks up.

Sorry's no good. Sorry doesn't help us here. Yes, the money is agreed. We agreed the money five months ago . . . the 'little people' agreed the money. The problem? The problem is the car. It's not a car, it's an insult.

No, she will not travel in a limousine . . . she travels stretch. She stretches. You stretch her to the première or you sit on the sequel and swivel, my friend.

How long is this car? Four metres? What the fuck does that mean, talk in feet, talk to me in feet, you metric cunt.

Thirty? No . . . thirty-five minimum. Yes, they make them

92

. . . well, build one or she walks. She is very angry. How do I know? Because she's with me right now. She's crying. Yeah . . . you made her cry. Sure . . . stars . . . what can you do. Thirty-five feet. We have a deal.

I will see you at the première. I will be bringing my tape measure. Thank you. I am having a nice day.

He puts the phone down. He speaks to the chair.

There you go. We got the car. You wanna have lunch?

The chair swivels round. It contains an eight-year-old girl.

GIRL: Cool.

BAR

Barry drinking alone. Ian approaches him.

IAN: Hallo.

Ian sits next to Barry.

BARRY: Hallo?

IAN: My name's Barry.

BARRY: Big deal.

IAN: I heard the barman call you Barry.

BARRY: Two Barrys. Crazy world.

IAN: And this bar is called 'Barry's'.

BARRY: Yes, I know. I own it.

IAN: Is everything you own called Barry's?

BARRY: Yeah, I label it with dymo.

Ian laughs a little too much.

IAN: That's funny.

Pause.

BARRY: Listen, Barry, I'm having a quiet drink, alone, in my bar which . . . is not a gay bar . . . you see what I'm saying . . .?

IAN: It is a gay bar.

BARRY: What?

IAN: This is a gay bar. It's featured in *The Gay Guide*.

BARRY: The what?

93

IAN: It's a guide to the gay hangouts of Europe and America. 'Barry's Bar is an informal, discreet modern bar. Non-scene. Recommended.' Something like that.

BARRY: Well, obviously some arse bandit editor has mistaken his cock for his pencil.

IAN: I'm very sorry to trouble you.

BARRY: No problem.

IAN: Very sorry to embarrass you.

BARRY: You didn't. You disturbed me.

IAN: I'm very sorry to have disturbed you.

BARRY: Thank you. Forget it.

Pause.

IAN: Mind if I finish my drink?

BARRY: Yes, yes, finish your drink, please.

Pause.

IAN: Can I get you one?

BARRY: No, thank you.

Silence. Ian drinks his beer.

IAN: Good beer.

BARRY: Yuh.

IAN: Thai.

Pause.

IAN: Sure I can't tempt you?

BARRY: I'm sure.

Pause.

You got a copy of that guide?

IAN: At home, I could bring it in . . .

BARRY: Nahh, forget it.

Pause.

Yes actually, bring it in, thank you. Just leave it with the barman. How much did it cost, I'll give you the money.

IAN: I couldn't part with it. It's very precious to me.

Beat.

BARRY: Well, maybe you could photocopy the relevant page?

IAN: The offending item?

BARRY: Yeah.

IAN: I can't do that. It would be a breach of copyright.

Pause.
BARRY: Are you taking the piss?
IAN: Yes.
Pause.
BARRY: Who are you and what do you want?
IAN: I'm a queer and I want to suck your cock.
BARRY: Well . . . I'm a heterosexual and I don't want you to suck my cock.
IAN: Your loss. Be seeing you. Barry.
Ian gets up and goes. Barry watches him leave. Thinks. Blackout.

BRASSERIE

Larry and Jake, drinking outside.
JAKE: I hate the summer.
LARRY: Look at that. She's naked, that woman is nude. Look at her. Brings out the stalker in all of us. One day they'll legislate against looking.
JAKE: They have. They've got us by the brains. We look, we feel guilty, it's not civilised.
LARRY: See that? Think she's got a degree?
JAKE: What?
LARRY: Jesus . . . the black one . . . look at her . . . no shame . . . no knickers. She knows what she's doing.
JAKE: That's her pitch, knowledge.
LARRY: Any other century, if we were aristos in the eighteenth century we could buy her.
JAKE: She's gone, file the image.
LARRY: Believe me it's in. She is in the wank bank. They can't take that away from us. We have our home movies. What are we, honestly, what are we?
JAKE: A couple of cunts shooting the breeze.
LARRY: No. We are prisoners, my friend. Never doubt it, they've got the power. Sit on my face . . . I beg you, please just sit on my face.
JAKE: I hate the summer.

Kirsty Seymour-Ure

THE RUSSIAN

I COME HOME from school one day to find a strange man in the kitchen. He is making something on the stove, peering intently into a saucepan and stirring vigorously.

'Who are you? What are you doing here?' I ask him. It is a week since my father left home.

The man says, 'Ssh. Not now. Just a minute.' He has a strong foreign accent. His hair is thick and bushy and he wears little round glasses. He needs a shave.

I recognise that he's concentrating and say, 'What's that you're making?'

This time he glances at me. He says a word. 'Polenta,' he says.

Dumping my satchel on the floor, I go over to the stove and look inside the saucepan. The man continues to stir its contents. The stuff is yellowy, gooey, a thick semolina. 'That looks disgusting,' I tell him. I watch him for a moment, then go in search of my mother.

I find her in the garden, looking at the bees humming round the roses. 'Mum, there's a man in the kitchen. He's cooking. He says he's making polenta.'

'Yes, darling? Polenta?' says my mother. I begin to suspect she may not be much help. I wish my father were here. 'I'm not exactly sure what that is,' my mother says vaguely.

'Mum, I don't care about the polenta. Who *is* he? What's he doing in our kitchen? Does Dad know he's here?'

'Ah!' exclaims my mother. She is wearing a thin flowery summer dress and I notice suddenly how thin she is. *My mother*, I think. Everything seems to pile on top of me and I find myself unexpectedly crying. 'Don't cry, love,' says my mother. 'It's all right. He's our new lodger.' She hugs me.

I wipe my eyes, sniffling. 'Lodger?'

'With your father gone,' my mother explains, 'I'm afraid I'm having to let out one of the spare rooms.' She turns and begins to walk back towards the house. We can see the lodger in the kitchen, moving about. I put my hand on my mother's arm to stop her going inside.

'Is he living here then?' I ask. 'With us? I mean, will he eat with us and everything? What about the bathroom?'

'This is his home now,' says my mother. 'We must make him feel at home.' She adds, as if it was an afterthought, 'His name's Konstantin. He's Russian.' Then she goes inside.

I pause to take in this information. A Russian. This sounds exotic and interesting and makes me inclined to forgive his rudeness. Perhaps he doesn't speak English? I watch my mother enter the kitchen. Konstantin the Russian looks up and a smile lights up his face. 'Maria!' he exclaims, as if she is the last person in the world he expected to see. He opens his arms and she goes up to him and they kiss on both cheeks as if they were old friends who hadn't seen each other for months. Finally my mother looks round and beckons to me.

'This is my daughter,' she says, a note in her voice that I can't identify. She stretches out her hand to me.

'Ah! You must be Anna,' the Russian says.

I am startled, not expecting him to have my name so readily on his lips. I look at my mother, who has a serene expression on her face. She is giving nothing away. The Russian holds out his hand, as if it is he who is welcoming me. 'Konstantin,' he says. 'I am very pleased to meet you. I hear so much about you.'

We shake hands. I want to know how he has heard so much about me, but can't think of a way of asking, at least not with my mother there.

The Russian turns back to his cooking. He seems familiar with our kitchen. He scrapes the congealing mass of semo-lina-like substance into a bowl. He sprinkles salt and pepper over the top of this, then carries it through to the living room. For some reason, my mother and I follow him. We all sit in armchairs and look at one another. Konstantin eats. I think I am the only one who feels any sense of unease.

My father calls. Konstantin answers the telephone. He has been here a week now. I am standing in the hall right next to him and I watch him as he picks up the phone and says our number without having to read it. He hands me the receiver. 'It is your father,' he says, smiling.

'Who the hell was that?' says my father.

'Hi, Dad,' I say.

'Hello, sweetheart. Who was that?'

'The lodger,' I tell him. 'He lives here now.' Konstantin is at my elbow. 'Hang on,' I say to my father. To Konstantin I say coldly, 'I'd like to speak to my father in private, if you don't mind.'

'What do you mean, he lives there?' says my father, sounding bemused and a little concerned.

'Well, he lives here, Dad. I can't think of another way to put it. He pays rent. We give him breakfast. Mum says she needs the money now that you've left.' I'm not trying to make him feel guilty, just give him the bare facts. I say, 'I wish you'd come back, Dad.'

'Anna, you know that's impossible,' he says. Do I know that?

'He's Russian,' I tell my father. 'If you came back, we wouldn't need to have him here. He eats this stuff like semolina, all the time.'

'Is your mother there? Put her on the line, please.'

'But Dad, we've hardly . . .'

'Anna, let me speak to your mother.' A hardness appears in my father's voice which I know it is useless to disobey. I call my mother. She waits till I leave before she begins to speak. I listen from the top of the stairs until they start arguing, and then I creep off to my room, just as if my father were still at home.

98

I bring my best friend, Juliet, home one day. Konstantin is in the kitchen, stirring away.

'Yuk, what *is* that?' says Juliet.

Konstantin stares at her. 'You English people,' he says, shaking his head. 'You have no soul. No imagination.'

'But Konstantin,' I say, 'you eat that stuff all the time. What's so imaginative about that?'

'It is all you can get to eat in Russia,' he says darkly.

'Then why do you eat it here? You can have anything you want here.'

Konstantin gazes mournfully at us as if we are wilfully misunderstanding some simple but profound fact. Juliet and I look at each other and shrug. Then we go outside. It's the beginning of a hot summer and we've got better places to be than in my mother's kitchen with a strange Russian man fixated on cornmeal.

'He's quite good-looking, though,' Juliet confides in me later, as we walk into the town centre to hang out. I've stolen one of my mother's old lipsticks and out of sight of my house we stop to smear it on our lips, bright red and sticky. I don't remember my mother ever wearing this colour. My lips feel heavy and numbed with the stuff, as if they've been covered in a layer of paste.

I pout experimentally and say, 'Good-looking? Konstantin? You can*not* be serious!'

'Well, without those glasses, and if he got a proper haircut, and lost about two stone . . .' she amends, giggling.

'. . . and stopped eating ze polenta,' I say, in what is intended to be a Russian accent. And we laugh and lick our red lips and prance into town with all thoughts of the Russian forgotten.

When I get home later that evening, Konstantin and my mother are deep in conversation over dinner. There are candles on the table. They are using the white linen tablecloth and napkins, and the silver cutlery.

'What's going on?' I ask.

'Are you hungry, darling?' says my mother. 'We've left you some, it's in the kitchen.'

I am starving. 'No thanks,' I say sullenly, 'I'm fine.'

I sit down and plant my elbows on the table and look at Konstantin. On his plate is a mess of little bones. Chicken. He has a small smear of grease on his chin. His eyes gleam out from behind his glasses and his face looks chubby. I am starting to become used to him. I turn my gaze to my mother. She looks tired, but it's a happy-looking tiredness. Her arms are bare and skinny as ever. She stretches out her hand and wipes the smear of grease off Konstantin's chin with her little finger. I have become invisible. Though it is early, I go upstairs to bed.

Later I hear my mother's footsteps on the stairs. She comes into my room and leans over me. I keep my eyes closed and breathe deeply. 'Anna?' she says. 'Anna, are you awake?'

I remain silent.

'I know you're awake,' she says.

There is a pause. I am on the point of giving in and opening my eyes when she speaks again. She says, 'You're not as clever as you think, you know.'

I ponder this for a moment. Then she says, 'Your father never loved me. You should not have had to know this. He did not love me.' She speaks each word with a terrible clarity, as if trying to burn it into my brain. I squeeze my eyes tight. Rigid in my bed, I wait for my mother to leave the room.

The following week school breaks up for the long summer holiday. I am to spend the first two weeks with my father in the country. He picks me up from the station in a very old red car that I've never seen before.

'It's new,' he says. He laughs, as if embarrassed.

'I like it,' I tell him, as it seems to matter to him, and he pats me on the shoulder.

'Attagirl,' he says, using an expression I have not heard him use before. The words don't sound like they belong to him.

My father takes the first week off work to spend time with

me, now that I'm the child of separated parents. He never used to spend time with me, but when I point this out to him he merely shrugs and says, 'That was then. This is now.' We smile at one another, a little sadly.

One of my father's friends in the village has a swimming pool and I spend most of the second week round there sunning myself by the side of it. The man whom the pool belongs to is called Jerry and my father tells me that he's 'in computers'. I don't know what this means except that he earns an enormous amount of money. One afternoon Jerry comes back early from work. I haul myself off my sun-lounger to say hello, politely. He is wearing a light summer suit and as he comes towards me he is loosening his tie.

'So, Anna,' says Jerry, looking me up and down. I know what the look is, I've seen it pass between the older boys and girls at school. I've even longed to be a participant in that slow, daring, cool exchange of glances. But now, I find myself uncomfortably aware of my barely clad body and sun-oiled skin, burning under Jerry's gaze.

'An-na,' says Jerry, lingering over each syllable of my name. A smell of whisky wafts towards me off his breath.

I grab my towel and book, shoving my feet into my sandals. 'Got to go,' I mutter gracelessly, yet rooted to the spot.

'Stay, stay,' he croons, 'have a drink with me.' I am not usually considered old enough to be offered drinks by adults. I feel flattered but even more nervous.

'Sorry,' I stammer. 'Sorry ... thanks ... bye ...' I back away from him, feeling ridiculous and yet certain that I am not wrong in being scared. At the gate, when safety is assured, I pull myself together and say in a high, clear voice, 'Bye, Jerry. Thanks for letting me use your pool.' Then I run home, all the way through the village where the evening's barbecues are already beginning to scent the air.

That evening my father cooks a special meal. We have wine. 'Tomorrow's my birthday,' he says. Tomorrow is the day I'm going home.

'Oh, Dad,' I say, mortified and ashamed. I'd lost track of

dates, but how can I have forgotten my father's birthday? 'I'll stay an extra day,' I offer, trying to make up for it.

He shakes his head wearily. 'It's OK, Anna,' he says. 'Your mother fixed these dates. She knew.'

'Oh, no!' I protest. 'She must have forgotten.'

'She knew all right,' he says quietly. He doesn't sound bitter or cross, just sad. He strokes my hand. He takes a drink of wine. He says, 'I just don't know what happened, Anna. I loved your mother. I really did. I want you to remember that.'

Despite my mother's words still ringing in my ears, I believe him. I want to believe him. I nod solemnly. 'OK, Dad.' He has tears in his eyes. I don't want to hear his confidences. Above all else I do not want to see him cry. I start to tell him about the scene with Jerry, making it funny, to make him laugh, but he won't laugh. We clear away the dishes in silence.

When I get off the train next day there is no one there to meet me. I phone my mother from the callbox. The phone rings for a long time before someone answers it. 'Hello?' says a female voice, not my mother's. In the background I can hear music and voices. It's the middle of the afternoon.

'Who's that?' I ask.

'Hello?' The girl's voice sounds foreign. I wonder if she is a friend of Konstantin's.

'This is Anna,' I say. 'I want to speak to my mother.'

'Anna?'

'I *live* there. Get me my mother!' For a few moments all I can hear are the sounds of the party. Then Konstantin comes to the phone.

'Hello?'

'Konstantin, it's Anna. I'm at the station. Where's my mother?'

'I come,' he says. The line goes dead.

Stunned, I stand holding the receiver and staring at it in confusion until someone behind me says, 'You finished with that or what?' I hand him the phone dumbly and he shakes

102

his head, muttering to himself. Filled with an unspecific anxiety, I walk to the edge of the station car park to wait for Konstantin to come. When I see my mother's little blue Mini approach for a moment I think it's her; but no, Konstantin is driving. He screeches up to me, leans over and throws open the passenger door.

'Hop in!' he cries, the English phrase sounding strange in his thick accent, as if he is practising a colloquialism he has just learnt in his language class.

I hop in. 'Konstantin,' I say firmly. 'Tell me what's going on. Where's my mother? Who was that who answered the phone?'

He is laughing. 'Little Anya,' he says. 'Always the worrier! Your mama she is half your age.' He roars with laughter and I sit coldly waiting for him to finish. Eventually he notices my lack of participation and his laughter winds down. He wipes his eyes, swerving dangerously across the road as he does so.

'Nothing, nothing,' he says. 'You are the paranoid, yes? Your mama have a few guests, that's all.'

'Why didn't she come and pick me up?' I demand, aware of sounding childish and petulant but not caring.

'What is wrong with me coming? You don't like me?' He glances sideways at me, shrewdly.

'Oh, Konstantin, it's not that,' I burst out. Suddenly, he stops the car, lurching up on to the kerb. A passing old lady gives us a fierce glare.

'Anna, Anna,' Konstantin says. 'Tell me, what is the matter? You are so sad.'

'Nothing. I don't know,' I say, and then: 'It's just, since my dad left home, everything seems to have gone funny.'

'Funny?'

'Well, I mean, for a start you moving in. Nobody told me. And I don't know who you are. And Mum's turned so weird lately . . .' I stammer to a halt, not knowing what I'm trying to say.

'Funny. Weird.' He rolls the words around in his mouth. 'No, Anna, your mother she is happy, that is all. Which perhaps you have not seen for a long time. She have not been.

103

And now she is.' He takes my chin in his hand and turns my head to look at him. The tips of his fingers are soft. 'Funny-weird it may be but sad it is not. Now you be happy.' He grins. 'We have a party,' he says. He starts the car and pulls out without looking in the mirror. I flinch and wait for the impact that does not come. In ten minutes we are home.

There are cars in the drive and music coming from the house, some kind of jazz. My mother floats down the front steps to meet me. She is wearing a 1920s beaded dress, with strands of jet beads round her neck, and pretty, strappy shoes. She looks interesting and exotic, not like my mother. I stare at her. She is smiling.

'Darling,' she says, kissing me on the forehead. 'Did you have a lovely time? You look well. Are you very brown all over? Doesn't she look well, Kostya?'

She turns to Konstantin as she says this. Since he came to live with us I have been reading Tolstoy and I know that Kostya must be the friendly short form of his name. This doesn't mean I am not taken aback by my mother's use of it. I am newly roused to hostility.

'What are all these cars doing?' I ask in a surly tone. 'Why are you dressed up like that?'

She laughs lightly. 'I'm just having a few friends round for tea in the garden. It's a sort of garden party, I suppose.'

My mother never has friends round for tea. Not like this. I look at her suspiciously. 'Come on,' she says. 'Come and meet people. Have some food. You must be hungry.'

I don't want to meet people. I follow her meekly into the house. Walking behind her, I am struck by a difference in her. I realise that she has put on weight. No longer is she stick-thin, wasted-looking: now she looks healthy and, well, plump. Why does this make me want to cry? I remember what Konstantin said to me in the car, about my mother being happy now. The flesh on her arms is tanned, taut, like beautiful risen bread dough.

Suddenly I say, 'It's Dad's birthday today.' I am almost shocked by the malice I hear in my own voice.

Abruptly my mother stops, so that I almost bump into her.

She doesn't turn to face me. She says very calmly, into the air: 'Anna, the date of your father's first coming into this world is no longer of any interest to me. However, if you felt you would have liked to spend today with him, you were entirely at liberty to do so. Both you and he knew that. Please do not taunt me like this.'

She says all this without looking at me. Her shoulders are very still and tense. I know that Konstantin will have heard everything. I feel ashamed. I feel too thin, too brown, too long-legged and young. Wordlessly I run away, I run upstairs, I hide in my room, refusing to cry. From the garden the sounds of jazz and laughter drift up to me.

It is Konstantin who comes to find me, later. He peeks his head round my door. His hair is short and bristly.

'You can come out now,' he says cheerfully. 'Everybody has gone home.'

'You've had your hair cut,' I say.

'Yes. You like?' He looks pleased that I've noticed. 'Your mama she cut it.'

'My mother can't cut hair,' I say, turning my face to the wall.

One day I find my mother in the kitchen surrounded by recipe books. Her hair is tied up with a scarf to keep it off her face, and she is barefoot. I am on my way out to meet Juliet, and was not expecting to meet my mother. I am wearing an extremely short dress, which I'd hoped to get out of the house without her seeing. I brace myself for the onslaught but all she says is, 'Oh, there you are, Anna.'

My mouth is already open to protest, 'But *all* my friends are wearing them this length', but I close it again rapidly without saying a word.

My mother continues, 'Off out, darling? Have a nice time.'

Perversely, this makes me want to stay. 'Are you cooking?' I ask. It is rare for my mother to cook from recipes. Something big must be happening.

'People to dinner tomorrow night,' she replies. 'I'm trying to get inspiration.'

I peer at the cookery books. *Chilled cucumber soup*, I read. *Gazpacho. Vichyssoise.* 'Who's coming? Am I invited?' I say.

'Do you want to be?'

I turn the pages of one of the books. *Penne with vodka sauce. Iced white grapes with garlic.* 'Yes, please,' I say shyly.

'Then you are,' says my mother.

When I come home that evening she and Konstantin have started cooking, making all the things that have to be served chilled. They're drinking wine, a lot of it, I can tell. I wake in the night and hear them downstairs still, laughing and clinking glasses together.

I get up very early, but Konstantin and my mother are downstairs before me. Possibly they have not been to bed. They are already cooking, and the kitchen is full of the smell of spices and slowly stewing meat.

Mainly to be awkward I say, 'Don't forget I'm vegetarian.'

Konstantin cries, 'No problem. So much food!'

They spend the whole day in the kitchen. I am roped in as taster and dish-washer. Sometimes I catch Konstantin and my mother exchanging glances and smiling. At six o'clock everything stops. Instructed by Konstantin, we sit down. He hands us tiny glasses of iced vodka. 'Calmness under fire!' he says and drinks his vodka by throwing back his head and gulping it down in one. My mother and I do the same. We gasp. 'You will be Russians yet,' he tells us.

I am sent off to have my bath and when I come back, wearing lipstick and my short dress, the table has been carried into the garden and laid with the white linen and silver. Big flaming torches have been planted at a strategic distance around it. Dusk is falling and the air is full of the scent of honeysuckle. Soft piano music wafts through the french windows. It is like a scene from a film.

When the guests turn up they are Russian. There are six of them, three women and three men. They are perfumed and dark and beautiful and, like Konstantin, speak heavily accented English. Next to them, my mother looks pale and silvery, like a rare and lovely moth. One of the men says to her, 'Is this your beautiful daughter?'

It is my first grown-up dinner party and I am practically silent throughout. I watch and listen. They talk about Russia, and about what has come after the Soviet Union. A woman says, 'The streets of Moscow are mud, just mud.' At first I think she says 'mad' and picture the streets filled with crazy people, gesticulating and frothing at the mouth. Some of their conversation passes over my head. One of them says, 'You can get anything there if only you are prepared to pay', and someone else answers in a knowing tone, 'There are ways and ways of paying.'

We eat our way through many courses of food. I have never known food like this at our house. I forget I am meant to be vegetarian and let Konstantin's beef marinaded in nutmeg melt in my mouth. The wine flows. No one says, 'Should Anna be drinking?' Everyone just fills my glass when the bottle goes round. Either my mother does not notice or she has ceased to object. It is not long before I am drunk, a happy tipsy dizziness that makes me loll back in my chair and see the scene as though it were out of a nineteenth-century oil painting, all rich colours of faded intensity, people's faces glowing. Eventually I hear my mother say, 'Is Anna still awake?' and someone gets up and shakes my shoulder. It is Konstantin. I smile up at him.

'Come on,' he says and helps me gently to my feet. Then he scoops me up in his arms. 'Say goodnight,' he commands.

'G'night,' I say, directing my face in the general direction of the dinner table. Konstantin carries me upstairs.

'Are you all right?' he asks when he has deposited me safely on my bed. The ceiling spins gently around me.

'Fine,' I mumble. He ruffles my hair and disappears. The next thing I know it's morning, the sun streaming in through my window, and my head pounding. I am still wearing last night's clothes and I feel sick. This is my first hangover.

Several days after the dinner party, the table is still out in the garden and two of the guests have not left. I find the situation disturbing. In the evenings, my mother and Konstantin and the guests – two women – sit in the garden, drinking vodka and talking until the early hours of the morning. I spend my days round at Juliet's. Once or twice I bring her home but I feel out of place with the Russian women swanning around like characters out of an old novel.

'How long are they staying for?' I ask my mother. She is learning Russian and looks up from her textbook to say, 'But as long as they want, darling. Are they bothering you?'

'No.'

'Don't you like them?'

'Yes, of course I do, Mum.'

She smiles vaguely, as if something has been settled. 'There you are then.'

Early one morning I see the younger of the Russian women coming out of the older one's bedroom. I wonder what conclusions to draw from this, if any. I discuss it with Juliet and she widens her eyes and says, 'How glamorous!'

'You don't have to live there,' I say.

But in some way I do feel that the house has suddenly become a glamorous, glittering place, a place where unexpected, fascinating people could turn up at any moment. I could walk into any of my old, familiar rooms and find a scientist deep in conversation with a poet, or my mother holding court to three handsome Russian youths, or a consumptive-looking figure playing a tragic sonata on the piano. None of this happens, but for some reason I feel as if it might.

And where do I fit in to all this?

The Russian ladies leave. They give me a small, exquisite bottle of musky perfume and tell me that in a few years I shall have the world at my feet.

'Why not now?' I say, and they laugh, although I had not meant to be funny. They give me their address in St Petersburg and say I can come and stay whenever I like. I think of the streets full of mad people and then remember that that was Moscow. I thank them. They climb into a taxi and we stand on the front steps waving them goodbye. Konstantin calls out to them in Russian. When their taxi has disappeared from view he shuts the front door and picks my mother up and twirls her round until she shrieks like a child. I don't know where to look.

Everyone gets over everything with time. Lots of people have told me this. I am beginning to believe it must be true.

A few days later, I arrive back one morning from staying at Juliet's. The house feels odd, not quite real, as if it is holding its breath. Then, without warning, I hear music start. It is loud, and beautiful. I pad through to the back of the house. The french windows have been flung wide open and speakers placed so as to carry the music far out into the garden. It is a waltz that is playing.

I run upstairs, take a deep breath and from my bedroom window look out into the garden. It is the middle of summer and the garden is full of flowers and sunlight. It is full of music. I gaze down on my mother and Konstantin, who are in each other's arms. My mother is wearing a dress of faded silk the colour of roses and her face is dreamy. They are dancing, around and around, like strange, sweet, serious butterflies. I watch them. It is a waltz. They are waltzing.

Nicholas Shakespeare

THE PRINCESS OF THE PAMPA

1.

ISABEL SAT IN the window and scoured the greying pampa for a pick-up. It was early afternoon, but already the wind had started to blow away the light. All day a thin rain had fallen. Now she thought she heard hail.

She switched her focus to the barn. A bird scrabbled for balance on the steep tin roof. It slipped down the far side, clawed back in urgent stabs to the summit and stood tipsy in the wind.

She observed the bird through her field-glasses. She didn't recognise the colouring and this, after a while, vexed her. She put down her glasses and fetched the second volume of *Birds of La Plata*, searching for an illustration to match the slate feathers. A Crested Screamer, she guessed.

Chauna chavaria. No illustration. Disappointed, she read Hudson's description which compared its voice to a bassoon. She strained to hear, but either the bird wasn't singing or the wind had swallowed its voice; or it wasn't a Crested Screamer.

The bird plunged its bill under a tired wing, and from nowhere she desired nothing more than to run to the side of the barn and break a scone for it. Only the thought of her husband restrained her. Where *was* Clem?

The bird flew off, ascending in laborious beats above a narrow strip of maize until she lost it in one of the hail trails sweeping across the window.

So she stood, scanning the plain for Clem.

The hill was bare. Lines of stiff stalks pulled to the level horizon and the gale continued to blow, clattering the windmill behind the house with such force that just now, when she tried to take a siesta, she couldn't sleep.

At least it wasn't a dust storm. Two winters earlier they'd woken to find the farm choking under a blanket of ash. Nine hundred and seventy-three sheep Clem reckoned the volcano in Chile had cost him: one for every mile to Mount FitzRoy.

At the horizon the colours of the land were sucked into a muddy sky. She could always tell if anyone moved through Clem's empire. Horseback, pick-up, on foot, she would track them with her field-glasses. But this afternoon nothing moved. A promising blur beyond the barn turned out to be a solitary cherry tree.

Feeling a sudden pang she sat down. 'Never look back at the past,' she told herself. 'It's a hawk that goes for the eyes.'

At the sound of an engine she leapt from her seat.

He'd left at six in the morning for San Julian, to sell the wool. Last night, after listening to the radio, he'd estimated twenty-five pesos a kilo.

She ran to meet him. She waved him down below the house and he turned off the engine so he could hear her words.

Eager under her umbrella, she asked: 'How much?'

He looked ahead, to where the rain pecked the bonnet. 'Twelve.'

She lowered her eyes to his arm. 'A man rang. The lorry's on its way.'

'But it's meant to be coming tomorrow.' His voice began to bruise. 'I told them not to come today.'

The butcher was driving from Port Desire to slaughter the bullocks. Twice a year, for a few hours, the barn became an abattoir.

She walked round the bonnet and opened the door and collapsed her umbrella and climbed in. *Twelve*. It had never been that low before.

111

'Did the man say anything else?' said Clem.

'Only that they'd left and they'd be here tonight.'

'I told them I wouldn't be here today,' he insisted. Since laying off his men, he depended on itinerant butchers from the coast, not always reliable.

He braked outside the kitchen door, waiting for her to get out.

'If they're coming tonight, I'd better bring the bullocks in.'

'You'll have a scone, won't you, Clem –'

He was already reversing the pick-up. They'd been married eight years.

It took Clem three more hours to bring in the bullocks. It was nearly nine when he appeared. He poured himself a whisky. The rain had extinguished his pipe, which he emptied in messy black gobbets into the grate, started to refill, and then abandoned beside the sink. His features were smudged, as if the rain which had lasted for five days had not fallen on his land but between the two of them.

The rain had painted his ears red and she could smell the bitterness of wet tobacco.

She'd been rehearsing her words. 'Is it the Australians?' All last year there'd been a wool mountain in Australia. 'They're not *still* undercutting us? It's never been twelve before.'

He sat at the kitchen table and tugged off one boot, then another, leaving both under the table. 'I don't know what it is,' was all he said. He used to talk enough to make himself hoarse.

'Did you accept the price?'

His nod was barely perceptible.

After dinner, her five-bean stew with rice, he continued to sit in silence. He had on a white jersey of ribbed wool with the mauve and black stripes of his school colours and a pair of cream flannel trousers, turned up, and a paisley cravat. It was the way he had dressed the first time they'd met, the way he always dressed.

On his feet he wore two olive-green velvet slippers.

'Don't say they're still worried about volcanic dust?' she persisted.

He refilled his glass. Drink had rounded his face and his lips relaxed together in an expression of discontent. She removed his plate, but he didn't look up and she could hear his feet fretting against the chair.

'What were you doing today?' he asked at last.

She delayed her response. 'I saw a new bird.'

Brightly, avoiding his recriminating glance, she hurried on. 'I thought it might be a Crested Screamer, but the wings were too green.'

His chair juddered back. 'We'll miss the play,' he said.

He gathered his glass and went through to the front room and switched on the radio. Five minutes later she joined him.

'. . . *with Ian Carmichael as Lord Peter Wimsey* . . .'

Because of the storm, the reception tonight was not good. It was never very good. She sat opposite Clem, who sat under his father's circular portrait, and they listened to the actor's voice booming and fading from London. Clem listened as if he understood those silences. They had sat like this for almost a week. The play made no sense to her. Sometimes minutes went by, they didn't hear anything.

'What's happening, Clem?'

'Shush.'

She watched the inelegant tilt of his glass. He'd been trim-figured once, under that cricket jersey. Only his legs, protruding stiffly into their slippers, guarded their lean shape.

Another silence, longer.

She met the eyes of her father-in-law, painted on a herring-barrel lid. That was always the story. She wanted to interrogate the old face: 'Was this how you spent your time? *Was it?*' At least, before they sent him abroad to school, Clem's parents had a child to look after.

Clem and she had only themselves, the BBC World Service, these books.

The voice of Lord Peter Wimsey, educated and superior, returned to the room. She closed her eyes, pretending to listen. But she was scaling a mountain made of wool.

Clem, after the play ended, pushed himself from his chair

and switched the radio off. She collected his glass, came to where he stood beside the piano. She put a hand on his shoulder, but her fingers rested there untouched.

'Another?'

'I'll get it.'

He trudged out and she thought for the thousandth time: 'Poor Clem, brought down by his upbringing.' He had no bright colours, no brilliant plumage. He was an ordinary person, but he had never pretended to be otherwise.

She heard Clem sneezing in the kitchen. He would bring them both down unless she found a means to make him soar. She looked hard at a shelf behind the piano. Tonight, she could think of only one way to restore his spirits. She wandered to the shelf, plucked out a book with a faded lavender spine.

Never, not even at his lowest ebb, did he ignore the call of his favourite character.

When Clem returned to the room Isabel sat under the reading lamp. The story which lay open on her lap had been written a hundred years before. She knew its words by heart.

She looked up, brilliant, steeled to make her husband happy. 'Shall I be Princess Tatiana?'

He hesitated. She saw his wild turmoil, how the name stroked at his face, how he clenched with everything in him to resist her allure. Abruptly, he turned his back on her. Not until he reached the doorway did he pause, speaking to the floor.

'That lorry's probably lost. I ought to put a light on the barn.'

2.

They'd met in mid-air, that's what he liked to say; eight years before. He was flying to England for his mother's funeral, the first time he'd been back since leaving school.

She was a stewardess. She'd flown both flights. In neither

crossing had she registered Clem Caskey. In her version, which she kept to herself, they met in the lobby of a Buenos Aires hotel.

It was her first time on the Argentina run and she had four days' leave. She thought she'd visit an estancia, go riding, maybe see a tango show. Janis, another stewardess, had very much recommended a travel agent in Calle Junin.

She stepped out of the lift, a narrow-faced woman in her mid-thirties with loose fair hair and large green eyes set wide apart. She was pretty, but no more. That morning she wore a knee-length maroon silk dress.

In the lobby some journalists discussed the breakfast while she battled with the map. Clem stood before her.

'Excuse me,' she asked. 'This is such a silly question. But what street are we in?'

Respectful, he took her map, unfolded it, showed her. He showed her Calle Junin as well. Then he told her they'd met already.

'My headset didn't work.'

'Oh yes, I remember.' She drew back, speaking automatically. She was suspicious of people who talked in soft voices. 'I remember you.'

'You were also on the London flight,' he said. 'You're thinner.'

He was right, she'd been ill. But it disconcerted her to think that someone might have noticed the difference, someone she couldn't recall.

She thanked him with a professional smile and was about to disengage herself when he invited her for coffee.

All her training obliged her to say no. The person before her was quite large with an untidy pink face and the forlorn appearance of an intelligent, not very graceful man who hadn't taken care of himself. He might have wanted to cut a dash in his cricket whites, but something seemed undone in his character through which escaped the narrow, honest, awkward truth of it.

Everything about him was indicative of awkwardness: the

tight white collar, the wintry eyes, the hands bunched into fists.

Then he dropped her map.

She started to bend down, but he lunged forward and in one seamless movement recovered it from the floor as if he was catching a ball at slip.

'Here.' He held out the map, boyish. There hadn't been a skip in his attention.

When she had forgotten all about Clem Caskey she would be able to recall his redemptive gesture: its energy, its ease and the colour of the back of his hands.

'You look like you've been out in the sun,' she said.

In an empty café on 9 de Julio, Isabel outlined the itinerary suggested with enthusiasm by Janis. The sun falling through the water jug caught the glint of her dress, making reddish ripples on the white tablecloth.

'No, don't do that,' said Clem. He gazed at her from a bottomless shyness. 'Come to La Lucia.'

His farm was nearly a thousand miles south. He was leaving that afternoon. 'You can ride. See the birds. We have wonderful birds. Do you like birds?'

He was horribly persuasive. What else would she do? Follow Janis, as always, then buy an expensive cardigan she didn't need with money she didn't have.

'It takes fourteen hours,' he was saying.

She looked straight at him. 'I want to make something perfectly clear. We're not going to have an affair.' She was being professional and decent – yet out it came sounding brittle.

He tried to look comfortable in a cane chair, but didn't know where to put his arm.

'I mean,' she went on, and something was deserting her.

Her cheeks were blazing when with his big man's odd precision he laid two fingers on her arm, putting aside her fear.

'Don't worry. You'll have your own room.'

They went down on the overnight bus and all weekend he gave her the full beam of his attention.

From Janis's description of an estancia, she'd expected something grander. Clem Caskey's house was single-storey, modest and built in red brick on a hill below a windmill that reminded her in its metallic greyness of a Birmingham sky.

He lived on his own and had turned off the refrigerator while he'd been in England.

'Warm gin and tonic?'

The tonic tasted flat.

'Tell me if it's flat.' He prepared a grimace.

'It's absolutely fine.'

The kitchen smelled strange. No one had emptied the grate and from the rafter a lump of decaying sheep fat hung in the shape of a shining skull.

Beer in one hand, he piloted her into the front room. A huge window overlooked the pampa. There was an upright black piano and, on two walls to the ceiling, shelves and shelves of books. She carried her glass to a shelf and ran a finger along the spines.

'What a lot of books you have!'

'All his,' Clem pointed.

She glanced at the herring-barrel lid, but the shelves interested her more: volumes of short stories mainly, dating from the 1920s, with gold on their spines. Turgenev, Maupassant, Somerset Maugham, Tchehov.

'Is that how you spell him?'

'It's how they spelled him then.'

'Let's see, what are you reading at the moment?'

A book rested open on the piano, its place marked by a woman's nail file. Careful not to lose the page, she sought the title. '*The Princess of the Steppes and other stories*,' she read. She pronounced the author's name. 'No. Not heard of him.'

Clem stood. 'He was a friend of Tchehov. He's not well known, but I like him.' There was a defensive quality to his voice, to the way he held himself. 'No matter how many times I read him, I always find something new. You can't say that about many writers.'

117

Isabel replaced the book and joined Clem at the window. Below, she saw a small orchard of crab-apples and a wooden barn with a corrugated roof. The day was hot, the sky on the horizon a rich blue. She followed the sunflowers to the sky.

'All yours?'

'As far as your eye can see,' he joked. But it was true, and her eyes darted over the view, the first time she had confronted a landscape owned by one person.

'What's that bird?' It perched on the barn roof, grey with a black tail and primrose chest.

Clem narrowed his eyes. 'I'm not sure. A cocoi heron?'

He produced two green, leather-bound volumes, offering Isabel one. *Birds of La Plata, Volume I*, by W. H. Hudson, with twenty-two coloured illustrations by H. Gronvold.

For Isabel's sake Clem spelled out the heron's name. He found it first. 'Cocoi! Here we go!'

She stood by his side. Together they read the description. He asked, tentative: 'Is that it?'

'No.' She had read ahead. Impatiently she turned his pages. Further on there was an illustration, of another species. 'Look! Isn't *that* it?'

'The Whistling Heron,' read Clem. Their shoulders touched. '*Ardea sibilatrix*. You may be right.'

He extracted from an ancient leather case a pair of field-glasses and she focused while he sifted the short entry.

'There should be a chestnut patch behind the eye,' he said.

'There is.' The discovery excited her.

What about a yellowish tinge on its chest?'

'Yes!'

The colours matched those in Gronvold's illustration. '"Its melodious notes prophesy changes in the weather",' quoted Clem. 'It's very scarce, it says here.' He sounded surprised by his own enthusiasm.

When Isabel handed him the glasses, he went on, 'We do get wonderful birds. They always rest here on their way south.'

She was looking at him looking at the whistling heron

when suddenly he turned his head. 'How's your drink? Another warm gin and tonic?'

Tired after the long bus journey, she took a siesta under the cherry tree. She said hello, goodbye, five hundred times a day. Here there was nothing to do and it thrilled her.

Later, Clem saddled a bay for her and they rode. Away from the tumult of airports, her spirits revived. The fields stretched enormous before her. She sensed the freedom of the geese swishing overhead, heard each clear sound. The cry of a lapwing; the rasp of a tongue on a cow's flank; two bullocks locking horns, like the cutlery of silent diners.

Isabel was riding ahead – thinking that in coming to La Lucia with a stranger she had done, for her, something quite extraordinary – when her horse stopped to urinate. She swivelled in her saddle, conscious of Clem's approach. She had slept under a straw hat and the strong sun had patterned her face. She looked at him through the latticemarks, listening to the urine steaming into the red earth.

She was too content to be embarrassed. She rose in her stirrups and stored her lungs with air.

It was after dinner when he introduced her properly to the Princess of the Steppes. She stood at the huge window, wearing an unprovocative dress, waiting for him to bring coffee. There was enough light in the sky to see the heron's lanky silhouette.

'"*Princess Tatiana intrigued Stolypin from the moment he saw her feeding the birds . . .*"'

She looked around. 'Say that again,' she said, struck by the conviction in his voice.

He repeated the line, placing the tray on the piano. 'You reminded me of Tatiana. You're just like her.'

'And who's she?'

'She's everything I desire.' No sooner had he uttered the phrase than he laughed at his own ridiculousness. 'What I

119

mean to say –' his arm in a graceful sweep took in the shelves – 'of all the hundreds of people in these books, she's the one I'd really like to know.'

'It sounds like you know her already.'

'I've never heard her voice.' His face was boyish again, animated. 'But if she had a voice, it would be like yours.'

'What's she like, this Tatiana?' she asked, fired by her gin and tonic.

Clem, removing the nail file, underlined a passage with its tip. 'See for yourself.'

Isabel read aloud:

'*There are people who feel in colour, that's what Stolypin believed. If he were to put a colour to Tatiana it would be the pale blue of a lake in Oslo. He had visited the city as a student. There was one night's ice on the lake and when he put down his foot, the ice broke with a pinging sound that he recognised in her voice. There was a crispness, a youthfulness about her . . .*'

'You think this is like me?' She could see Clem's body poised, as when he had been watching the heron.

'That's the first thing I noticed about you, your voice.'

She read on, in silence. A minute later, she said: 'This is really good.'

'We always used to read to each other after dinner.'

'You mean *aloud*? That's very old-fashioned.'

'There's not an enormous amount to do in the evenings. I should have warned –'

'But I want to know what happens!'

'Then you'll have to begin at the beginning.'

She sat in the window and started at the first line, reading slowly and clearly, pausing only to sip at her glass. Twice she raised her eyes from the text. Clem sat on the piano stool. His face, observing her enunciate the words, had life in it and she felt calm and intimate, the room idealised by the gin, her voice, the story. She smiled at him, and became aware, for the first time, of feeling nothing professional on her face.

'*Tatiana lay waiting for him in her room. When she heard*

*the door open she propped herself on her elbows and looked
at Stolypin with such intense longing –'*

She stopped, glanced sharply up. He must have known this
was coming. But his eyes were closed. When he opened them,
she blushed, looked down at the page, continued.

She read to the end, hearing in her voice the cold sunniness
of the stewardess.

Next morning he showed her round the farm in an old Ford
truck. It was painted Bolivian army green and the passenger
door didn't work. She had to squeeze over the driver's seat.

At each gate she waited for Clem to climb out, open the
gate, drive the pick-up through, close the gate. The process
tired her patience. Clem didn't appear to mind.

They drove to a shed where he spoke to two men who
stood in shadow doing nothing in particular. One, spanner in
hand, listened to a soccer match on a radio. The other, seeing
Isabel, raised his hat, but it was to scratch his head.

Two more gates brought them to the boundary stream.
Clem parked and they watched the parrots in quick flutters
screech in and out of a cliff honeycombed with burrows.

Set back from the stream under a spread of acacias, the
roofs of a dozen beehives poked from the rushes. They
belonged to a neighbour, Clem told her. 'My sunflowers
welcome the bees.'

'Does your neighbour give you honey?'

'No.'

'Why not? His bees make honey from your flowers.'

He thought about it. 'You live here, but you don't know
your neighbours two away.'

On the way back, as if a decision had been reached by the
stream, he opened up to her. His father had started the farm,
he explained, and its history seemed a race he had to finish
before they reached the house. Before, he had spoken one
sentence at a time. Now he talked at a gallop.

Alec Caskey from the Falklands was granted his land as a
bastion against an Indian threat that never materialised. He

had built it up as a sheep station. The price of wool had slipped ever since.

'No one's buying wool because everyone has central heating and wears acrylic.' From Bahia Blanca to Port Desire, the farmers were steadily going bust. This was why, after his father's death, Clem had diversified. 'Although no one warned me about Patagonian parrots.' After losing one crop of sunflowers, he had planted a band of maize. That seemed to stunt their attacks. 'They're not very good at precision landing.'

He survived on sunflowers, sheep, a few cattle. The flight to London was not an expense he could afford. His father, he said, had bankrupted himself through spending so much on Clem's private education. 'Like Alyokhin's father.'

'Who?'

'A character in Tchehov.'

Alec Caskey had died five years before, but his presence clung to the farm he had hewn out of nothing. Later, Isabel would come across half-sucked lozenges wrapped in tissue in the pockets of his suits. They still smelt of a man's saliva. At the time, she thought: Clem's inherited a love of the land that's not yet requited. She would learn it was not so much love as the energy of an illegitimate determined to outrun his stigma.

Clem's situation was indicated by the Ford pick-up: Isabel's unopenable door rattled at the smallest bump.

'You're sure it can't be opened?'

'It's always been like that.'

He got out to open another gate. As he walked back to the pick-up, two sharp bangs startled him.

He raced forward. 'Isabel! Are you all right?'

Isabel opened her door, stepped down, stretched. Apologetic, she said: 'We were trained on doors like this.'

'I don't believe it! But it's been like that for nineteen years!'

'You haven't used this for nineteen years? What happened to you when your father was driving?'

'I used to climb out of the window.'

His gratitude was extraordinary. He was still smiling when

the pick-up halted at the last fence. 'Passenger side opens the gates.'

She read to him that night and the next. His favourite stories were Russian. 'They're so at ease with their landscape.' She saw by the way he listened that he was drawn to what she became when she read. It was the concentration of a man listening to someone reading his own poetry aloud.

As the moment approached for her to leave, Isabel felt her heart go out to him, this man who was not an obvious part of the landscape he struggled with.

On Monday afternoon he drove her back to the bus station in San Julian, four hours away.

On the outskirts of town, a crop-sprayer wobbled over-head. 'It's been lovely,' she said, breaking a long silence.

'Yes.'

'I'll wave down at you.'

'Next week where will you be?'

'London, Toronto, Cape Town.'

'You go everywhere.'

'I fly the world, but I don't know it.' Grim-faced, she contemplated her schedule.

He said something. The words stumbled out in a quiet, awkward rush and seconds passed before their meaning penetrated. She was too stunned to keep the thought upright in her head.

It was not how her father had proposed to her mother, on the other side of the Wye. He had taken her there in his brown Austin Seven and parked in Far Forest. Something of the kind she had envisaged for herself.

She would have to think about it, she said.

She returned to work unravelled, with a reckless energy.

A fortnight later he telephoned. 'The birds are missing you.'

She found herself smiling. 'And the whistling heron?'

'He's there every morning. He's pining for you – and he never got to know you.'

'Give him my love.'

'How was Toronto?'

'I slept.' In Clem's pick-up, she had told the truth. She flew the world, yet she didn't see anything. She met all these people, but she didn't meet anybody.

'And you, Isabel, how are you?' he asked.

'I'm well – apart from some bruised fingers.'

Two nights before, on the flight to Moscow, a passenger had poked his head round the pantry curtain, pulled Isabel's face to his, kissed her. When she didn't respond he had lingered, winking.

'With those legs you shouldn't sit down.'

In that moment, in that man's drunken leer, she saw the numberless bodies she had strapped to their seats, the faces she had served with how many trays, the snot-encrusted noses of the children she had wiped. She put down on the floor the mineral water she was about to carry to 42G and her hand formed itself into a fist and with all the energy she had denied herself, with every regret at the passing of her impertinent hopes, she ploughed it into the man's face.

Since then the pinging in her hand reminded Isabel at the slightest movement of Stolypin, sinking with loud cracks into the ice. Clear, cold, true, beautiful.

'Have you thought about it?' asked Clem.

'Give me another week.'

A week later, her lungs still fresh with the air of his pampa, her eyes still rippling with his yellow empire of flowers, Isabel agreed to Clem Caskey's proposal.

3.

She had offered herself as Princess Tatiana and Clem had rejected her. Unable to sleep, she listened out, awaiting his return from the barn.

The windmill squeaked and the light she had left on for

him in the hallway stretched flat and pale under her door. They slept in separate rooms, but how she longed sometimes for Clem to open her door, come in with the rest of the light. She imagined that light, unused, building up over the nights and weeks until the weight was too much to endure and he burst into her room, silent and fluent, with his body composed of the same athletic grace as when he had retrieved her map.

He never came.

At five in the morning she was woken by the sound of a lorry. Next door she heard Clem rise, and feel for his slippers in the dark. Her imagination followed him into the bathroom, through the kitchen, down the hill. In the hiatus of the abattoir and scraping hoofs, of slaughterhouse offal and the shouts of itinerant butchers, he would tread in a daze until dawn.

At seven she got up. The rain having eased, she decided to spend the morning riding. The need to be away from the house, the farm buildings, suddenly overwhelmed her. She never was able to harden herself to the killing, and Clem's behaviour last night disturbed her.

His boots stood under the kitchen table where he had left them. He must have taken hers in the dark. Clem's, although bigger, would do for her ride. She would watch the ewes lambing.

She guided her bay up the hill, a pair of Detolled gloves in her saddle-bag. The horse trod in nervous steps through the damp char grass and once or twice to the top a hoof slithered in the mud. Last time she rode this way, Clem was burning the grass and the stumps were black and the smoke got into her eyes and stayed there.

She came to an earth bank and kicked, intending to pause at the summit where the clouds were touchably close. At that moment, concealed in the grass, a chimango thrust itself from an armadillo carcase and beat into the air.

The horse shied in fright at the hawk and when Isabel lost balance, broke into a gallop. She tried to fall, but Clem's boots remained stuck in her stirrups.

By two o'clock, the men had finished loading the warm meat into the refrigerator van. Exhausted, they sat around on bloody bales prolonging the ritual of maté until the foreman, standing at the second attempt, barked: 'Time to go.'

Clem, surprised to find that Isabel had not prepared lunch, concocted a sandwich for himself. After eating most of it he lay on his bed. Half an hour later he stood at his window, buttoning on a clean shirt, when he saw her horse grazing on the hill.

He ran to the pick-up. He accelerated up the bank, wheels spinning and careering in the wet soil. At first he thought she was dead. Her body lay stretched out on the grass, not moving, her trousers splattered with mud.

'Isabel!'

She raised her head, tried to smile. 'My ankle. Can't move.'

He gathered her up. Only when he lowered her into the pick-up bed did he hear the clicking. Her hands gripped his arm and her green eyes looked into his and he could tell the pain was excruciating.

He drove her, covered in blankets, through the dusk to San Julian.

After two hours on the road he pulled in to see how she was.

'Fine. Absolutely fine,' she said feebly. Her vision slipped from Clem to the burning horizon.

At the hospital, a nurse fitted a metal bib in preparation for the X-ray machine. It was hot in the waiting-room and Isabel fainted.

Two men lifted her on to a trolley. The nurse brought a pair of crutches and a young doctor came to reassure Clem. 'You can go home.'

Clem said, 'I'll come by tomorrow afternoon.'

'We'll have her in plaster,' said the doctor.

At four the next day Clem returned. The doctor took him aside. He had lost some of his springiness.

'How is she?' asked Clem. Seeing Isabel at the end of the ward, propped up on pillows, one leg raised in plaster, he waved his pipe.

'She's obviously taken a bump. She was in and out of consciousness and she's now a bit forgetful.'

'What do you mean?'

'It's disturbed her, the pain. She's not quite herself.'

Clem approached the bed. Isabel's face twisted in his direction, awake.

'I saw you talking to the doctor,' she said. 'Isn't he nice? He's been so good.'

He sat beside her. 'Yes, he does seem nice.'

She gave him a look, curious but bright, and he was relieved.

He asked, reaching out to touch the plaster with his pipe-stem, 'How's the pain? I called this morning to check up.'

'Are you a doctor too?'

'Am I –?' The words stopped, waylaid in his throat. 'No, darling,' and with the mechanical response of someone who has driven an empty road for four hours, he said: 'I'm your husband.'

'My husband?' She seemed rather indignant.

He noticed the stoop of her gaze. He was sweating slightly and bits of straw stuck to his forearm. Her eyes rose up his arm to meet his stricken smile.

In a very formal voice she said: 'You look like you've been out in the sun.'

It was the nausea of feeling himself alone. A most terrible wrong had been committed. 'I delivered her to you with a broken ankle,' he told the doctor.

At some point in the night Isabel's mind had turned blank on itself. Her own name, who she was, what she'd done: she could not remember anything from her life prior to the accident.

'The lesion may have been there before the fall,' the doctor cautioned. He was acknowledging something serious, while making an effort to sound up-beat. In every probability her memory would return. Full recovery occurred usually within a short space. Either gradually, he said, or unblocked suddenly by an isolated memory. Patience, that's all they required.

For three days the hospital kept Isabel under observation, without medication. Urged on by the doctor, Clem compiled a list of details which might stir a memory. She greeted each with the same devastating expression: Lord Peter Wimsey, the whistling heron, La Lucia. They had no meaning for her, produced no bombardment of associated images.

Only one detail elicited any sense of familiarity. Asked about volcanic dust, she said: 'Is it to do with the Australians?'

'Darling . . .' Defeated, Clem reached for her, tried to hold her eyes, and it was as if he was feeling for two lost slippers in the dark.

On the fourth day the doctor started her on a sedation of valium and sodium amytal.

'Retrograde amnesia is still a grey area. We know so little . . .' The best course was for Clem to talk to her, remind her of who she was.

'Sometimes we only know what we're told.'

Late on the fifth day Clem reappeared with a hold-all.

Isabel, when she heard his footsteps in the corridor, exclaimed to the nurse: 'That's Clem!'

Alert and inquisitive, she observed him unpack, arranging each object on the bed.

'I've brought some things for you to look at,' he said.

She accepted the framed photograph. Engrossed, she scrutinised the wedding in the chapel of St George's, Quilmes.

'She's smart,' she said, indicating Janis in a Hermès scarf. 'Who's she?'

'Your bridesmaid.' Agitated, he retrieved the photograph. 'What about this map?' He traced with her finger the location of the hotel where they'd met on Calle Lavalle. She did not recall a single episode of the circumstances.

'Does this ring any bell?'

She inspected herself in the silver stewardess badge.

'No.' She pushed it away, distressed at his distress. Fear and tension scored her face. She glanced at him with the withheld breath of an animal under threat and suddenly he was back in the darkness of the barn, watched by living creatures he couldn't see.

Then she said something in such a quiet way that he had to ask her to repeat it. 'Did we have a nice time?'

He sat back, staring into the bowl of his pipe. 'Yes, I think so.'

She searched his face. Her lower lip trembled. She was lost on a massive plain.

'I can't remember. I can't remember,' and she sounded as if she were snowing.

From the hold-all he selected another object, a book which he rested on the bed. 'What about –'

Isabel, unable any longer to contain her frustration, kicked out under the blanket. 'What is the point of showing me these things, what's the point?'

The book slipped from the blanket, but Clem with an acrobatic gesture lunged forward and scooped it from the air. When he stood up he noticed a change in his wife. She held her head at an angle, bird-like, her eyes fastened on the back of his hands.

'Don't you remember?' said Clem. He gripped even tighter the faded lavender cover. 'You were my princess.' It was a sigh from the marrow.

'Princess Tatiana?' She gazed at him in a concentrated way. And then in an altered, interested voice, she said, '"Princess Tatiana intrigued Stolypin from the moment he saw her feeding the birds."'

Ten days later, Clem Caskey drove his wife home.

'What a view!' cried Isabel. She rested on her cane, taking in the hill, the windmill, the fields. When he offered his arm, she squeezed it trustingly and with a coltish rub pressed her head into his shoulder. Like that they entered the house.

He had prepared for her return with scrupulous care. He

had stripped the front room of shelves, of books, of his father's portrait. In her bedroom, too, he had removed all traces of her past.

'Look!' She took his hand, gestured through the window at the barn. 'That's where I fed the birds.'

Garaged word for word in a corner of her memory was the story of his favourite character, which she understood to be her story. It was the only part of her life she remembered, to which she had access. She knew it by heart.

And Clem, responding to her warmth, couldn't help himself. He had the power at any moment to break the spell, but why do so? Hadn't the doctor advised him, in the hope of one spontaneous recovery leading to another: 'Just play with her, go with it. With luck she'll remember everything else'?

No. He would respect the natural law of things. He would say nothing.

She touched his face. 'You're very withdrawn.'

At her touch he felt a mad charge of omnipotence. 'I'm just happy to have you back.'

'I'm happy to be back.' It was a sensuous smile.

Nothing in her change of manner could have prepared Clem for the joy he felt that night when, with clattering heart, he opened the door to her bedroom and saw the light fall on her eager face. She lay propped on her elbow in an attitude of the most intense expectation, as if she had waited a hundred years for him.

Over the following weeks, the familiarity which had built up in a vague but co-operative sort of way in the hospital developed into a childlike sense of awe at her surroundings. This was true especially of her feelings towards Clem. Or – as she called him – Stolypin.

Whenever she addressed him by that name, he felt the same charge of energy. He didn't care if Stolypin wasn't his real name, that Tatiana wasn't hers. Who was there to challenge Isabel's new sense of herself? As far as her eye could see she was his Princess.

Under his guidance, she learnt very well. Soon all concern vanished about her defective memory – although, because of her cast, she continued to walk with difficulty. The injury to her ankle restricted her to Tatiana's universe of kitchen, bedroom and the orchard she could see from the window.

She moved through that world with splendid ease. Surfaces gleamed for the first time. She scoured the floor tiles, rafters, pans. She stewed jam from the young crab-apples and cherries. She labelled the jars, lined them up as little gifts for her Stolypin. In the kitchen the warm, sweet smell of baking cakes replaced the odour of sheep fat.

Sometimes he heard her in the front room naming the birds in a sing-song voice. 'That's a J, could it be?' At first she was able to recall them by their first letter alone, not by the whole word, and her evident frustration worried him to the extent that one day he arrived home with a gift which thrilled her more than anything: a pair of bird-books entitled *Birds of La Plata*. They were the only two books in the house, but it relieved and gratified him to see the satisfaction they produced in her. From that day on, with one or other volume resting against her leg, she reclined for at least an hour each morning on the window-seat.

Nowhere did she move with greater ease than in bed. In the bedroom, she was not hindered by her ankle. Each night when he opened the door, her eyes looked up at him, open and shining.

So with each day did he come into his own. He completed projects long abandoned. He reorganised the vegetable garden; he filled in the cracks in the swimming pool, so that Tatiana would be able to exercise once her cast came off; he prised from his Basque neighbour a box containing twenty-two glass jars of acacia honey.

Neighbours who met him in the street in San Julian noticed that he had gained authority. He walked straighter, with a leaner body, and seemed in every respect to be taking care of himself. The few whose business took them on the cinder road past La Lucia noticed how amazingly healthy all of a sudden his crops looked.

Even the price of wool responded.

Seven weeks went by like this.

One morning, Princess Tatiana was watching the tin roof when she heard a rattling. She lowered her field-glasses. When she understood the reason for the noise, she adjusted the lens adoringly.

Stolypin stood at the barn door, absorbed in opening a padlock. At last he succeeded in wrenching free the lock. He opened the door and disappeared inside. She observed him a few minutes later heading in brisk steps towards the pick-up.

It struck her as peculiar, long after he had driven away, that over his shoulder he should be carrying a woman's maroon dress when only a short while before, at breakfast, he announced he was going into town and was there anything she required.

'There is,' she said. 'I need a new dress.'

On the point of leaving the house, he had come back to find her.

'I forgot to ask. What size are you?'

Puzzled at his question, she stared down at herself. 'I don't know.'

Until this morning she had never spared a thought for the inside of the barn, only for the birds resting on its roof. She couldn't help noticing that her husband, in his haste to be off, had left the door unpadlocked. She wondered with a mild curiosity what he stored inside.

She was now able to walk short distances without discomfort. She estimated the distance across the orchard. With the aid of her stick, she ought to be able to manage. It would be a good thing to test her ankle.

Twenty minutes later, panting heavily, her knees brushed in the dark against a straw bale. She collapsed on the straw. The tendons pulled at the top of her foot and she couldn't work out why her weight on the stick had woken in her hand such a throbbing pain.

Glad to rest, she looked about, her eyes adapting to the gloomy interior. The barn smelt of urine and animal sweat and dust from the hay. She sneezed, frightening something on the roof.

Down at her feet, two pale trackmarks curved across a

wooden floor. She followed their direction, surprised to see various cardboard boxes stacked against the wall and, beside the boxes, a black tin trunk. Somehow the trunk, even more so than the boxes, looked out of place.

Her breath recovered, she hauled herself up.

The lid was unlocked, the trunk inside packed to the brim with women's clothes: skirts, shirts, scarves – and, laid flat on top, a book. She picked out the book, stepped back a pace and held it to the light streaming through the door behind her. She rotated the cover. Something about the purplish colour pricked at her. She had the sensation of having seen this precise colour before. But where? On a bird? A fruit? In a sunset?

She gained the door in less than a minute. She stepped outside into the mid-morning sun and leant against the side of the barn. She did not see the cherries on the tree or the water sparkling in the pool or the ruffled feathers on a pigeon's neck. She saw only the book in her hand.

She opened the cover.

The book was published in London in 1922 by Chatto & Windus and translated from the Russian by Constance Garnett. She noted that it had first appeared in print in 1897.

She turned to the first page.

Susan Wicks

ONE WHITE

We are unlearning vision. Under rain the snow
rises into mist, the earth itself is lighter.
Pale clods shrink back, part to show
a bowl of dark leaves, the sudden fruit of water.

Mist ghosts the high trees, their ragged
rigging of needles. A barn
drifts into focus like the barns of childhood
rising through dusk and gone.

Let them go. Let this one wreck
shake off its rags, single
and forgettable, this one shade of white

spread between air and earth. No sight
to speak of. Only the cornea's tingle,
the rank smell of the brook.

THE MORNING AFTER

Grey light, and the animals
have gone, a slur of footprints.
The world creaks. Rotten tree-trunks
lie down on a bed of splinters
to be covered, and Mary
is pie-eyed, yawning, the blue folds
hiding the ragged places
of new blood, as Joseph scrubs at
his hands. Angels
have become ordinary,

a matter of straw and torchlight.
Now the stars
have shrunk back into the grey.

The parents listen
for their child's breath,
not quite believing
he is real, this perfect flesh
is real and can be satisfied
with simple milk, not quite believing
him born into a time
of census and grey footprints
where their own lives continue.

Penelope Fitzgerald Talks to Hermione Lee

A VERY ENGLISH GENIUS

Penelope Fitzgerald was born in 1916 and educated at Wycombe Abbey and Somerville College, Oxford, graduating in 1939. She married Desmond Fitzgerald in 1941; he died in 1976. They had one son and two daughters and she has nine grandchildren. After working in the Ministry of Food, at the BBC, in a bookshop and as a teacher, she began writing in the mid-1970s. She has published three biographies, of *Edward Burne-Jones* (1975), of her father and her uncles, *The Knox Brothers* (1977), and of *Charlotte Mew* (1984), and nine novels: *The Golden Child* (1977), *The Bookshop* (1978), the Booker Prize-winning *Offshore* (1979), *Human Voices* (1980), *At Freddie's* (1982), *Innocence* (1986), *The Beginning of Spring* (1988), *The Gate of Angels* (1990) and *The Blue Flower* (1995).

I ask Penelope Fitzgerald about the shape of her novels, about whether she cuts a great deal out of them. She looks at me askance and says, in her mild, apparently absent-minded manner, 'I always feel the reader is very insulted by being told too much.' This remark strikes me as telling. It explains the way her short novels, though limpidly clear, also give off a sense of depth, of something withheld, of mystery. It illustrates the sharpness underlying her benign manner. It points to one of the most appealing qualities in her writing, her respect for other people's dignity. And it incidentally provides a comment on why she is not an easy subject for interview. Not telling too much is an art with her.

She is not a formidable figure, but you want to treat her with great respect. Eighty at the end of last year, she looks well: short, solid, active, with cropped grey hair, a wide, watchful, slightly anxious face, strong blue eyes, a good smile, and every so often, an appealing childish giggle. Her voice is clear, light, rather melodious, and tends to run upwards into puzzled, ironical exclamations.

She lives, as she has for some years, in a separate annexe of her daughter's house in Highgate, which once belonged to Arnold Wesker. Her son-in-law has just bought a house in Wales, and there is much talk of family (she has three children), of one daughter's job as a professor of neurobiology, of the grandchildren, of travel plans; also of PEN meetings, of publishers, of translations and readings. This seems a rich, busy, full, unsolitary life.

The flat is friendly and tidy and crammed with books, though many more of them, she says ruefully, are up in the attic where the electrical wiring is, and can't be got down. ('The man who comes to buy my manuscripts from Austin Texas, he's dying to get up there! He says he won't be electrocuted – he's sure there'll be diaries – but I never kept a diary. It's Gibbon's *Decline and Fall* up there . . . Still, I'm sure it's very good insulation.') She is kind to me when I arrive, late and flustered from hold-ups on the tube, gives me tea and chocolate cake and sits on the little sofa opposite me with her hands obediently folded, looking obliging.

We embark on an affable, rambling conversation marked on her part by sudden switches of subject, short bursts of excitement, profound hesitations, polite abstentions, and self-protective side-steppings skilfully masquerading as musing *non sequiturs*. She is particularly pleased and relieved when the conversation leaves her and gets on to other writers. So she talks with enthusiasm about Charlotte Mew's 'four or five great poems', how Scott mixed up historical and fictional characters, the Victorian novelists always setting their narratives back in time, Dickens having to do research for his material ('I feel awfully sorry for him having to go to all those opium dens'), Tolstoy's short novel, *Master and Man*, being

137

her favourite of his books, how she admires Lawrence 'for having these immense gifts and then throwing them all away', how no one can write now with James's formality (but 'Henry James was fine'), and about Anita Brookner's marvellously 'timeless' novels.

By contrast, direct questions about her life and her writing methods are met with the gentlest of diversionary tactics. I couldn't decide whether this was a deep unwillingness to explain how she does it, a desire to keep her secrets, or a reluctance to consider herself a suitable subject for interview. The effect of her modesty and complete unpretentiousness is to give the impression of genuine surprise that anyone should be wanting to ask her questions about *her*.

But, even if her manner in interview has allowed people to think so, this is no minor figure, no amateur lady scribbler, but one of the most brilliant, original, imaginative writers of fiction in the country. She began to be published over twenty years ago and has written nine novels, three biographies and a large number of excellent review-pieces (which she would probably never dream of collecting). Yet this body of work, though justly admired and respected, has still not turned Penelope Fitzgerald into a major 'name'. She is not talked of alongside Murdoch or Spark, and she certainly does not convey, in interview, the sort of established, constructed novelist's persona you would get from an interview with – say – Martin Amis or Salman Rushdie. And even though her last novel, *The Blue Flower*, received the kind of passionately admiring reviews which confirmed her importance and centrality in English fiction, she is still not widely known.

Perhaps she has not acquired such status because the novels are short, and so perceived as 'light'. No one, she says, likes being called a 'light' novelist: 'You've put a lot of yourself into it, but being English, you feel you shouldn't make a fuss.' She often refers in interviews to the awkward start of her fictional career, when her first publisher, Colin Haycraft, told her that her 1977 thriller, *The Golden Child*, was too long, cut it by eight chapters and so, she says, wrecked the working-out of lots of the clues. After that she was inhibited about writing long books but 'if your books are too short, the librarians mind'. Perhaps she has suffered in terms of reputation for having started in her sixties. It would have been nice, she says wistfully, to have been a young novelist. Perhaps she still falls victim to the lasting assumption that short novels by elderly English ladies cannot be rated alongside great male intercontinental epics or bravura postmodernist exercises.

Fitzgerald's biographies, written in the 1970s and early 1980s, of Burne-Jones, the Knox brothers and Charlotte Mew, have the sympathy, the evocativeness and the psychological clarity of fiction. The novels, beginning in the late 1970s, inhabit their periods, their places and their touching, troubled characters with the precision and attention of biography or history. And she has drawn very fully for her work on her own life, her associations and memories. All three biographies derive from a personal link, and to write them, she needed a living connection to the subject: 'I wouldn't like to write a biography unless you could speak to someone who knew the person.' She adds, looking at me wryly, 'I'm a bit snobbish about biography – I only want to write about people who haven't been written about.'

The link to Burne-Jones was an old lady who knew him; but she had also grown up thinking of him as almost a relation, because he 'did' the west windows of Birmingham Cathedral (once St Philip's), where her grandfather, bishop of Coventry, officiated. '*He* didn't care about them, he had no aesthetic sense at all, he was far too busy – as far as he was concerned they might have been filled with whitewash!' But she was often taken up to look at those red and pink windows, now, she says sadly, boarded up against vandalism.

Her religious, literary, Sussex and Hampstead family background ('tweedy and establishment') provided the materials for her second biography, an affectionate life of the four Knoxes, her father, 'Evoe', editor of and contributor to *Punch*; and her uncles, the classics don and cryptographer

Dillwyn, the Anglican priest Wilfred, and the famous Roman Catholic convert and apologist Ronald. In her stories of her childhood, she often speaks of her father's weekly struggle to write his humorous column, or of her brilliant, dominant brother Rawle, who was good at everything and always made her feel inferior. ('He was the absolute ideal ... I used to think everything came "After Rawle".') He went on to work as a war correspondent and to write a life of E. H. Shepard, whose daughter was Evoe Knox's second wife. She and her brother produced a humorous magazine; they listened to the radio a lot. (She remembers that the first thing she ever heard on the radio, when she was about seven, was Yeats, reading 'His Pheonix': 'I knew a Phoenix in my youth . . .')

But this was not an entirely male-dominated world. Penelope Fitzgerald's mother, who died when she was eighteen, was also a writer – and she has said that her mother must have given up a professional career in order to bring up her children, though they were not aware of it at the time. 'She used to cut down *Pilgrim's Progress* and *Pickwick Papers*, for schools. Everyone in the house in Well Walk was writing. My father had a study – that was the only warm room in the house. My mother wrote in the drawing room. Alida Munro used to say that every woman must freeze or starve for an hour and a half before she starts the day, because some woman or other has to get the range going and boil the kettle.' Was she close to her mother? 'Oh yes, very much so.' And was she writing as a child? 'I wrote poems and stories and little pictures.' And long epic novels when she was thirteen? 'Oh sure, yes. But we had to get scholarships, without that things couldn't be afforded. I worked very hard. When I went in to do my finals at Oxford I knew all the Folio and Quarto variants of all the Shakespeare plays. But really, what was the use of it? I never meet anyone who wants to know the Folio variants . . .' I ask her how she remembers herself as a child. 'Rather a miserable object really, I think.'

Charlotte Mew, the subject of Fitzgerald's 1984 biography, was also a 'reading and writing child'. And there was a direct link between them. When she reviewed my biography of

Virginia Woolf, Fitzgerald remembered how different her 'Georgian' childhood had been from 'Bloomsbury': 'My world was Hampstead, muffin men, autumn leaves, *Peter Pan* at Christmas, the Poetry Bookshop where Walter de la Mare, W. H. Davies and Eleanor Farjeon read aloud our favourite verses.'*

She knew Alida Munro, the wife of Harold Munro of the Poetry Bookshop, who was a friend and memoirist of Mew. ('What happened to her?' 'She took to dog-breeding actually.') And Fitzgerald was lucky in meeting, at PEN, an old lady who had known Mew well, and who had never shown anyone her collection of the poet's letters. 'Then one day, she was sitting next to me at PEN, she dropped a paper-bag in my lap – it might have had fish and chips in it – and the letters were in that. They made me understand Charlotte Mew in middle life. But I'm sure I didn't find out everything there was.'

Fitzgerald's sense of Mew, in this book of extraordinary feeling, perception and vividness, is intense. We get very close to her unhappiness ('From adolescence she was one of those whom Colette called "restless ghosts, unrecovered from wounds sustained in the past"'), her hopeless loves, her painful family life, her need in her poems to 'impersonate', her idiosyncrasy and lack of self-esteem. 'Are you Charlotte Mew?' she was asked on her first arrival at the Poetry Bookshop. 'I am sorry to say I am.' Fitzgerald speaks of her as a divided personality, half proper lady, shocked at going to tea with the bohemian Ella D'Arcy and finding 'no flowers and no cake', half 'a wild spirit'. It is tempting to draw analogies with her biographer.

I ask if the novels are connected to the processes of biography: *At Freddie's* (1982), for instance, feels to me like a fictional biography of the indomitable manageress of the stage school (in fact the Italia Conti, where Fitzgerald taught in the 1960s). 'And so it was,' she agrees. But biography, she thinks, is safer than fiction. 'You look through your notes,

* *Prospect*, October 1996, p. 66.

and you feel you're doing something. With a novel you don't have that.' Readers, however, make little distinction between real-life stories and fictional stories. 'People's standards of truth for a novel are not different from a biography.' When she wrote *Human Voices* (1980), closely based on her wartime work at the BBC, she thought all the people she wrote about would be dead, but, on the contrary, they all wrote in to say that she had got things quite wrong: 'Somebody had a blue pencil and I'd given them a red one.'

Such literal-minded readings might be excused, given the closeness of her first five novels to her earlier experiences. Sometimes all she needed was an atmosphere: *The Golden Child* (1977), written to amuse her husband when he was ill, derived its wickedly accurate comedy of the workings of the British Museum from a succession of visits to the Tutankhamun exhibition. *The Bookshop* (1978) recalled the time in the 1950s when she and her family lived in Southwold; its evocation of post-war Suffolk life is as vivid as its painful account of the heroine's struggle to keep the shop going against the local bigwigs. The terrifying and entirely convincing appearance of a poltergeist in the bookshop is also based on life. 'Oh, I'm quite sure about it,' she says matter-of-factly. 'But it's not a *high* manifestation, it doesn't really lead to anything.'

The family moved from Suffolk to a barge called 'Grace' on Battersea Reach, which sank twice. This gave her the material for *Offshore*, which to her great surprise won the Booker Prize in 1979. (She is funny about what a 'hole in corner' event it was then. 'It's all right for you,' was all her publisher said, 'you don't have to borrow a dinner jacket.') After the barge, the family moved to Cambridge for a time; Fitzgerald taught at the stage school and at Westminster Tutors (and was enthusiastically remembered by many of her students). Her husband, Desmond Fitzgerald, whom she had married in 1941, died in 1976. With her three children grown up, she began to write full-time.

After five novels, she felt she had 'used up' her personal materials: 'I felt I had finished writing about the things in my own life which I wanted to write about – then you must look and find other experiences, you must launch out.' The novel *Innocence* (1986), a richly imagined story of an old Florentine family and its matrimonial problems in the 1950s, seems to have marked a turning away from autobiography. She became increasingly attracted to the idea of going back to a world with *rules*: 'If there are things you mustn't do it makes it easier for a novelist. Prohibitions were a great help – look at Jane Austen.' In the last ten years, she has written three magnificent 'historical' novels (though the term doesn't seem quite right for her subtle re-entries into the past). *The Beginning of Spring* (1988), her favourite of her books, is set in Moscow in 1913, before the revolution. *The Gate of Angels* (1991) is set in Cambridge in 1912. *The Blue Flower* (1995) is a reconstruction of the young life of the German philosopher Novalis, at the very end of the eighteenth century. The novel's epigram, from Novalis, is: 'Novels arise out of the shortcomings of history.'

Yet the division in her work, often referred to, between 'personal' and 'historical' novels, is perhaps misleading. The earlier novels are just as concerned with pinpointing the atmosphere, the mood of a time (like the comedy of *Lolita*'s shattering impact on rural England in *The Bookshop*, or the euphoric 1960s carnival of the King's Road in *Offshore*). Though *The Blue Flower* is of all her novels the most dependent on historical sources, she has always enjoyed mixing up real and fictional characters, having Gramsci appear in *Innocence* ('He was ... something', she says suddenly), or M. R. James in *The Gate of Angels*. And her own feelings and memories get into the 'historical' novels as well: her deep interest in Russia and Russian literature for *The Beginning of Spring* ('It was post-Chekhov Russia, when they'd started to have electricity and gas – yes, I'd always wanted to do that'), or her family knowledge of Cambridge history for the setting of *The Gate of Angels*, at the time when nuclear research was beginning at the Cavendish Laboratory, a time of debate between scientific rationalism and belief in the supernatural and the spiritual.

I ask her why she wants to set the books in particular historical periods and she gives me a sideways answer, to do with the practical difficulties of establishing the date in a novel. 'You can't say – he glanced up at the calendar . . . If you're writing about the BBC before television, you can't have people say, "What a pity there's no TV!"' This is typical of how she answers: she would much rather talk technically than personally about her work. So she will speak about her pleasure in dealing with institutions and closed societies ('Is that a weakness?'), about how much she cuts down, about her need to have a beginning and an ending in mind for every book: 'I do need the title and the last paragraph and the opening – then I can do it.' She says that her greatest technical problem is making more than two people talk to each other – as in Handel's operas, you never get more than a duet. But, I object, she does have a large family on stage in *The Blue Flower*. 'Yes, but I cut the family down, everyone was called either Fritz or Caroline and it was too confusing.'

She is severely matter-of-fact about her imagination. When I ask her if she ever feels (as some authors say they do) that her characters are running away with her, that she has no idea what they will do next, she says: 'I think if you get that feeling you must stop them at once, because they're out of order.' So it is all in her head from the start? 'People say you should have a plan, yes, I've seen that. But I couldn't write down schemes, I could never have done serial publication . . . Well . . . I just hope for the best, really.'

Fitzgerald always talks about her work with this kind of self-deprecating irony. When I ask her how much she writes in a morning, the answer she gives me is: 'Oh, women are always interrupted.' This resistance to all notions of a high calling or of professional status, and the determination not to speak about the imagination except in terms of craft or strategy, does not begin to explain the strange effect of her novels. She has nothing to say about the amazing deftness and precision with which, in a very little space, a whole complex historical moment is imagined, nor about the haunting darkness that lies under their quiet manner.

In all the novels, there is a sense of people puzzled or baffled by their lives, coming up against a point where they must make a choice or recognise a change. They have a chance, but they often miss it. There is a strong investment in likeable, not very effective, honest, diffident, undemanding types – particularly men. There is sympathy and interest for characters who don't fit in – the boat people in *Offshore*, the Moscow oddities in *The Beginning of Spring*. There is, almost always, a consuming passion which starts very suddenly, cannot be cured, and goes hopelessly wrong. Happy endings only get in by the skin of their teeth. ('It goes against the grain. I'm deeply pessimistic.') Most of these characters – courageous innocents, kind-hearted losers – are defeated or balked. Fitzgerald often refers to the struggle between 'exterminators and exterminatees'. In this struggle, it is not the good or the innocent who triumph. The cruelty as well as the comedy of life is very marked in her books. At the same time there is great respect for human weakness and decency: 'I don't want more contempt in the world, I want less,' says the young Italian doctor in *Innocence*.

When Fitzgerald talks about writing novels she talks about inventing a 'moral structure'. 'I think that when you write, you should make it clear where you stand. And if you don't stand anywhere . . . I think it shows.' The politics that 'show' in these novels came out of a long-term admiration for William Morris, and politically charged years at Oxford before the war (she got a First from Somerville in 1939). 'We were always going to political meetings about the Spanish War – everyone was asking you to join the Communist Party. It was quite different by the time my daughter went up . . . But we were right, it did matter. There's no political home for me any more. But for some reason I feel you ought to vote.' She describes herself as a Lansburyite – invoking a now-forgotten figure, the much loved Labour leader of the 1930s, editor of the *Daily Herald*, champion of local government and idealistic pacifist. 'It was such a marvellous idea really –

but that's all a thing of the past.' Lansbury, like any Fitzgerald hero, lost out to the more forceful socialism of Ernest Bevin. Fitzgerald describes herself as 'mild', but I once saw her old-style politics in action, sharing a platform with her about the future of public libraries. A man from the Adam Smith Institute who had been arguing that libraries should all charge admission fees, and were in any case socially redundant, was startled to find the gentle grey-haired old lady next to him transformed into a fireball of scathing, fiercely-reasoned hostility.

I ask her if she thinks (as I do) that her politics get into her novels. She gives me one of her indirect answers: 'I would like my religion to get into my novels and I'm very ashamed that it doesn't.' I have heard her say this before – that she wishes she had made it plainer that 'the material world is not all there is'. And yet it is apparent, especially in the last three novels, that there is a debate going on between different forms of belief: between the rationalist conviction, like Fred's in *The Gate of Angels*, that 'what is completely described is completely explained', and the probability of 'The Unobservables' (the book's first title) suggesting 'a life beyond the life we know'. In pre-revolutionary Russia, in *The Beginning of Spring*, the possibility of different kinds of faith – a faith without beliefs? – and of respect for other faiths, is always being mulled over: 'As long as mankind doesn't pretend to believe in something they see no reason to believe, because there might be an advantage in pretending – as long as they don't do that, they won't have sunk to the lowest depths.' And *The Blue Flower* is in part a meditation on the irrational faith of love, and on the reaches of human nature that can't be explained or accounted for. Its particular quality comes from the odd, funny, moving juxtaposition of very precise, domestic historical details, and that sense of the soul's mystery.

But Penelope Fitzgerald does not think she has succeeded. She never rereads her books. She hates writing, only likes to have written. She never feels that what she has done is good enough. She accounts for this by calling herself a characteristically English depressive humourist. 'I think in general everything goes wrong and is disappointing,' she says, smiling at me. There is a lot of regret in her books, isn't there, I ask her. Yes, she says, and there is then a very long silence.

Louis de Bernières

MAMACITA'S TREASURE

THE OLD MIDWIFE swung her legs over the side of the bed, and rubbed her eyes with the heels of her palms. A cruel and implacable light had already invaded the house, stamping a brilliant rectangle upon the floor where the door stood open. She moved her feet a little to one side, so that the sun would not scald them, and took an experimental breath of air. She breathed out with resignation, reconciled in advance to one of those days when each inhalation would be a desiccation of the lungs, so that little oxygen would be absorbed. One would have only to move a hand to brush a wisp of hair from the eyes, and the sweat would pour down one's back and between the crease of the buttocks, it would trickle down from the neck between one's breasts, and one would thank the Good Saviour for the gift of eyebrows that prevented the salty water from running down from the forehead and stinging the eyes.

They called her 'Mamacita' or 'Abuela', 'Little Mother' and 'Grandmother' being the only terms that seemed adequate to express the respect and affection in which she was held. Her true name had long since been forgotten, sometimes even by herself, and she possessed the happiness of one who has been useful all her life even though none of her youthful aspirations had been fulfilled. She had never had a husband, had never had money, had never learned to read, and had never travelled further than the town of Domiciano, but on the other hand she had delivered three generations'

148

worth of babies, had never starved, and had never made an enemy.

Mamacita sat on the edge of her bed, and looked down at the speckled and loosened skin of her hands. She held them up to the ruthless light and marvelled at the way that they had become transparent. One could almost see the bones and blood vessels. She tried to still the tremor that had been worsening for the last ten years, and thought back to the time when they had been strong and self-confident, easing infants from the womb as if they possessed a knowledge that she herself had never consciously acquired. There was barely a soul within the radius of a day's walk that had come into this world without her firm hands cradling its head, and that included a fair number of the animals. It was true that for the most part it was only the women who bore the curse of agonising birth, but it did happen from time to time that a foal tried to come out the bad way, and that was when Mamacita might be called.

Mamacita had never been accused of sorcery or malice, even upon those few occasions when the child or the mother had died, and she was indeed quite famous for some spectacular feats of life-saving, the most celebrated being the occasion when Don Balcazar had insisted that the child's life be saved rather than the mother's, so desperate was he for an heir. Mamacita had stood up to him, pronouncing that the child would be a mooncalf, and a curse to him for the rest of his life, and she had ordered his brothers to take him away so that she could save the life of his wife, who lay upon the bed delirious and begging for death. Mamacita sent everyone out of the room, and cut the infant to pieces inside the womb, taking the limbs out one by one, until she had assembled upon a towel the complete body of a devil with a horny head and a monkey's tail. So horrified and repentant was Don Balcazar that he had crossed the sea to make a pilgrimage to the shrine at Santiago de Compostela, and after his return had produced a family of six normal children. From Spain he had brought back a silver crucifix to present to Mamacita, and she had hung it above her bed, the only rich thing that she was ever to possess, and which now hangs in the side-chapel of the Church of Our Lady of the Sorrows at Domiciano, with a yellowed and curled morsel of paper stuck on to the wall beside it, explaining its provenance and the story of the mooncalf.

On this day Mamacita reflected wryly that in the dry seasons one longs for rain, and in the rainy seasons one thirsts for the brutal sun. Still, the advantage of so much dust was that one could draw in it, and she hoisted herself slowly to her feet so that she could go to the table. She bent down to check against the light that there was indeed enough dust, and made a pair of experimental lines just to make sure. Then, pursing her lips, she drew the details of the map that she had remembered upon awakening. On the other end of the table she set down a plate, a small cup, and a steel tumbler.

Struggling with the matches and the knobs, she lit two rings of her petrol cooker, and on one she toasted a tortilla that was half wheat flour and half maize flour, whilst on the other she set a diminutive saucepan in which shavings of panela and grounds of coffee would boil up to produce a redolent brew that would wake a dead horse. She reached into her cupboard and drew out a half-bottle of aniseed-flavoured *aguardiente*, which she poured into the steel tumbler. She knocked it back in one slug, experiencing all over again, as she had every day of her adult life, the delicious and startling assault of strong alcohol on an empty stomach. This was a morning ritual in every household, and was designed to kill intestinal parasites. Those that were not killed would be stunned and horrified, and such small revenges had their own satisfaction.

Mamacita sliced a platano and fried the pieces in corn oil. She wrapped them in the warm tortilla, and masticated slowly and painfully with her toothless gums. There was something comforting about eating the same breakfast every morning, she reflected, and besides, when she went to see Don Agostin, he would undoubtedly give her some avocados to take away with her, and she would have the glorious obligation imposed upon her of eating all of them before they turned black and slushy. Her mouth watered at the thought.

Mamacita sipped the sweet strong coffee. It was like tasting the distilled essence of one's entire country; the tyrannical rain, the arrogant earth, the perverse savannahs, the obstinate jungles, the supercilious mountains, the playful rivers. She lit a cigar, and felt the sweet fumes fill up all the empty spaces in her skull.

Her breakfast finished, she ventured out into the white light, her *puro* still clenched between her teeth, and squinted for a moment. She shuffled slowly past the chickens that pecked and squabbled in the dust, and entered the little shop where Conchita sold alcohol and machetes. Both of the women raised a hand in greeting and drawled, 'Buen' dia.'

'I want a pencil and a piece of paper,' said Mamacita, 'I want a good pencil, and the paper should also be good.'

'I will give you a piece of paper,' said Conchita, 'but such a pencil will cost from two to ten pesos, depending upon how much of it is left. I have a good one here –' she produced a pencil from a drawer – 'and with careful sharpening it will last a long time. Who knows? Perhaps a year. The cost is four pesos.'

Mamacita inspected the pencil suspiciously. It was important to appear knowledgeable even if one was not. She turned it over in her fingers, and said, 'I will give you an avocado from Don Agostin's *finca*. I don't have it yet, but I will have it later.'

Conchita sighed. She had tried for years to consolidate a habit of cash-for-goods amongst her customers, but the village had only been well connected to other places for a few years, and the old habits had not been easy to change. Still, an avocado was not such a bad idea, so she said, 'OK, an avocado, but a big one.'

'A very big one,' agreed Mamacita, chewing the end of her *puro*, 'but don't forget to give me the paper.'

Conchita reached under her table for a spiral-bound notebook of the type used in schools, and carefully tore out one sheet, which she handed to the old midwife, who took it reverentially between thumb and forefinger. 'Paper,' she said, in the same tone of voice as one says 'thunder' when it is about to rain.

Back in her little dwelling, Mamacita carefully transcribed on to the paper the map that she had drawn in the dust on the table. It was very difficult. If one pressed hard, the fingers went into a clench that was hard to control, but on the other hand, if one pressed lightly, then the lines were faint and wobbly and did not go in the right direction, and neither did they stop at the right place. 'Hijo'e puta,' she swore to herself, revelling in the delightful luxury of using in solitude an obscenity which never in her life had passed her lips in public.

Mamacita scrutinised her completed work with some dissatisfaction, and felt the bitterness of ill-education mingle with the bitter taste of tobacco on her tongue. Her eyes were not in any case as good as they had been, and, when she peered hard, the lines faded and duplicated themselves, wandering about like ants and slipping away like snakes. 'It will have to do,' she told herself, 'and Don Agostin can always improve it if he wishes, with God's help.'

She put her chart into her *mochila*, and hung it from one shoulder. It had been made of heavy white linen by the Indians in the foothills, and had a pretty double-stripe around its top, in natural shades of maroon and green. She went out once more into the white light, and made her way towards the beginning of the long track that led down to Don Agostin's hacienda. On one side was the reedy swamp where small caymans lazed and grunted, only their snouts and their arched eyesockets above the level of the water, and on the other side was the field with the fallen trees where one of Don Agostin's mares was cavorting about with her foal. Mamacita laid her *mochila* on the grass, muttered a charm against coral snakes, and sat down on it, forgetting that this would crumple the map. She was waiting for Don Agostin's tractor driver, who passed this way several times a day, toing-and-froing between the different halves of the farm.

Mamacita arrived at Don Agostin's feeling like a queen.

The tractor was a venerable but lovingly-tended bright red Massey-Ferguson, a very large one, and today it had had the bucket mounted on the front so that it could be used for earth-moving. Mamacita had been installed in the bucket, and then raised high in the air, so that she became lady of all she surveyed. It was perilous, no doubt, and once or twice she had experienced tricky moments involving low-hanging branches, but it had been marvellous to be able to see the world at speed from such a novel angle, and she had also contrived to pick some lemons, a large grapefruit, and two avocados. It was not stealing, she reasoned, because Don Agostin would not have minded. Besides, the cooling effect of the air as it passed her by made her feel just a little irresponsible on such an otherwise oppressive day.

It was difficult to maintain dignity as Mamacita was lowered to the ground in a series of jerks, but she clung grimly to the side of the bucket, and continued to puff at her cigar with every affectation of nonchalance. The *vaqueros* who were saddling up their ponies and mules at the tackhouse gave her an ironic cheer as she stepped to the earth, and she beamed at them shyly but brightly, so that for one evanescent moment they caught a glimpse of Mamacita as she had been when young, when her father had become accustomed every night to having to chase away the boys who came to sing *rancheros* outside her window.

Mamacita crossed the flagstones shaded by bougainvillea, and tapped on the frame of the door. Through the fine green mesh that let in the air without also admitting the insects, and which served the place of glass in that tropical inferno, she could see Don Agostin himself, hunched over his papers at the dining table. Beyond him she could glimpse the cook in the kitchen, apparently skinning an iguana.

At the sound of her knock, Don Agostin called 'Enter' without even looking up, which struck Mamacita as a little marvellous, because she had herself tried not looking up when somebody knocked at her door, but had always looked up none the less, as if by reflex. Perhaps only those born to importance were capable of such coolness in the face of a knock.

Mamacita entered, and Don Agostin stood up to greet her. In his youth he had been a rakehell and an unmitigated dog, but at the age of forty-five he had become gallant and urbane, and so he seized her right hand and kissed it, not once but twice. 'Abuela,' he exclaimed, 'what a pleasure this is.' He waved her to a chair with an elegant sweep of his arm, and called out to the kitchen 'Emma, a jug of *guarapo* for my guest.' He turned to Mamacita, and wiped his forehead with the tail of his shirt. 'Another infernal day,' he observed.

Mamacita pointed to the fan that was rotating slowly and half-heartedly above them. 'This is very nice,' she said drily, 'but it would be nicer if we could all have them. It is the heat that makes us behave badly.'

'We become ill-natured, do we not?' agreed Don Agostin. 'However, I have finally bullied and bribed the State Governor into electrifying the village, and soon we will have every sort of convenience, including refrigeration.'

'You are a good patron,' said Mamacita, 'everyone admits it.'

'Very kind, very kind,' replied Don Agostin, 'but all the same I am frequently reminded of my shortcomings.'

'At least you look after all your little bastards,' said Mamacita bluntly. 'There is many a patrón who doesn't.'

Don Agostin flushed, but remained dignified. 'Now what can I do for you? As you know, Abuela, nothing is too trivial or too great when matters concern the person who delivered me into this world.'

Mamacita came straight to the point. 'I have come to sell you a dream,' she said.

'A dream,' repeated Don Agostin.

'Yes,' she said. 'I have dreamed something, and you are the only person I can think of who can take advantage of it, since you have a Land Rover.'

Don Agostin was curious. He had been to a fine school in Cali and could have been a café intellectual anywhere in the world were it not for his duty to the family farm – he could cite instances from philosophy, and quote Neruda with the best of them – but he had learned to listen with more than half an ear to these dogged *campesinos*. He had become familiar with their syncretistic religion, their fantastical beliefs and quirky rituals, and could not in all honesty deny that sometimes they knew things in a manner that could not in the ordinary run of things be called knowledge. Had he not witnessed his own cattle cured of an inexplicable epilepsy by an itinerant mountebank who kissed them on the mouth and muttered secrets in their ears? It seemed that in different parts of the world there were entirely different laws of nature. You could not apply scientific principles in this place, any more than you could cure a European cow by kissing it.

'What is the nature of this dream?' he inquired. 'Naturally one must inspect the goods before purchase.'

'I dreamed of gold,' she said, 'I know exactly where it is.'

'Don't you want it for yourself, Abuela? Why don't you go and find it?'

Mamacita gestured loosely towards the foothills. 'It's over there. I think that one would need a Land Rover, or even mules. It's too far for me, I'm an old woman, and I don't have the means. That's why I thought I would sell the dream to you.'

'Is it a *huaca*, by any chance?' asked Don Agostin, referring to the huge urns in which the Indians used to bury their dead.

'I can't say,' said Mamacita. 'All I know is that I saw the exact spot, with a golden light above it. Like an angel.'

'It's funny,' mused the patron, 'but I have always thought of angelic light as being more silver than gold. One has such funny ideas.'

'There might be silver,' said the old woman. She rummaged in her *mochila* and produced the rumpled piece of paper. 'I drew a map, and I am prepared to sell it to you.'

'And how much are you asking?'

'I am asking two thousand pesos, and a share of the find.' She looked at him resolutely, the cigar, now extinguished, still protruding soggily from the corner of her mouth.

The patrón whistled. 'Two thousand? That's enough to pay a *vaquero* for ten weeks. And what share do you want?'

Mamacita raised all ten fingers, and then folded back seven of them. 'I want three out of ten, because three is the number of the trinity, and lucky. Also, three is made by the adding of the first two numbers, and therefore it is a very perfect number.'

Don Agostin was pricked by curiosity, and also by a feeling of obligation. How many times had his mother insisted that he would not have survived his birth if Mamacita had not greased her arm with lard, and reached in and turned him? Two thousand pesos was not too much money to help such an old lady for a time, and indeed, perhaps he should settle one hundred pesos a week upon her in any case. The good that one does in this world lives beyond the grave. 'I will give you three thousand pesos, and a fourth of the share,' he said, willing himself not to regret it the moment that it was said.

'It is too much,' said the ancient midwife, her mouth working, and her rheumy eyes flicking from side to side.

'I insist,' he said.

'Who am I to contradict the patrón?' she asked rhetorically. 'I accept, but not willingly.'

'Your reluctance shows great graciousness,' he said.

'I want it notified,' she remarked suddenly, 'I want it done before a magistrate.'

'I am a magistrate,' said Don Agostin, mildly offended that she appeared not to take his word. In fact Mamacita had recently become impressed by this business of bits of paper, and it appealed to her to have an official one.

'Forgive me, I forgot, Don patrón, but I would like a piece of paper all the same.'

Don Agostin removed a notepad from beneath his heap of paperwork, and wrote, in a beautiful cursive script:

'I, Don Agostin Leonaldo Jesús de Santayana, certify that on this day I have purchased from –' Here he stopped, and said, 'Forgive me in my turn, but what is your real name? I cannot write "Mamacita" on an official document.'

156

'It's Liliana,' she said, 'Liliana Morales. But Mamacita is better.'

The patron continued to write. '– Liliana Morales, spinster and midwife of this village, the right to a map indicating a place of treasure, revealed in a dream, for the sum of three thousand pesos and a fourth of the gross sale value of the aforementioned treasure, should it be found. Witnessed by God and by the aforementioned Liliana Morales.' He dated it, signed it with an exuberant elaboration of curlicues, and passed it over to her, saying, 'Keep this in a place where you can powder it with insecticide, or the termites will eat it, and we will have no agreement. Now, perhaps you would permit me to see the map?'

Mamacita passed it over, and Don Agostin scrutinised it. He felt both amused and cheated, for it was no more than a web of errant scribbles. 'I think that you should explain this,' he said.

Mamacita leaned over and jabbed at the paper with a trembling forefinger. 'This is a stream,' she said, 'and this is a goat track, and that is a rock that looks like a man, and this is a bush that is dead and has been burned, and this is a black rock that looks like a jaguar, and here you will find the skeleton of a horse, and this is where the sun rises, and at this place between all these things, you will find the treasure.'

The patron noted all of this, naming the features on the map. 'Perhaps you could give me an indication of distances,' he said.

Mamacita ran her forefinger over the scribbles, reciting, 'This is ten paces, this is five minutes' walk for a grown man, this is the same as from here to the waterfall, and this is about the length of a lemon tree's shadow an hour before sunset.'

'That seems very clear,' said Don Agostin with an irony that he knew she would not perceive. He scratched his head with the pencil.

Mamacita rose and offered him her hand, which he kissed again, this time less gallantly than before, as he was beginning to suspect that he had somehow been nudged into making a fool of himself. Mamacita reminded him, 'Don't forget the four thousand pesos.'

'It was three thousand pesos,' he said, 'and a fourth of the treasure.'

'Oh, forgive me, it's my old brain. It's not what it was.'

'An understandable error,' he said, drily. He left the room and returned a few minutes later with a sheaf of five hundred peso notes, which he handed to the old lady. She had never had so much money in her life, and she counted it shamelessly before rolling it up and stuffing it carefully into the bottom of her *mochila*. 'Another thing,' she said, 'whilst I am here. I have heard that you have a good crop of avocados.'

'Of course,' said the patron, 'you shall have some.' He called through to the cook, 'Emma, bring through some avocados, would you? Nice big ones with no blemishes.'

Mamacita was returned to the village by the same means that she had arrived and went promptly to pay Conchita for the pencil. Conchita took the avocado and prodded its apex appreciatively. 'Just a few hours and it will be perfect. Thank you, Abuela.'

'I can sell you back the pencil now,' said Mamacita. 'I don't think I'll need it again, and if I do, I can always come back and buy it again. I will sell it back to you for three pesos and another bit of paper, and then you can sell the pencil again for four pesos.'

'You old fox,' exclaimed Conchita admiringly.

What came of all this? Don Agostin and his foreman made several exasperating expeditions into the foothills, greatly perplexed to find hundreds of rocks that might look like a jaguar or a man. Stupefied and baffled by the heat, disorientated by insects, startled by armadillos, lacerated by thorns, they blundered from one incandescent rock to another, futilely stabbing with a pick at the unyielding baked pale earth of each location that seemed propitious.

They found numerous goat-tracks, many a stream, a fair quota of burned bushes, and a large number of horse skeletons, besides the skeletons of cattle, donkeys, mules, pumas, and the gruesome mummified cadaver of a ginger-haired human being clad entirely in the leather garments of an old-fashioned hunter. In view of this evidential prodigality, Don Agostin felt just as incapable of blaming Mamacita for misleading him, as he felt of ever finding the treasure. He eventually developed the intention of trying a few more times, but somehow never quite got round to it.

As for the old midwife, she had little immediate use for such a large sum of money, and she sealed it into a small clay pot, which she buried in her back yard at a depth of two handspans. On her spare piece of paper she indicated its whereabouts by means of another wobbly and undecipherable map, which she placed in the same termite-proofed drawer as her contract with Don Agostin, before going to sell the pencil back to Conchita for the agreed three pesos.

After Mamacita's death, her nephews found the contract, and wondered what she might have done with the money, but they could make neither head nor tail of the scrap of paper covered with shaky lines and arcane blobs, so one of them who had been caught short used it in the outhouse and then dropped it into the cess-pit.

One morning, not long after the funeral, Conchita awoke, having dreamed that there was buried treasure in the place where Mamacita used to live, and she took a lift on the tractor down to the hacienda, to try to sell the notion to an obdurately sceptical Don Agostin.

Paul Muldoon

THE HOPEWELL HAIKU

An extract

XLVIII

From under the shed
a stench that's beyond belief.
Pangur Ban is dead.

XLIX

I lean to one side
to let a funeral pass.
It leans to one side.

L

Now I must take stock.
The axe I swaggered and swung's
split the chopping-block.

LI

In a slow puddle
two dragon-flies, Oxford blues,
rest on their paddles.

XLIV

A Saharan boil.
Oscar stretched under a hide
by the toilet-bowl.

XLV

There's a trail of slime
that runs from the ladysmock.
I'll show you sometime.

XLVI

At my birthday bash,
a yellow bin for bottles
and a green for trash.

XLVII

Sunflower with fence-posts.
Communion-rail. Crozier. Cope.
The monstrance. The host.

Peter Straughan

ORPHAN

MY GRANDFATHER WAS an orphan from County Mayo; from a village on the coast, near Leedarne. In the photographs that survive you can see the orphan in him, his thin arms and narrow face, his lightness, his unanchored nature. He stares past the photographer, slightly frowning through rough, black hair. He stares far away, as if noting a distant, returning figure.

William – a bastard – was a shameful thing. A priest brought him to the village in the spring, the product of a young girl from Tuan and a theatre manager. The priest had the little thing baptised and found a suitable family for him – a shopkeeper and his wife who already had three grown-up girls and would receive money every year from the Parish Poor Fund for the upkeep of the child.

It was the grocer, O'Hannlon, a pious man, who had persuaded his wife to accept my grandfather.

'You can't blame the child for his mother, can you?' he reasoned, staring down at William's tight-wrapped, silent self.

'Suffer the little ones, Mr O'Hannlon. Suffer the little ones . . .' murmured the priest in agreement.

But Mary O'Hannlon observed her new son, tight-lipped, as her new son, tight-lipped, observed her, and both reserved judgement.

'Well,' she said at last, 'tell the neighbours he's my sister's boy and she's too ill to raise him.'

The silent baby grew into a silent boy. He ate every meal as if it was his last – ate enough for two – but still grew razor-thin and ghost-faced. That's what the other children called him – 'Ghost' – distrusting his silence, his stares.

One photograph shows him sitting on the rocks, the ocean behind him. Pinched features and hollow eyes, the blue black hair. Mary stands awkwardly beside him, a big, fine-looking woman, shielding her eyes from the sun with one hand. With the other she grips William's shoulder. Grips. She stares at the camera with a frozen smile. William, as always, is staring past us all with that slight frown of concentration. His hands are crossed primly upon his knees, his expression a curious mixture of dignity and imbecility.

Two days before William's eleventh birthday O'Hannlon went and died. My grandfather was carrying a mug of tea through to the shop front, for the grocer's breakfast, as he did every morning, and so was the first to find him sitting in the corner by the till, his legs spread out before him, his face a stormy purple, grinning with a kind of desperate intensity.

Mary took it grimly, almost angrily, as if her husband had died against her express wishes. She arranged the wake, mass and burial – all with a kind of suppressed fury. At night, in bed, she thought of the grocer's bulk upon her, and searched her emotions guiltily for grief. She remembered her embarrassment when the doctor had arrived in his car with his beautiful suit and O'Hannlon lying there with one trouser leg dragged up past his knee, and that painful grin still upon his stiffening face. He had looked such a fool. And that great gligeen of a boy! Again and again she saw him, coming back into the scullery with the mug of tea still in his hand, sitting at the table and never a word, not a damn word, until she had gone through to the shop front herself and found him lying there. Sitting with that vacant look and all the time her poor

163

husband lying dead next door. It roused her so, she felt she could strike him, slap his face as hard as she could.

And now O'Hannlon had gone and left her to run the shop all alone, and bring up that idiot, a boy she had never wanted, all alone. Overcome by the pity she felt for her own situation Mary blinked out a few, silent tears. God is good – the priest had said – God is good and brings his own back home to him. She could have slapped his face as well.

The funeral was dismal. A freezing, salty rain slanted in from the ocean and the priest dragged out the service in a quite unnecessary manner.

The three O'Hannlon girls had come with their husbands and stood in a huddle of wet, black coats on the other side of the grave to their mother. William stood with them. Anne, the youngest, stood next to him. She noticed him shivering and put her arm about his shoulder. Dry eyed, Mary thought, watching the boy's face. Not a tear, not one – not for all O'Hannlon had done for him, saving him from the poor house or his mother doing away with him – bringing a bastard up as their own. For all that, not one tear.

A gust of wind sent the rain against her face, stinging it fiercely. She herself was dry eyed.

After they had all gone she began clearing the plates into the scullery. At the sink she heard his soft padding step and knew he would be behind her. Her ghost. And this her only company through the coming years. She glanced irritably over her shoulder. Sure enough he was standing there, holding a pile of dirty crockery, staring vaguely at the floor.

'Well?' she said. 'What is it you're waiting for? Put them on the table.' He turned to do so and two plates slid free from the pile and shattered on the stone tiles by her feet.

'Ah, will you look what you've done now!' she cried, exasperated. 'Clean them up, will ye, man! Don't stand there looking at them!' She watched him fetch the broom and pan and begin slowly and clumsily to brush up the pieces, all the time her anger building and building until she could feel the small hairs on her hands lift.

'What use are you?' she said bitterly. 'Yer no use at all!' And then repeating this: 'Yer no use at all!' Finished, he stood up. He was wearing the glasses her husband had found for him shortly before he died. Behind their lenses his fish eyes blinked at her. He was all things infuriatingly weak and she gave in to the delicious sensation of her anger.

'You couldn't even manage a tear for your poor dead Da!' she said, and not knowing why she felt herself blush.

'He wasn't my Da,' said William turning away.

For a second she thought she'd misheard.

'What's that? What did you say?'

'He wasn't my Da,' he repeated, his voice hoarse, 'and you're not my Ma. They're dead and you're only paid to keep me.'

And then she had slapped him. She was a big woman and she hit him as hard as she could. Later she remembered how he had searched for his glasses on the floor while she had stood above him, her hand still raised, feeling a sudden cooling inside.

Not a tear of course – only the angry red on his face from her hand.

'My Ma's dead,' he had repeated, 'and she was a better woman than you.'

'Was she now? Well it's a shame she didn't like you enough to keep you, isn't it?' But the fight had left her – suddenly.

That night he stayed in his room, crying, while she banged pots in the sink. Each of them spent the night listening to the other. And so they stayed.

I have other photographs of my grandfather, of course. As a young man, after he had come to England to work on the railways. After he had been called up. I have a photograph of him in France in the sun with other soldiers; he is tanned but still thin, smiling but still his eyes . . . Perhaps his comrades also distrusted his silences, like the children from his village. And later still, sitting on English rocks at Tynemouth or Cullercoats, a solid family man with daughters of his own and my solid grandmother standing beside him, caught laughing, a hand upon his shoulder, even then he has the ghost about him, as if he might fade into the sea behind, leaving only solid brogues and a crumpled jacket on a rock, a sense of incompletion in the air.

He kept himself tidy, as he entered his teens, washed his own shirts and collars, combed down his rebellious hair. Everything in his little room had a place. Even Mary had to admit that he didn't take much keeping. But still there was nothing much to him – the type you barely notice as they pass.

He worked every day in the shop, slow but careful, and gradually Mary began to rely on him more and more. She still felt she ran the shop because she dealt with the customers, chatting and joking – the ghost was no good at that – but he ordered all the goods, stocked the shelves, cashed the till, kept the books.

It was Anne, of course, who had caused all the trouble. Mary had never doubted that. She had found him crying on the beach. Two of the boys had told him he was a bastard, flung the word lightly, perhaps even without malice, at him. His mother hadn't wanted him, they had explained, so Mary O'Hannlon was paid to keep him. Upset for the boy, Anne had told him that his parents had wanted him but they had died when he was just a babe. She had told him what she felt she would have wanted to hear in his place: to have been wanted. Mary was furious.

'You've filled his head with nonsense. No one else is good enough for him now. You can see it in his face. We're all muck compared to his Ma and Da in Heaven! I've got a good mind to tell him the truth . . .'

'You'll do no such thing!' said Anne. So Mary didn't. William kept the shop while Mary chatted and gossiped and at night they listened to each other in the empty house. They wore at each other like two stones, never becoming comfortable but somehow fitting, somehow continuing. And all the while Mary grew older and thinned a little and began to stoop a little, while my grandfather grew taller and broadened a little.

When William was seventeen one of the suppliers told him he wouldn't be coming any more. He was selling up and moving to England. He had a brother there, working on the railways, who had told him that jobs were plentiful and the money good.

Mary had whooped with laughter when my grandfather had told her that night that he was going to England to be a navvy.

'Ye can barely lift your knife and fork, let alone a pickaxe!' she said. 'Sure, what else are you good for but shop work?' But she felt quite unexpectedly a sharp pang of unease.

'I don't think it's what my Da would have wanted me to do,' he answered gravely.

'Your Da? And what in Jesus' name would you know about your Da?'

'I know he's in Heaven, looking down on me, and I know he wants the best for me.'

'You know nothing!'

'Mary,' he said, and his voice was steady though he blushed at saying it, 'Mary, you didn't think I would stay for ever, did you?' And when she couldn't answer he had calmly left the room.

She couldn't sleep that night. She had seen in that moment of awful clarity how utterly dependent upon her idiot boy she had become. The shop would fail were he to go, and she would be alone, totally alone. He had called her 'Mary' instead of Ma. It was this, not the shop, that she could not forget. Let that slut and that whoremaster have him, she thought to herself. Let his precious, saintly parents have him, for I'm finished with him!

The next morning she left the house early. When she

returned she found William eating in the scullery. She put the scrap of paper on the table in front of him.

'There,' she said, 'you want to know what your precious mother wants for you? You can go and ask her. That's where you'll find her in Tuan. Ask her about your caring Da.' Then she fled to the shop front and busied herself chattering madly to a customer, all the while her heart thumping in her ears.

He was gone for a week and Mary was sick with fear. What had she done? She couldn't sleep or eat and the realisation finally came to her: she had no one else. Her husband was dead. Her daughters were gone. William was all she had left.

He came home the following Monday. She made him tea as he sat, silent, at the table and inside she was jubilant. He'd come back to her. He'd seen his real Ma for what she was and he'd come back to her!

'Well,' she said, setting his tea before him, 'and how did you find your precious mother?' She had meant to sound stern, wounded even, but she could not keep the grin from her voice.

'I looked,' he said, 'but she wasn't there. I couldn't find either of them.' He was lying, of course; she saw that. And in an instant she was ashamed and bending forward she saw the ghost in him and knew she could never fill his loss.

I have a photograph of my grandfather. It is my mother's wedding day and he is smiling, surrounded by the family he made and anchored himself with. And his eyes stare through us all and far, far away. Perhaps as far as Heaven, where his circle is complete.

With the photographs I have a little bundle of letters he kept. They are from Mary O'Hannlon, written as she grew older and thinner, as her mind began to wander a little and she forgot the girls' names and would stare at them with distrust when they called, but would tell the neighbours how her son lived in England now but had said he was coming to see her. She sent the letters overseas. He never wrote back.

Ian McEwan

THE PLEASURE DOME

SCIENCE BUILDING. NIGHT.

An array of video monitors in the security guard room shows a number of empty corridors and lobbies. We are in a research institute attached to a large teaching hospital. Out of shot but for feet on desk, a guard is murmuring into the telephone to his girl.

GUARD: What'ja think I think? Every time I tell you, the next night I got to tell you all over ... Sure I do ... Yeah, well she's got a right, she's got a past, you know what I mean? (etc)

As he speaks, a blur of movement on one of the monitors. We pan across the array, and pick up a man and a woman passing across the end of a corridor. Panning again, we find them hurriedly crossing a lobby in front of an elevator. On a fourth monitor, they glance around and slip through a door.

STEPHEN'S LAB. NIGHT.

On the cut, Stephen Godwin, a neuroscientist, mid-thirties, leans hard against the door and locks it, and sighs with relief. Across the room, Carol Sergeant, also a neuroscientist, about the same age, turns on a desk lamp. The atmosphere is nervous, jokey. This is not something she would normally do, but quietly she cares strongly for Stephen.

CAROL: Is half an hour OK?

STEPHEN: I need you to come.

CAROL: Well, uh. We'll see . . .

STEPHEN: Could you clear the things off the table?

While Carol moves stuff off a sliding table, Stephen crosses to a battery of MRI equipment and is pulling switches, making adjustments. Lights flash on, three monitors come to life. He smiles at her teasingly.

STEPHEN: Half an hour should be fine.

Carol is sitting on the edge of the table, her blouse unbuttoned. Stephen is bent over his recording equipment. He makes his last adjustments.

I've been doing chin-ups, getting in shape. Now . . . main thing is, can you keep still?

He starts to undress.

CAROL: As long as you can.

Wearing unbuttoned blouse and panties, Carol spreads a blanket and climbs on to the table.

You got a hypothesis? Or are you fishing?

STEPHEN: S' the real thing. The cognitive subtraction in the last experiment . . .

CAROL: The cingulate again?

STEPHEN: It's a network, the whole shebang – nucleus accumbens, septal nuclei, posterior hypothalamus . . .

He gets on to the table beside her. She is lying on her back. To one side, Stephen has a view of a monitor. Picked out in computer-enhanced colour is the entire limbic system high-lighted against the background of the rest of Carol's brain.

OK if I record for sound?

She grimaces.

CAROL: No video.

STEPHEN: No video. And uh I'd prefer a low acoustic input . . .

He reaches across and sets a tape running. Then presses another couple of switches. Carol grimaces.

CAROL: So er do we get any foreplay?

He holds her gaze, speaks with sudden seriousness.

STEPHEN: Carol, I love you.

He glances across at the monitor which Carol from her

position cannot see. There is a shift, a little swirl of colour change in different regions.

CAROL: Uhuh. Not credible. Therefore, no response.

STEPHEN: You'd be surprised what those little words can do. But listen. You're a dedicated scientist. This was the only way I could get you into – er – on to the table . . .

She smiles at him and draws his face towards hers and kisses him.

CAROL: Not bad . . .

cut to

Several minutes later. Stephen and Carol make love. With his hands tenderly pressed against her cheeks, he holds her head still. Long, slow strokes. Carol approaches her orgasm with softly breathed repeated notes at a single pitch. At a critical moment she opens her eyes and looks up at him, mouths his name. But he is not entirely with her. He glances across his shoulder towards the monitor. We follow his gaze. The image of Carol's brain fills the screen.

We see illuminated a shifting pattern of neural activity in the cingulate and the thalamus – a slowly enfolding penumbra of brilliant colours rhythmically coalescing and separating, with myriad brightening and fading clusters pulsing to Carol's breathy, flute-like note. The impression is not of a merely interesting technological gadget, but of something wondrously beautiful revealed. We are witnessing Carol's secret life. We are seeing love from another point of view. A music cue picks up and elaborates Carol's sound.

Over the scan – title credit – The Pleasure Dome.

Carol's sound is gradually replaced by a voice, echoing and indistinct at first, floating in from far away; and then, as music fades to nothing, becoming recognisable as Stephen's voice. The acoustic is that of a filled, high-ceilinged lecture hall. We catch the rustle and murmur of an audience. We continue to watch the scan.

STEPHEN: . . . and there it is, in the full glory of its functioning, the most complex object in the known universe, made out of cosmic dust and gas, the stuff of stones and water, and yet somehow capable of thought, feeling, memory, vision, anticipation, pain, love. Why did the universe come to arrange some of its atoms in this way? In order to think about itself? Or love itself? Or is the brain simply an incredible accident? I doubt that we can ever know.

LECTURE HALL. NIGHT.

We pull back from the image to discover it is formed on a screen on a lecture platform. The occasion is a public lecture at the university. The hall is in grand nineteenth-century style. Stephen is behind a lectern wearing a tux. His delivery is passionate, assured.

Stephen: How does consciousness spring out of a bunch of molecules? Is this one of life's sacred untouchable mysteries? No! It's a set of complex problems for science to solve. One day we will know how the brain works. There's a vast continent to explore. The great achievement of the late twentieth century has been to arrive on its shore and take the first faltering steps up the beach. This is no less than a scientific revolution. Neuroscientists will be the first to have truly responded to the challenge of the ancient Delphic Oracle: know thyself!

On the first wave of applause and Stephen's bow, cut to–

RECEPTION ROOM. NIGHT.

A crowded, noisy reception after the lecture. Highest echelons of the university establishment, down to the lowliest post-graduate research student are here. Waiters circulate with trays of drinks and canapes. Stephen is being steered at speed across the room by his departmental head, Jack Pace. Jack is in his fifties, more of an administrator and fund-raiser than an academic. He is energetic and hugely ambitious for his department. He whisks Stephen by colleagues and well-wishers who want to congratulate him.

JACK: You were perfect, Stephen. It was a great pitch, man. I really . . .

Stephen catches sight of Carol nearby.

STEPHEN: Hey, Carol . . .

But she turns and slips away into the crowd.

. . . It wasn't a pitch, Jack. It was a lecture.

JACK: Sure, sure, but all the right people are here.

Jack gets Stephen into a relatively quiet corner.

I'm taking you to meet some people. From the Buzzkid Corporation . . .

STEPHEN: Computer games?

JACK: They're over there, talking to the president.

We are looking through the crowd at an elderly stooping, birdlike man, and a younger, smoother-looking type at his side.

Best behaviour, OK. For the department? For the money?

cut to

Jack, the practised networker, makes the introductions.

JACK: . . . Professor Kalman, Mr Baldwin, Mr Butler, Dr Stephen Godwin.

KALMAN: Congratulations, Doctor. Very stimulating.

As Stephen is about to respond to the President, Baldwin takes his hand to shake it. He leans in on the younger man.

BALDWIN: Dr Godwin, we're very interested in your work on pleasure.

STEPHEN: Really. Well, it's a fascinating area.

JACK: Mr Baldwin would like to send Tom Butler here over to your lab.

Butler is Kalman's head of research. He's about Stephen's age, cool, poised.

BUTLER: Some general questions . . .

Stephen is nodding, smiling, doing his bit.

STEPHEN: Sure. I'd be delighted. Anytime you like . . .

End close on Jack's big, satisfied grin.

STEPHEN'S HOUSE. WORK ROOM. NIGHT.

Later the same night. Stephen has discarded his dinner jacket and bow-tie and is at his work station, examining a still of a scan on a small back projection screen, typing at his computer. Among the clutter on his table, by a bottle of Scotch, a framed photograph of a young woman, Rachael. He stands wearily, and leaves the room without switching off his machines. We follow him into the bedroom. He sits on the edge of the bed and begins to remove his shoe.

STEPHEN'S DREAM.

The same bedroom, another time. The room is darkened, and we are approaching the bed where a beautiful young woman, Rachael, lies on her back with her eyes closed. She is suddenly flooded with light, as though a curtain has been drawn. A pulse of fear: a fly is crawling across her forehead.

INT. STEPHEN'S BEDROOM. NIGHT.

Stephen gropes for the bedside light switch. He sits on the edge of the bed, naked, drenched with sweat. The dream is familiar . . .

EXT. DAWN. STEPHEN'S HOUSE! – LONG SHOT.

A solitary light in the window. The rest of the city still sleeping.

INT. STEPHEN'S WORK STATION. DAWN.

Wearing a bathrobe, Stephen types away at his terminal, preferring work to sleep. A glass of Scotch is at his elbow. Our impression is of a lonely, driven man fleeing his past, escaping into his work.

PSYCHIATRIC WARD. DAY.

Long shot down ward.

ROOM OFF WARD. DAY.

Stephen sits facing his patient, Patrick, an Irishman, a depressive in his early sixties. His face is void of expression. His voice is flat. Stephen takes from a battered case a beautiful country fiddle.
STEPHEN: Look. I brought your fiddle . . .
PATRICK: I don't want it.
STEPHEN: Patrick, a couple of months back you told me that one of the happiest days of your life was when your daughter was born.
PATRICK: She married a very stupid boy who—
STEPHEN: Let's stay with that day, let's try and bring it alive again.
PATRICK: It wasn't such a big deal. I got drunk was all.
STEPHEN: You told me you played your fiddle in the hospital ward . . .
PATRICK: Agh!
STEPHEN: I'd like you to try and think how the way you feel now might have changed that memory . . .
Patrick sighs. He seems to ponder.
PATRICK: I think I'd like to be getting back to the ward now.

SCIENCE BUILDING/STEPHEN'S LAB. DAY.

Stephen is late. We track behind him as he strides along a bustling corridor and sweeps into the lab. His team consists of half a dozen medical researchers and postgraduates. The most senior of the team, Alex, comes towards Stephen.
ALEX: Great talk. You made the local paper.
STEPHEN: Is everyone here? Can you round them up?

175

cut to

Stephen sits on the edge of a table and addresses his team.
I know I say this every day, but if one word of this experiment gets out, we're finished. Not just for scientific reasons. The administration here is like some borderline personality – paranoid, jealous, timid . . .
He takes some pages offered by Hermione, a postgraduate.
Is that the final draft description?
HERMIONE: Ken's got a non-technical summary
STEPHEN takes a single sheet from KEN.
STEPHEN: So. They want me at three o'clock.
Amidst murmurs of 'good luck' from the team, the meeting breaks up.

ELEVATOR. DAY.

Stephen steps into a crowded elevator. It goes up one floor. Two nerdish-looking researchers, Fred and Bob, step in. The elevator continues to rise. Fred and Bob look at Stephen. Then they look at each other. Fred nods. Bob clears his throat.
BOB: Er, Dr Godwin, we were wondering if you would step into our lab. There's something we wanted to show you . . .
STEPHEN: Sorry, guys. I don't have time.
Bob has pressed a button. The elevator stops, the doors open. Fred and Bob are steering Stephen out.
FRED: Won't take a minute. You gotta see it.
BOB: It's a breakthrough.
FRED: You'll love it . . .
Stephen shrugs and resigns himself.
STEPHEN: You've got two minutes.
BOB: We only need one.

SECOND LAB. DAY.

The lab is crammed with equipment and is very untidy. Bob

*ushers Stephen on to a wooden kitchen chair. Fred fusses
with a kind of hairnet to which three electrodes are
connected.*
BOB: You make yourself comfortable here . . .
FRED: This might be a little tight . . .
STEPHEN: I can't even remember what you guys were
working on.
Bob places a large custard pie in Stephen's hand.
BOB: Rest your right hand on your right knee . . .
STEPHEN: You want me to throw this at you?
BOB: We want you to look at it.
FRED: Just relax. Empty your mind. Stare at the pie.
Bob and Fred are by the door.
STEPHEN: Free associate?
*Fred points a remote controller at a bank of equipment and
presses. Instantly Stephen's right arm jerks up to splat the pie
right into his own face.*

CORRIDOR BY SECOND LAB. DAY.

*Fred and Bob run off down the corridor, hooting with
laughter.*

SECOND LAB. DAY.

*Stephen immediately understands the significance of what lies
behind the practical joke, and he is excited. He is still blinded.
As he wipes his face –*
STEPHEN: Brilliant! Magnetic stimulation. Now I remember. Straight to the hand and arm representation on the
motor cortex. Fantastic accuracy. You guys should be . . .
*He looks around. No Fred or Bob. Instead, Carol. She pauses
in front of him for a moment, then walks past towards a set
of wall shelves. Her manner is cool, but Stephen does not
register immediately.*
Oh, they've gone. You should have been here just now. These

177

guys magnetically stimulated my motor cortex. Amazing feeling, completely out of control . . . you all right?

CAROL: I just came to pick up a file.

STEPHEN: What's up?

CAROL: Nothing.

STEPHEN: Something I said?

Carol is searching the shelves.

CAROL: I'll be out of here in one minute.

Stephen goes over to her. Patches of foam are still on his face.

STEPHEN: You're angry. What have I done?

She goes to move away. He blocks her.

Carol, tell me.

She faces him. Her feelings are painful and confused. She is reluctant to have this out.

CAROL: The scan you used in your lecture last night. It was me . . .

STEPHEN: Oh come on!

Carol's anger flashes out.

CAROL: I know. No one else knew. Just you and me. A really intimate humiliation. You made a mockery of my privacy.

STEPHEN: It was on top of the pile, godammit! I could have used anything.

CAROL: Exactly. And why didn't you?

In his exasperation Stephen is suddenly desperate to get the foam off his face. He crosses to a small hand basin and splashes his face vigorously.

You think good science has got something to do with being heartless?

Carol leaves, pushing past Hermione and Susanne (another member of the research team) who have just arrived. Stephen at the basin does not see Carol go.

STEPHEN: This is so predictable! Staking out a claim because of the other night . . .

Hermione and Susanne watch from the door, hugely amused. Stephen has his face in a towel.

Oh, you were a big girl then. Doing it for science. And now

178

you want me in your soap opera. Well, you can ... ah, Hermione, Susanne ...

HERMIONE: Five past three, Dr Godwin. The ethics committee is waiting ...

COMMITTEE ROOM. DAY.

The committee sits at three tables arranged in a horseshoe shape. Jack Pace is in the chair. Stephen is standing by an easel out front. Percival Latimer, an elderly, distinguished professor of anatomy has stood up and is trying to address the room. As we come in, several people are trying to speak at once.

JACK: Order please. Professor Latimer ...

LATIMER: Thank you, Jack. Look, let's face it. Neurologists everywhere are excited with their new toys, these scanners. New data is easy to come by, reputations can be made, so they're racing each other like crazy to come up with something different, something oddball ...

One of the younger doctors butts in.

SYKES: Stephen's doing pretty well in that race.

Knowing smiles and murmurs round the room. Stephen takes a breath, but Latimer waves him down.

LATIMER: It's a fad, and it'll pass. Meanwhile we have to remember, humans are not rats. He wants to get young people in his lab at a critical instant in their lives – to investigate what exactly? Joy? Sorrow? Boredom?

Lamont is also an older member of the committee.

LAMONT: Exactly so. Way beyond the legitimate concerns of science ...

Sally Fielding is a doctor of about Stephen's age.

FIELDING: That's ridiculous. How can you research the brain without touching on those things?

LATIMER: It's intrusive, and it's immoral ...

LAMONT: The thin end of a very long wedge ...

SYKES: Intrusive? These kids are going to be volunteers ...

JACK: Hold it everyone ...

179

STEPHEN: Look. Joy, sorrow, boredom, memories, dreams –
all patterns of neuronal activity. Are you telling me they
aren't a legitimate concern of science?
JACK: Hold it right there. I said I'd bring this to the vote in
one hour and our time is up. As usual, a two-thirds majority
is needed. Those in favour of permitting Dr Godwin to
proceed with his experiment as proposed . . .
cut to

STEPHEN'S DREAM.

*A mountain ridge trail. Views of mountain ranges, forests,
sunlight. Stephen and Rachael are walking side by side, much
in love. She is frail and beautiful. They stop, he takes her
hand, kisses her.*

STEPHEN'S OFFICE. DAY.

*Same time. Stephen has fallen asleep at his desk. A hand
touches his shoulder. He comes to with a start. The voice is
gentle, dreamy.*
BUTLER: Dr Godwin? Tom Butler. Buzzkid Corporation.
We have an appointment for eleven?

STEPHEN'S LAB. DAY.

*We are close on a man in his sixties who sits under the
headset of a scanner talking quietly.*
MAN: . . . I guess I would have been about sixteen at the time
. . . so, we went on down across the shore. We weren't
holding hands or speaking. There was a half moon, enough to
give us, you know, a great road of, you know, phosphores-
cence out across the ocean. Then we lay on our backs in the
sand, staring at the skies, and this was when she touched my

hand – and I suddenly realised – she wants it to happen, it's going to happen . . .

As the man speaks, we pull back to find Butler and Stephen. To one side we see also two members of Stephen's team, Ken and Hermione, monitoring the experiment.

STEPHEN: We're looking at the close relationship between emotion and memory.

He steers Butler to another monitor showing a clear cross-section of the brain. Butler follows. Stephen traces on the screen with his finger.

As far as pleasure goes, everything's still pretty obscure. We know this curved region here called the anterior cingulate gyrus is associated, among other things, with feelings of satisfaction, well-being, elation, joy, right on up to sheer ecstasy.

BUTLER: So if I was looking for a pleasure centre . . .

STEPHEN: Doesn't really exist. We're talking about a neuronal ensemble. But this region would have to be involved. And this is what we've been concentrating on . . . ah Alex – this is Tom Butler. My colleague, Alex Conrad.

As the two men greet each other –

Tom's from the Buzzkid Corporation.

Alex is thrown off balance.

ALEX: Oh, right, er, computer games . . .

Butler is unruffled by what he knows is hastily suppressed hostility. He remains courteous.

BUTLER: Computer games, TV stations, theme parks . . .

ALEX: Serious business.

BUTLER: If you call pleasure serious, Dr Conrad.

ALEX: I sure do, so, if you'll excuse me . . .

As Alex leaves, Stephen steers Butler out into the corridor.

STEPHEN: A lot of us were sorry to lose our federal funding. Let's step out here . . .

TERRACE. DAY.

The terrace is thirty floors up and gives a view across the city towards mountains. The two men lean against a railing and gaze out.

STEPHEN: Why is the Buzzkid Corporation interested in us?

BUTLER: When science gets interested in pleasure, you can hardly expect the entertainment industry to sit on its hands.

STEPHEN: But this is pure science. We're mapping out brain function. What do you want from us?

BUTLER: A first look at what you're doing . . .

STEPHEN: Subscribe to the journals. We don't have any secrets here.

Butler breathes the air, and decides on another tack. We follow his gaze across the city.

BUTLER: Look at it. Three-quarters of the American people have shelter and their bellies are full. For most of us the struggle for survival that shaped us biologically is over. So what do we have left to live for when our basic needs are met? Pleasure. And more pleasure, different pleasure, new pleasure. And America, more than any nation on earth has shaped itself to that pursuit . . .

STEPHEN: It's great to hear the Corporation philosophy. What do you want from us?

BUTLER: We want you, Stephen.

STEPHEN: I'm not free.

BUTLER: We can wait. You know more about the neural basis of pleasure than anyone in the field. We have a very ambitious project. You could say it's where the pursuit of pleasure was always bound to lead. So, we're prepared to fund your department – to stay close to you . . .

STEPHEN'S HOUSE. STUDY.

Late at night. Stephen examines slides of various scans and writes notes. He takes a long pull of Scotch.

STEPHEN'S DREAM.

Stephen is walking down the stairs of his house carrying a briefcase. At the sound of a woman's voice softly calling his name, he turns, but continues on down the stairs. Then we see her. Rachael is at the top of the stairs, leaning over the banister. Her hair is dishevelled. She is wearing a nightdress. She pleads softly.

RACHAEL: Stay with me . . . please stay with me . . .

STEPHEN'S BEDROOM. DAY.

Stephen wakes. He lies on his back, recovering from the dream. Then he glances at his clock. He's late. He tears back the covers.

CORRIDOR OUTSIDE LAB. DAY.

The corridor is packed with men and women in their mid-twenties – medical students waiting to hear their final exam results and who have agreed to take part in Stephen's experiment. Stephen pushes his way through the crush to the door of his lab.

STEPHEN'S LAB. DAY.

At one end of the lab Stephen's team, with Carol and another senior researcher, John Mayhew, are in a huddle. We have Stephen's point of view as he closes the door on the students' chatter and turns – an unmistakable sense, in the sudden silence, that he has been the subject of the conversation. He goes towards them, dropping his briefcase on a table as he does so.

STEPHEN: Morning everyone . . . our subjects are here. Are we all set? . . . Something wrong?

Silence again as he approaches, then Alex clears his throat.

ALEX: We heard from Jack that the Buzzkid Corporation is taking over our funding.

STEPHEN: Isn't that great? We can carry on with our work.

MAYHEW: They mass-produce these tacky TV game shows . . .

SUSANNE: And buy up virgin land for their obscene theme parks . . .

STEPHEN: You're above these kind of things. Fine. But their money's good.

CAROL: What do they want from us, Stephen?

ALEX: Yeah, what are we going to have to do for this money?

STEPHEN: Nothing . . .

A chorus of disbelief. 'Are you kidding', etc.

Listen . . . no, listen to me. You know how they did so well over at UCLA during the eighties? The US Air Force came to them and said, We want our fighter pilots to control their machines directly with their thoughts. A completely half-assed idea, but our colleagues took the money and said they'd look into it, which they did, and meanwhile they got on with their serious work on vision . . .

HERMIONE: So what's Buzzkid's half-assed idea?

STEPHEN: They think they're in our field. Pleasure. They give it, we research it . . .

Disbelieving groans from the team. Suddenly Stephen is angry.

How do you guys afford your goddamn morals! You're doing pure research in a recession, goddammit! Who's going to pay? I'm trying to hold our work together. If I fail, half of you are going to be out of a job . . .

They all turn at the sound of a door opening. A small, neatly dressed man steps in.

KATZ: Am I in the right room?

INT. LAB. DAY.

Twenty minutes later. The students – about fifty of them – have been gathered at one end of the lab to learn about the procedures. We look at the faces – the extreme anxiety, the jittery, jokey nervousness. Careers, lives, hang in the balance. Stephen is to one side busy with equipment. Carol talks to the students.

CAROL: . . . One very important thing. We have to ask you to keep dead still while you're under the scanner, and especially still when you hear your score. Feel free to speak your thoughts, but no jumping up and down for joy. There are no control groups or double blinds in this research. We want you to be confident that your results are genuine, so we've asked along Professor Katz, Dean of the Medical Examining Board, to read them to you. We'll take you alphabetically – and good luck.

STEPHEN'S LAB. EXPERIMENT
SET UP. DAY.

The subjects are brought into the lab from another room one at a time. They lie in the scanner. Three of Stephen's team are at this end (Hermione, Susanne, Ed), giving instructions to the subject, attaching and regulating the monitoring equipment, and of course, the scanner. The proceedings are video recorded. Professor Katz stands just behind the subjects' chair in order to give no advance visual clues of the exam results he reads from a list. At some distance away, three vdu's show different sections across the subjects' brains. Other displays show us heart and respiration rates and the video recording. Stephen, Alex, Carol and others are gathered here. They are sufficiently far away to be able to talk in low voices.

We cut between the two groups, and between the subject, for real and on video, and as seen through the scanner. The first subject is being settled and attachments made.

HERMIONE: How do you feel, Suzy?

SUZY: Kinda numb, I guess. Like being at the dentist.

The others laugh softly as they finish the attachments.

ALEX: Numb? 120 resting heart rate and her bp showing a systolic of 150!

STEPHEN: We have at least eight results that might give the subjects joy.

ED: We're all set this end.

CAROL: We're OK here.

SUSANNE: Good luck, Suzy.

KATZ: Your name and hometown, please.

SUZY: Suzy Ah Chan, Oakland, California.

KATZ: Your average result over three practical and seven written exams was 54 per cent, which rates as a pass.

Suzy gives a little sigh, closes her eyes.

HERMIONE: Hold still, Suzy. If you want to, tell us how you feel.

STEPHEN: Look at this, here . . . and here.

ALEX: She's happy . . .

SUZY: I scraped through . . . I can't quite believe it . . . something must have gone wrong . . .

cut to

Next subject, Quentin, handsome, muscled, smilingly confident, is being wired up.

ALEX: Heart rate normal . . .

CAROL: He's in trouble. Spent too long chasing girls . . .

HERMIONE: We're ready to go.

STEPHEN: OK.

KATZ: Your name and hometown, please.

QUENTIN: Quentin Carter, Jackson.

KATZ: Your average result over three practical and seven written exams was 28 per cent, which rates as a fail.

The big smile on Quentin's face simply doesn't fade.

CAROL: Did he hear it?

HERMIONE: Would you like to tell us how you feel, Quentin?

Quentin is triumphant.

QUENTIN: I told my folks – they wouldn't listen. I'm not a doctor. Man, I'm a *guitarist*!

cut to

The next subject is a solemn, upright young woman.

STEPHEN: She's in for a nice surprise. Watch the activity in the cingulate.

JANE: Jane Mary Benwell, Boston.

KATZ: Your average result over three practical and seven written exams was 91 per cent, which rates as a pass with distinction.

Close on Jane. For a moment impassive.

ALEX: There's nothing. There's no activity.

STEPHEN: Uh uh. It's here, round the hippocampus, the anterior nucleus of the thalamus. Memory!

Tears are welling up in Jane's eyes and pouring down her cheeks. This is sadness not joy. Hermione, Susanne and ED surround her.

ED: Hey, what's up Jane? You came top in your year.

Jane recovers sufficiently.

JANE: I'm sorry . . . my dad died last year. I just wish . . . I just wish I . . . could have told him . . .

cut to

Fifteen minutes later. Daniel, a plump, shy, unhappy looking young man, is being seated. He looks flustered, uncomfortable. As he lies down, he loosens the top buttons of his shirt.

DANIEL: It's really hot in here.

Small beads of perspiration are forming on his face.

SUSANNE: Just relax. There's no big hurry here . . .

She is attaching an electrode to his chest.

DANIEL: Feels kind of tight here . . .

CAROL: 140 resting pulse and his systolic bp's 170. Want to let him settle?

STEPHEN: Uhuh. He's got a good exam score. We should see a little joy here.

ED: Take a deep breath and . . .

DANIEL: OK, OK, let's get on with it.

KATZ: Your name and hometown, please.

Daniel's head lolls as he says his name. He catches his breath with difficulty.

STEPHEN: Keep his head still.

DANIEL: Daniel Hamond, Pasadena.

KATZ: Your average result over three practical and seven written . . .

Daniel's legs suddenly shoot out in front of him. He clutches at his chest.

STEPHEN: Cardiac arrest . . .

Carol has already picked up a phone and is speaking rapidly.

CAROL: Emergency room? We have a cardiac arrest in room 2507. Get the crash team up here right away . . .

Meanwhile Ed and Hermione are beginning resuscitation procedures – chest thumping, mouth to mouth. Professor Katz stands by, distraught. Stephen comes and takes over from Ed.

cut to

The emergency team arrives. Daniel is still lying in the scanner as they set about using the fibrillator. Stephen goes back to the control desk.

STEPHEN: We may as well watch this.

He begins throwing switches in rapid sequence.

CAROL: Stephen . . .

STEPHEN: We've got no oxygen utilisation so we'll go for regional lactate production . . .

cut to

The emergency team is packing up its equipment and is leaving. Silence in the laboratory. The team in the different positions around the room do not, cannot move. Out of shot, someone is speaking softly into the phone, arranging for the porters to collect the body. Stephen speaks in flat monotone.

STEPHEN: Play it back.

Heads turn in astonishment towards Stephen. No one moves or speaks. Stephen walks quickly over to the recording equipment and starts the replay. We are on to him and cannot see the monitor. We watch his face instead – a dawning incredulity. Slowly, the other members of the team, apart from Professor Katz, move down the room to see what Stephen can see.

The screen. The familiar curve of the cingulate, and around it, a hiatus of brilliant reds, yellows and blues throbbing. Then sudden white-outs, as electrical interference from the fibrillator surges through the brain.

STEPHEN: That's the fibrillator ...

Drawn by the awe on all the faces, Katz cannot resist joining the others.

The screen again. Stephen whispers.

And this must be bliss ...

The door opens. Two hospital porters with a gurney. The one who speaks is scraggily thin.

PORTER: You got a dead body in ...

We follow his gaze, from the body in the scanner, to the group by the monitor. The young man's eyes bulge.

Wow! Is this an experiment?

PARK. DAY.

Longshot: Stephen and Jack walk along a path on rising ground in a park near the hospital. Their heads are close in serious conversation. Then we go in tight.

JACK: Our own people have been through this. They could eat us alive in court ...

STEPHEN: Jack, the boy had a history of heart problems. He could have died reading his scores on the noticeboard ...

JACK: Wrong thinking. He had a medical history and we – you – failed to check him out. He died in our lab, under our supervision. The parents could have had us for millions ...

Stephen stops.

STEPHEN: You talked them out of it?

JACK: These are deep people. They're not interested in the courts or the money ...

STEPHEN: Well, that's great ...

JACK: Yeah, it's great ... but there's a price. They ... um. They want a head on a plate ...

Close on Stephen as the realisation sinks in. His accusation is vehement.

STEPHEN: You've done a deal . . .
JACK: It was you or all of us . . . I'm sorry, Stephen.

STEPHEN'S ROOM, CORRIDOR. NIGHT.

Stephen's room has been stripped bare of equipment. The bookshelves are empty. He takes one last look round and steps out into the corridor. Two janitors are finishing loading up the last of Stephen's stuff on to document carts.
STEPHEN: That's it. Thanks, guys.
Stephen begins to walk away.
JANITOR: Dr Godwin?
Stephen turns. The man is smiling. For a moment we might think Stephen is about to be offered sympathy.
The keys . . .
Stephen tosses them and walks on.

ROOM OFF PSYCHIATRIC WARD. DAY.

As before, Stephen sits facing Patrick who stares at his own knee.
STEPHEN: Patrick, I'm not going to be able to continue our sessions. I might come and see you in the ward. But – no more long talks. I'm sorry.
Patrick looks up, shrugs.
PATRICK: Does it matter?

STEPHEN'S CAR, HIGHWAY. DAY.

Stephen drives the highway from the Institute to his home. He glances in his rearview mirror. A black, smoked glass sports saloon is sitting on his tail. It flashes him. He frowns, and accelerates. The car sticks close. He slows. The car does not overtake. It sits right on his tail, then pulls out to

*overtake and pulls alongside. A little pulse of fear in Stephen.
The driver's window rolls down to reveal Tom Butler.
Stephen pulls over on to the roadside. Butler follows.*

ROADSIDE. DAY.

*The two men get out. They talk over the roof of STEPHEN's
car. Butler is playing cool.*
STEPHEN: What's going on?
BUTLER: Stephen. You're not answering your phone.
STEPHEN: That's right.
BUTLER: I'm sorry to hear what happened to that kid. I'd
like you to know our offer still stands. In fact, we need you
badly ...
STEPHEN: Thanks. But I've got a lot of data to work
through, three papers to write while the material's still
fresh ...
Stephen goes to get back in his car. Butler offers his card.
BUTLER: In case you change your mind.
STEPHEN: I already have one.
He slams his door and pulls away.

STEPHEN'S HOUSE, STUDY. NIGHT.

*Late night. Stephen is at his work station. Piled around him
are the contents of his room at the Institute – cardboard
boxes piled high, papers spilling across the floor. He is
startled from his concentration by the sound of the doorbell.
He opens the door to Carol. His face tightens.*
CAROL: I'm sorry. I know it's late ...
STEPHEN: Yeah ...
CAROL: Are you going to ask me in?
*A second's hesitation, then he opens the door and steps back
for her.*
cut to

Carol follows Stephen into the study and takes in the scene. Then she looks at him. He appears exhausted.

CAROL: Working late . . .

STEPHEN: Yup.

CAROL: Did you get all the discs?

STEPHEN: Carol, what is it you want?

CAROL: I haven't had a chance to talk with you since we heard . . .

STEPHEN: There's nothing to say.

CAROL: You're wrong. A lot of us admire your work. We're all involved in what happened. You don't have to be alone in this . . .

STEPHEN: *You're* wrong. I do have to be alone . . .

CAROL: I thought if there's anything you need . . .

STEPHEN: I don't need a thing.

Carol loses patience.

CAROL: OK, OK, spare me the lonely hero. For whatever dumb loopy reason I've become very fond of you, hard heart tough guy and all. You aren't answering your phone so I came round to offer help in whatever form you want it . . .

STEPHEN: Not honest enough, Carol. You think you're entitled to something from me.

CAROL: My God, that's mean –

STEPHEN: So let me set you straight about what I want and need. One thing only. I want to do my work. Nothing else. Just the work. I don't want emotion, tangle, mess, I don't want affairs, I don't want to live with someone, I don't want to get married again –

CAROL: Again?

He hasn't intended to let this out. He is terse.

STEPHEN: I don't want to talk about it.

CAROL: Sounds like you should.

STEPHEN: To you. You'd like to be indispensable . . .

Carol is beyond anger. She shakes her head wonderingly and makes to leave.

CAROL: So long, tough guy. You want to arm wrestle, you've got my number . . .

192

STEPHEN'S DREAM.

The psychiatric ward. Rachael and Patrick, in identical hospital gowns are walking arm in arm, away from us. They turn back to look at us. Both are smiling broadly.
RACHAEL: Does it matter?

STEPHEN'S HOUSE. BEDROOM. NIGHT

Stephen lies on his back, wide awake. We are close on him. Sweat streams from his face.

STREET. DAY

A poor neighbourhood of Los Angeles. Stephen gets out of a taxi and crosses the street towards a shabby apartment block.

LOBBY. DAY.

Stephen steps out of an elevator into a dingy lobby. He peers at the various doors surrounding him, rings one. The door is opened by Dean, about Stephen's age, overweight, strong. He stares at Stephen with undisguised hostility.
STEPHEN: Hello, I think I'm expected. My name . . .
Dean calls over his shoulder.
DEAN: He's here.
He leaves the door open and slouches away into the gloom of the apartment. Stephen follows tentatively. Suddenly, at the far end of the corridor, the face of a man appears, a pale mask of sadness, suspended in the obscurity. The face of Godfrey Hamond stares long and hard at Stephen who goes forward.
STEPHEN: Mr Hamond . . .
GODFREY: You're not how I've imagined you . . .

STEPHEN: Well . . .

GODFREY: It's this way.

He leads the way into a small over-furnished sitting room. By a window, in a wheelchair, is Godfrey's wife, Nora Hamond. She has a perceptible tremor in one hand. The face is intelligent and, like her husband's, sharpened by grief. She watches him closely. Godfrey indicates a chair to Stephen and goes and sits by Nora. He stills her tremulous hand in his own.

GODFREY: It's Dr Godwin, dear.

NORA: Yes, I know.

For a moment Stephen suffers their penetrating looks in silence.

STEPHEN: Look, I don't know how to begin to say it, but this terrible tragedy –

NORA: Dr Godwin, please. We didn't ask you here to make a speech.

STEPHEN: You think I'm to blame for your son's death . . .

NORA: We don't know enough to blame you, but we hold you accountable. Someone at the hospital has to take responsibility.

STEPHEN: Does it help you to know I've lost my job?

NORA: I'm afraid so, Dr Godwin. It's important that my son's death has serious consequences for someone. That's why we wouldn't settle for money. The hospital balances the books and no one gives a damn.

GODFREY: Do you believe in God, Dr Godwin?

Stephen is momentarily thrown.

STEPHEN: Ah, you mean a god that watches over people?

GODFREY: I mean God. The one we pray to. You have any use for Him in your science?

STEPHEN: I guess all a scientist can do is leave God out of his calculations and see how far he can get.

The elderly couple look at him intently. Nora's voice is small.

NORA: And how far would you say you have got now?

Stephen looks away, sighs. The meeting is even more painful than he anticipated.

STEPHEN: There's something you should know. You probably heard we were looking at activity in the brain in an area associated with pleasure. Well, after . . . we went on recording and it seems that in Daniel's last moments he experienced something extraordinary – a kind of ecstasy . . .
GODFREY: And then oblivion, Dr Godwin?
NORA: Is it true what they say? That right at the end you turned on the recording equipment? For the sake of science?
Stephen's silence is confirmation. He rises.
STEPHEN: I'll go . . .
Stephen reaches the door and turns. Nora has her face in her hands and is sobbing silently. Godfrey has his arm round her shoulder. Stephen is shocked, and tries to find the right words as Nora, all composure and authority suddenly gone, makes a chilling keening sound, and blurts out over her sobs.
NORA: He was the youngest . . . he was the baby . . .
STEPHEN: I'm sorry, I . . .
Godfrey speaks quietly.
GODFREY: Yes, please go now.

HAMOND'S APARTMENT BUILDING. DAY.

Stephen walks quickly away from the apartment building. He passes a parked car, glances at it over his shoulder, but does not break his stride.

STEPHEN'S HOUSE. NIGHT.

The bedroom. Stephen is asleep. From far away the sound of breaking glass. He stirs, but does not wake. Then the sound of footsteps, a creaking board, silence, a low murmur of voices, then a deafening crash of metal and glass. Stephen sits bolt upright. Was the sound in his dream? He listens. Then the creak of a board again, a man's voice. Stephen is about to reach for the phone then changes his mind. He slips out of bed, naked. He wraps a towel around his waist and steps out

*on to the landing. From the stairs he has a view into his work
room below. Two large figures are there. One we recognise as
he turns as Dean. He has a baseball bat in his hand and is
about to take a swing at one of the computer screens. Stephen
comes running down the stairs shouting.*

STEPHEN: Don't! Don't touch it!

Dean swings the bat and the screen shatters.

STEPHEN: You dumb asshole! I didn't kill your brother. His
heart did.

*Stephen runs down shouting and launches himself straight at
Dean. Stephen is in good shape, handy in a fight and has the
advantage of colossal fury. He could be about to lose his life's
work. He gets in a good hit at Dean and in a short struggle,
before the other man, Rex, can join in, he has wrestled the
bat away from Dean. Stephen stands with his back to the
work station, the bat raised. The two men face him, getting
ready to attack. Dean has a bad cut on his face. Stephen's
towel has worked loose and drops to the floor. The intruders
smirk.*

DEAN: Trying to tell us something, doc?

STEPHEN: You touch another thing I swear to you I'll kill
you . . .

*Dean lashes out. Rex charges. Stephen catches him hard
across the back, dodges Dean, and again the three confront
each other.*

DEAN: C'mon, doc. Go and get dressed while we finish off
here . . .

*This time Stephen attacks first. They fight. For half a minute
it looks like Stephen can beat the men off, but they are big,
and there are two of them. By the end, Rex, who is even
bigger than Dean, has Stephen pinned to the floor and is
cuffing him about the face. Meanwhile Dean is destroying
Stephen's work station. In the open fireplace a huge confla-
gration is made of all his papers, discs, etc. Pinned to the
floor, Stephen shouts and weeps. Beyond him, the flames
rising higher.*

STEPHEN: You fucking jerks. God, I hate you! I hate you!

A blow from Rex's fist knocks him unconscious.

STEPHEN'S HOUSE. DAY.

Dawn. Naked, shivering, Stephen surveys the devastation of his work room. All his work, all his research, destroyed.

CITY LOCATION. DAY.

Long shot. Stephen takes a lonely walk through the city.

STEPHEN'S HOUSE. DAY.

The work room. Back from his walk, Stephen crosses the work room to the open fire. He crouches down, sifts the blackened remains. He straightens, picks up the phone with blackened hand, dials.
STEPHEN: Buzzkid Corporation? I want to talk to Mr Butler . . .

BUZZKID RESEARCH INSTITUTE. DAY.

Late afternoon. Stephen parks his car in front of a late nineteenth-century mansion set in beautiful gardens in the Santa Monica Hills. He steps out and looks about him. Golden light. A fountain. Old stonework, old trees, deep shade. Lawns. Exotic flowers. Humming birds. Peace. He is taking all this in. He turns at the sound of Tom Butler coming down the steps of the house. As the two men shake hands, Butler registers the cuts on Stephen's face.
BUTLER: It doesn't look too bad.
STEPHEN: You should've seen it last week.
BUTLER: I'll show you the lab first. Then I've arranged two little demonstrations for you.

BUZZKID INST. ATRIUM. DAY.

Stephen follows Butler across the atrium – a large, communal area where Buzzkid staff meet to chat and take refreshments. Trees, shrubs, a central fountain, arbours where people sit. Two formally dressed waiters circulate, taking orders. It's happy hour now and the place is quietly humming. At the sight of Stephen, one young scientist, Quinn, detaches himself from his group and approaches enthusiastically. Butler keeps Stephen moving.

QUINN: Hey, excuse me. Are you Stephen Godwin?

STEPHEN: Yes.

QUINN: I know you from your lectures. I've read your work on cortical integration and the binding problem. Brilliant, man. And that exchange of letters with Edelman –

STEPHEN: I think he had the better of me. His ideas on re-entry suggest . . .

BUTLER: You guys can shop talk later.

QUINN: You mean you're working here? Wow! That's amazing. If you've got half an hour . . .

BUTLER: I'm sorry. It's this way.

BUZZKID INST. CORRIDOR AND LAB. DAY.

Butler opens the door for Stephen. We step with him into the lab – into a high-ceilinged room filled with sunlight. No one here, only equipment, state of the art tools of neurological investigation. The space is rich in colours and textures. Paintings on the walls, plants, wide second-floor views over the gardens. Stephen stops by the largest scanner.

BUTLER: The CR 20. Just delivered. Only two in the country.

Stephen's tone is guarded.

STEPHEN: It's, uh, good stuff . . .

BUTLER: We like our people to be comfortable.

STEPHEN: . . . but I still don't know what you want from me.

BUTLER: All we want are maps, routes . . .
STEPHEN: Maps?
BUTLER: Remember we were talking about pleasure . . .
A beeper sounds in Butler's pocket.
. . . they're ready for us . . .

SECOND CORRIDOR AND VR LAB. DAY.

Butler steers Stephen through a door, and hurries him down a busy corridor. Various labs and offices glimpsed through open doorways.
BUTLER: You know who's putting money into this, anonymously? The two largest Hollywood studios, and a cartel from the Japanese electronics industry. They all ride with us or they're finished. Movies, TV, hi-fi – soon that'll be the old pleasure junk. No one's talking about it because they're all protecting their current investments – but there's a new generation of pleasure machines and we hold all the key patents . . . here we are . . .
We are in a small electronics lab – steel racks packed with equipment. An electronics expert, a strange-looking fellow, Ollie, is waiting.
Ollie, Pat, Dr Stephen Godwin.
A round of 'hello's'.
If you'd like to step round here . . .
Stephen sees a headset and finger glove on a chair. He picks up the headset then contemptuously lets it drop.
STEPHEN: Virtual reality? You're not serious. Is this the big secret?
In the cramped space, Stephen is trying to get to the door.
OLLIE: He's being rather offensive.
BUTLER: Stephen, you've got this wrong . . .
STEPHEN: You don't need a neuroscientist. Get a TV engineer.
Ollie blocks the doorway.
OLLIE: A dozen dedicated seven-series chips on the visual field enhancement, micro-sensor circuitry in pure gold,

twenty-four channel sound in layered coil feed-through ...
State of the art, pal ...

STEPHEN: It's theme parks, game shows, pop junk cheese-cake. Get out of my way ...

Butler smoothly interposes himself.

BUTLER: Stephen ... Ollie, excuse me. You're right, of course. Virtual reality, it's a marvellous toy, hardly a revolution. But it's only part of the explanation. You won't be bored, I promise.

As Butler soothes, Stephen shrugs and lets himself be led towards the chair.

STEPHEN: The guessing game is getting on my nerves.

Ollie fits the headset and finger glove and fiddles with the equipment.

OLLIE: You know about finger gloves? Here ...

BUTLER: Our mutual interest is pleasure, so we'll begin with the myth at the beginning of human time, when there was nothing but pleasure ...

VR Sequence.

As Butler speaks, our vision fills with an intricate, luminous street scene. We are in a modern city, with the dazzle of Manhattan and the impacted human density, liveliness and squalor of Bombay. The sky is bathed in crepuscular light. The forms of what we see hover tantalisingly between naturalistic images and computer-generated lines. A version of Butler himself is walking at our side.

BUTLER: Keep walking. Don't talk to anyone or you'll be sucked into a whole other adventure.

We begin to make our way through the crowds. The noise of voices, traffic, buskers, bells, is deafening. Odd characters, old men with faces by Dürer, young women with impossible beauty, call out to us, sell us things, make obscene proposi-tions, try to pull our lapel. But we keep going. Ahead, there's a car parked by the sidewalk.

That's your car.

Stephen opens the door and sits in. Butler leans down to give directions. His face fills the window. He has to talk loudly over the din of the street.

Now, you're on your own. Stay on this main drag and head straight out of town. Careful in the traffic. You get into a collision, you'll be in another story. Keep heading west and follow the signs to Arcadia. The Garden of Eden, Stephen. You'll be the first and only man in the world. Take your place in paradise . . .

Stephen's hand goes to reach for the ignition, but Butler reaches into the car to restrain him.

One last thing. When you're there – if you meet someone without a face, speak to her. Memory and desire will do the rest . . . Good luck.

Stephen starts the engine. Butler thumps the car's roof in farewell. We swing out into the dense, wildly unpredictable traffic. Stephen swerves to avoid a truck, and then brakes hard to miss hitting a sudden swarm of cyclists. Very soon we are moving out of town on a packed twelve-lane highway through an industrial landscape of colossal power stations, ruined factories, abandoned pit-heads. At a huge clover-leaf junction, dozens of signs to neighbouring cities, road warnings and commercial billboards obscure the small rickety pointer to Arcadia. Stephen only sees it at the last moment and has to cut across the lanes.

We are out in open countryside now, travelling fast on a straight two-lane road. The sign points us down a smaller road. Off that, a narrow bumpy track. We pass through a wood, ford a creek, and begin to mount a sharp rise. Then the car gives out. Stephen curses under his breath. He tries the ignition. And again. Nothing. The fuel gauge reads empty. He opens the door and steps out. He follows a footpath which continues up the hill to the crest of the rise. We reach the crest, and see paradise spread below us.

It is a vision drawn from medieval and early Renaissance painting: benevolent and sensual, with exotic trees and flowers, woodland glades bathed in gentle sunlight, normally fierce animals grazing peaceably, and everywhere water, tumbling down creeks to a lake of a pure glacial blue. We hear Stephen's chuckle of admiration and incredulity. With him, we begin to move down the gentle grassy slope towards the vision. Paradise draws us in, and as we approach, pleasantly shifting harmonies swell and eddy around us. We come through the trees and flowers to the lake. Stephen bends down and touches the indigo blue water. Strange fish glide away from his fingertip. As he straightens he sees a figure some distance off, standing by the edge of the lake. We begin to walk towards her. She turns and drifts away among the trees. For a moment we lose her. Stephen increases his speed. As we come into a sunny clearing we see her again. She is standing in the deep shadow of a tree, waiting for us. We approach. She looks up, and it is as Butler said. Her face is indistinct, undrawn. Stephen comes nearer, extends his hand to her.

STEPHEN: Rachael . . . Rachael?

She looks at us again, and slowly her features compose themselves into those of Stephen's dead wife. She smiles uncertainly.

RACHAEL: Stephen . . . You took so long . . .

She stretches out her hand. He takes it. They go to kiss. It is then that he sees the fly on Rachael's cheek – the image from his nightmare. His shout resounds across the landscape. The whole of Paradise shakes, bucks, and then buckles as –

VR LAB. DAY.

Stephen struggles to remove the headset. He is screaming.

STEPHEN: Get this off me! Get this thing off me!

Stephen manages to wrench the equipment off. He's on his feet, glaring at Butler. His mood is dangerous.

STEPHEN: You did this . . .

BUTLER: It's OK, Stephen. Just pop junk . . .

STEPHEN: You got your hands on a picture of Rachael.

Butler nods at Ollie who bends to the electronic equipment. Behind Stephen's head a video screen comes to life.

BUTLER: I shouldn't have to explain to a neurologist . . .
STEPHEN: What did you do? Break into my house? I should smack your stupid face . . .
BUTLER: Look behind you. It wasn't even a woman. It's just a shape, Stephen. You filled her in.
We are looking with Stephen at the video screen. Paradise re-run. The image is pitifully reduced. Once more we see the figure standing by the lake, then turning away. It is a blank, undrawn, ambiguous human shape.
OLLIE: Best fit, as they say. You met your Eve, Dr Godwin.
BUTLER: I'm sorry if it upset you. Women watch this and see their Adam. Other subjects see nothing but the shape. Like I said, it's memory and desire, pure fantasy.
OLLIE: So who's this Rachael?
Stephen has subsided into his seat, deeply shaken. The hand he raises to his forehead is trembling.
STEPHEN: Someone I knew . . .
Butler exchanges a glance with Ollie and lays a hand on Stephen's shoulder.
BUTLER: They're waiting for us upstairs.

Upstairs Lab. Day.

A small ante-room. Stephen is seated in a comfortable chair facing a blank TV screen. He wears a headset with wires trailing away to the lab next door. Various other monitors with flickering screens are banked on either side. Past Stephen, through a large plate-glass window we can see into the lab. Two scientists are busy in there, but we cannot see their faces. They communicate with the ante-room by way of a PA.
PA VOICE: We're ready for you now. Please keep perfectly still, Dr Godwin.
The monitors in front of Butler and Stephen come to life – the familiar computer-generated colour-intense images of the brain. Various angles and slices are shuffled.
STEPHEN: Good pictures. What are you using?

BUTLER: Just watch this . . .

On the screen, an image is settled upon, then enlarged.

STEPHEN: Medial pre-frontal cortex.

Two fine moving straight lines appear on the video screen. The point of intersection is adjusted, fine-tuned, then enlarged. Another angle, and the lines are slightly adjusted again.

Anterior cingulate cortex.

The procedure is rapidly repeated. A voice over the PA murmurs, 'We're ready.' Butler turns to a vtr machine.

BUTLER: Relax and enjoy.

On the central screen a Bugs Bunny cartoon begins.

STEPHEN: You're stretching my patience.

On the monitors – at the point of intersection of the lines – there is a faint continuous glow, representing electromagnetic stimulation. Tight on Stephen. His lips are tightly pursed. Then, against his will, he snickers. He tries to prevent a smile. The cartoon action. Stephen chuckles. He splutters.

STEPHEN: Haven't seen this in years . . . The visual gags are better than ever.

His words are lost to his own sudden shout of laughter. And another. And then he is helpless. Every fresh antic redoubles his mirth. Tears are pouring down his cheek.

PA VOICE: Keep your head still, Dr Godwin, please.

Stephen is clutching his stomach, barely able to breathe.

On screen – 'That's all, folks.'

STEPHEN: You got any more?

Butler speaks into a microphone.

BUTLER: Fred, Bob, you better come through.

Fred and Bob burst into the ante-room.

FRED: Hey! What's up doc!

FRED: Better than cream pies, huh? You impressed?

Stephen is wiping his eyes.

STEPHEN: I'm impressed.

BOB: And three spots simultaneously! We hit the medial pre-frontal for the laughs, the anterior cingulate to push up your attention and the ventral tegmentum to beef up your interest in life.

FRED: D'you hear him rationalise? The gags are better than ever!

BOB: The machine is amazing. It's the Japanese team. Accurate down to ten thousand cells. But we're blundering. This was really crude . . .

FRED: Yeah, we don't know our way round the cingulate cortex . . .

BUTLER: We need a map, Stephen. Look—

Butler has picked up from a table behind him a copy of the virtual reality and the electromagnetic headsets. He puts them on. They slot together neatly, so that he suddenly resembles a bald, bump-headed, bug-eyed alien.

Our prototype is the Garden of Eden. Now we need a programme for the emotions. When we find ourselves on a crowded street in an unknown city you're going to give us anxiety, and when we almost hit that truck, fear, and rage when we run out of gas, then happiness when we see paradise spread beneath us, laughter as we go down that slope, joy when we get to that blue blue lake, and bliss, sheer melting agony of bliss when we see our darling Eve, with every hot little pleasure centre that four billion years of evolution have given us zapped by electromagnetic pulses.

He removes his mask. He's fired up.

We'll give them the drama *and* the emotional responses. The ultimate entertainment. Bigger than life! It's where all our pleasure-seeking was bound to lead – to the brain.

Fred and Bob raise their fists in ironic salute.

FRED and BOB: To the brain!

GARDENS. DAY.

The gardens are lush and extravagantly attended. The Corporation's version of paradise, perhaps. Stephen and Butler reach an ornamental pond. Stephen speaks calmly, trying to conceal the shock of his encounter with Rachael.

STEPHEN: You're going to have problems with the medical ethics.

BUTLER: We got people researching that, preparing the ground. There's a secrecy issue too. That's why I'm asking you to experiment only on yourself.

Stephen looks up sharply. Butler shrugs and smiles.

Paying you a lot of money.

Stephen glances at the sky. A storm is on its way. A few drops of rain are beginning to fall.

STEPHEN: There's something else. It's not so difficult to make someone laugh. But there isn't a single place in the brain where you can press a button and get happiness or joy.

BUTLER: You're telling me it's going to be hard.

STEPHEN: It's unknown territory. You go looking for an emotion in the limbic system you might find something else . . .

BUTLER: Like what?

STEPHEN: I'm not sure. Memories perhaps . . .

BUTLER: You scared off by what happened to you down by the lake?

It is raining lightly. Close on Stephen. He shakes his head and speaks softly.

STEPHEN: I'd like to see her again . . .

GARDENS. DAY.

The rain is falling harder. Butler and Stephen hurry through the gardens, back towards the house.

CAR. END OF DAY.

The rain is falling in sheets – a cloudburst – as Stephen pulls into his driveway. His point of view (POV) through the windshield. The wipers can barely clear the screen, but the figure of a woman sheltering by the front porch is unmistakable. The colour of the clothes suggest Rachael. Stephen's reaction as he switches off the ignition: a beat of fear – and intense curiosity.

FRONT OF HOUSE. END OF DAY.

Stephen's pov as he runs through the blinding rain to the porch towards the woman. Only when we are under cover and she steps clear of doorway is her identity clear.
STEPHEN: Carol!
CAROL: My car broke down two blocks away . . .
She's drenched.
STEPHEN: You better come inside.

STEPHEN'S HOUSE. END OF DAY.

Carol, barefoot, dressed in shirt, sweater and pants belonging to Stephen, surveys the devastation of the work station. Stephen is getting a fire going.
CAROL: Did you call the police?
STEPHEN: Uhuh. It's too difficult. You know the family thinks I killed the boy.
The fire blazes up. Stephen pours coffee from a flask.
Here . . .
They settle down on cushions in front of the glow. The rest of the room is in darkness. From Carol, a sexual charge which Stephen tries to ignore.
CAROL: What if he comes back?
Stephen takes in his hands the baseball bat he has left leaning by the fire. He shrugs.
STEPHEN: Look, I'm sorry about last time . . .
CAROL: It's OK.
STEPHEN: I've taken a job out at Buzzkid.
Carol's wry disbelief.
Well, I've got nothing left here . . .
CAROL: What are they working on?
STEPHEN: Selective magnetic stimulation targeted at reward sites with a miniaturised MRI scanner and interfaced to virtual reality . . .
Carol is silent, staring at him. Stephen's jokiness is unconvincing.

207

Hey, it's the biggest thing since TV. You see it and feel it. The feelies!

CAROL: It's dangerous ... You could trigger an epileptic state.

STEPHEN: Accurate down to a single neuronal group.

CAROL: It's worse than dangerous. It's frivolous. Stephen ...

With Stephen, we are looking at Carol. By the firelight, and in her oversized clothes she looks especially beautiful, poised. They exchange a long look.

STEPHEN: Yeah, well. It could help me with something.

Carol places her hand on his knee.

CAROL: So could I ...

They kiss.

STEPHEN: Carol, this is a really bad idea.

Right down on the cushions now. As they kiss again –

CAROL: OK. I'll go ...

cut to

Minutes later. They make love languorously, in the glow of the fire. We close in on Carol's face. She knows she might regret this, but for now ... Then, on Stephen. A sudden flash to the VR Garden of Eden; the brilliant light, the trees near the lake, and Rachael turning to look at him as he approaches. Over this image, Carol's voice whispering –

CAROL: Stephen. Stephen?

STEPHEN: Mmm ...

Now we are back at the fireside.

CAROL: Hey. You. You're so far away. Where have you gone?

STEPHEN: Paradise ...

OUTSIDE STEPHEN'S HOUSE. DAY.

Following morning. We are watching the house through the windshield of a parked car. Stephen comes out the house, gets into his car and drives away. The waiting car begins to tail Stephen.

BUZZKID INST. STEPHEN'S LAB. DAY.

Stephen sits at a table writing notes, while Fred, Bob and Ollie noisily supervise a number of lab technicians who are fussing round the equipment and material associated with the project. Butler is to one side, watching.

STEPHEN: Let's get started.

FRED: OK, gentlemen. Clear the room now please. Finish this later, thank you . . .

Bob bolts the door behind the last technician. Stephen stands, goes to a whiteboard and draws a rough cross-section of a skull, then a curving shape within that. The atmosphere is tense. Stephen draws a deep breath.

STEPHEN: Pleasure, anxiety, fear, they all have their complicated origins in here, the limbic system. This is where we'll be fishing. It's possible we'll find ways of generating pure, detached pleasure, well-being, even ecstasy. But it's more likely that these feelings will come with unwanted baggage. That's also, in effect, what we'll be investigating. Another thing. You stimulate one emotion, and that in turn can fire another.

BOB: Where are we going to start?

STEPHEN: I want to explore the amygdaloid nucleus around area 34. We'll move into it by a three-degree arc from the tip of the hippocampus.

FRED: We suggest working on the big machine and downloading.

STEPHEN: How many positions does the headset hold?

FRED: Sixty.

BUTLER: Dr Godwin tells me there's a theoretical risk of an epileptic seizure. A doctor's standing by on extension 306, but he's to know nothing about the work. And that, as always, applies generally. Nothing leaves this room.

BUZZKID INST. STEPHEN'S LAB. DAY.

A little later. Stephen is in the machine which, like the headset, both scans the brain to pinpoint the appropriate location, and electromagnetically stimulates. He sits upright, with his head held very still. He is naked to the waist. His pulse rate, EEG and EEC are being monitored. In front of him is a monitor showing his own brain image. On the screen, the crossed lines of the targeting device. Nearby is a microphone connected to a tape recorder. Fred and Bob sit at a console. Butler stands apart.

BOB: That's area 28 you have now.

STEPHEN: OK. Move a millimetre along the *x* plane. Right. When you're ready, give me 200 mv.

From behind the console, we have a view of a monitor, and beyond, Stephen. Fred types the co-ordinates of position on a computer screen.

BOB: Three . . . two . . . one.

Faint glow at the cross-lines.

STEPHEN: One take one. Nothing. Increase it by twenty per cent . . .

FRED: Twenty?

A brief silence. BOB's voice is quieter.

BOB: Here goes. Three . . . two . . . one . . .

Into this relative hush, a sudden explosion of sound – a violent thunderous roar, and the impression of something vast, black, unidentifiable rushing past. In its wake, the sound of a child's piercing cry and then sounds of adult voices, fading into confusion. Close on Stephen – his features momentarily frozen in childlike fear. Then he grimaces.

FRED: You got 135 resting heart rate. Better take five.

BOB: You able to tag that one for us?

Stephen gathers himself.

STEPHEN: One take two. Shock . . . fear. Tied to, well, uh, it's a memory . . . a childhood memory, uh, stepping into the road. I guess I was about five.

FRED: You want to take a walk around the garden?

STEPHEN: I think we hit one of the negative sites. We might have been too far forward. We'll go on. But let's get across to the medial forebrain bundle, where it projects to the accumbens.

BOB: Area 25? –

STEPHEN: Check the co-ordinates. z minus 8, x minus 8 and y minus 10.

The changing cross-sections on the monitors, then the zoom in on the chosen area.

This is a well-mapped reward system . . . dopamine terminal field. You're almost there . . . This time I want you to move slowly along the x axis from 0 to minus 8.

BOB: Here goes. Perfectly still. Three . . . two . . . one . . .

Butler's beeper sounds. He glances at his watch and moves towards the door. He is on the point of unlocking it when a sound from Stephen makes him pause. It is a long, contented sigh. Butler moves back into the room. Fred whispers.

FRED: Head still, Stephen. Or you'll lose it.

Stephen's eyes are closed, his face assumes a beatific calmness. His breathing is slow and steady.

BOB: Where are you, Stephen? Can you give it a name for me?

STEPHEN: Uh . . . high above the ocean . . . peace . . . very stoned . . . but pure . . .

Fred glances at Bob.

FRED: What are you on, would you say?

Butler moves in closer to hear what Stephen is saying. His voice is dreamy, distant, but under control.

STEPHEN: Uh . . . an opiate, morphine perhaps, but pure . . . big space . . . light pouring over me . . . now it's milk, a jug of milk . . .

STEPHEN MENTAL TRAVELLING.

At last we cut into Stephen's world. Close up – milk pouring from a jug, a woman's hand, now the woman's face smiling. Children's voices in background. Now we fade into another time. The same woman, smiling, speaking gently, bends down to us and lifts us from a crib. Her breast is a vast white hill. The baby closes his mouth over the nipple and sucks and gazes into the eyes of the woman. The woman looks down on us, calm, loving. The feeling is of infinite peace. Stephen's voice floats in from a great distance.

STEPHEN: ... a breast ... ah ... my mother's face ...

The sound of children's voices again, and laughter. We are running into a wood with dozens of children. A girl – about eleven years old – looks over her shoulder at us and laughs 'Come on!'

... a birthday in Vermont ...

We go deeper into the wood. Sunlight slants across the darkness. The little girl puts her arms around our neck and goes to kiss us ... Then we are somewhere else, another time, with dark shadows over whiteness.

I don't know ... I can't ...

Now the image begins to resolve. These are other arms about us. We are in a bed. By us is Rachael, naked. Whispering lovingly, possessively. As she speaks he is kissing her.

Rachael: I've been waiting for you ... waiting for you ... wanting you ... waiting for you to come home ...

BUZZKID INST. STEPHEN'S LAB. DAY.

Stephen's eyes are closed. His eyelashes are wet. He goes to speak, but at first the words do not come. Pulling back a little we find we are in the lab.

STEPHEN: Honey, I came as quickly as I could ... It's not always so easy to get away ...

FRED: Stephen?

Stephen's head lolls. His eyes open. He takes in the room, remembers where he is.

STEPHEN: I lost her ...

FRED: You moved your head.

BUTLER: But you're on to something. That pure big space ...

Stephen is still clearing his head of the encounter with Rachael.

Something good we can use?

Stephen begins to detach himself from the monitoring lines. He is mumbling, vague, collecting himself as he puts on his shirt.

STEPHEN: Oh yeah . . . sure. There's a variety of ascending dopamine pathways, any number of sites . . . er, I'll be taking a look at the dorsolateral pre-frontal cortex, but right now . . . look, let's call it a day.

BOB: You OK?

Fred pours him a glass of water.

STEPHEN: I just need to sit alone. It was, er, kind of intense.

Fred and Bob call goodnight as they leave. Butler speaks from the doorway.

BUTLER: Good work, Stephen.

Stephen is seated at the table. He forces a little cheerfulness.

STEPHEN: An amazing experience.

As soon as Butler leaves, Stephen sinks his face into his hands. He shakes his head slowly. In close to catch his whisper.

I love you . . . I love you . . . I love you . . .

STEPHEN'S HOUSE. NIGHT.

Stephen stops his car in the drive, gets out hurriedly and opens the trunk. He lifts out a large cardboard box and carries it towards the house.

STEPHEN'S HOUSE. BEDROOM NIGHT.

Stephen rummages in a wardrobe and pulls out a laptop computer.

STEPHEN'S HOUSE.
WORK STATION. NIGHT.

The laptop sits among the still uncleared mess of Dean's visit. Stephen takes from his pocket a disc and inserts it. Tight on the screen. A list comes up of activation strength, scanner co-ordinates giving the 'address' in the brain and their respective 'tags', i.e. Stephen's response—

take one...	millivolts	...address in brain	...nothing
take two...	"	... "	...shock/ stepped in road as a child
take three...	"	... "	...ocean/peace/stoned/pure
take four...	"	... "	...milk from jug
take five...	"	... "	...breast/deeply contented

And so on.

Working at speed, almost in a frenzy, Stephen takes from the cardboard box what looks like hi-fi amplifiers, three of them, and plugs them together. From the third he runs a lead to the laptop. He lifts his TV set on to the table and runs a lead into one of the electronic boxes. Finally he lifts out the headset, VR viewer and finger glove and connects them to the array. He pulls an armchair into position. Shivering – with cold, with excitement – he picks up a blanket from among the cushions where he was lying with Carol the night before and wraps it about him. The headset and finger glove are on, the computer and one of the electronic black boxes are on his lap. On the TV screen, in a matter of seconds, a high-speed fast-forward of the VR. Paradise scenario – the drive out of the city, the bumpy track, the footpath through the woods. On the crest of the rise, he freezes the frame. On the laptop we watch the cursor drop three positions on the list to hold at 'ocean/peace'. He punches a key with his free hand. Briefly a TV cartoon gives way to successive brain images as the right 'address' is sought out by the electronics. He clips on the VR viewer and settles back. Medium shot across the room. Surrounded by the chaos of damage, and by his small array of equipment, Stephen, huddling in his blanket, begins to drift down the electronically created slope to Paradise, wrapped in a magnetically induced bliss, towards an imaginary meeting with his dead wife which he will play over and over again through the night. He groans and sighs with pleasure.

VR SEQUENCE.

We are descending the slope with Stephen. As before, but the light now is richer – milky and golden, and a seemingly infinite spread of dense and luscious harmonies unfold around us. Beyond, his groans of pleasure are still audible. A sudden blurred confusion as he fast-forwards. Suddenly we are crossing the clearing in the woods towards Rachael. She turns, smiles uncertainly.
Rachael: Stephen . . . you took so long.
She stretches out her hand. They go to kiss. Stephen raises his hand to her face—

STEPHEN'S HOUSE.
WORK STATION. NIGHT.

Stephen in his chair, raises his gloved finger—

VR SEQUENCE.

– And brushes the fly from Rachael's face. Then he kisses her. Different parts of this same sequence are repeated. Approaching paradise, arriving by the lake, seeing the figure of Rachael, following her through the trees . . .
RACHAEL: Stephen . . . You took so long . . .
He kisses her. And again. Entering paradise, touching the water of the lake, crossing the clearing towards Rachael.
RACHAEL: Stephen . . . You took so long . . .
He kisses her. And whispers urgently—
STEPHEN: Rachael, I want you to come home with me now. I want you to come home . . .

STEPHEN'S HOUSE.
WORK STATION. NIGHT.

Tight on the laptop screen. The cursor drops down through the list, right to the bottom, to the item tagged 'Honey I came as quickly . . .' Stephen's free hand punches a key. The TV screen. Shifting slices of brain imaging. The cross-lines adjust, then glow at their intersection. Stephen lifts the VR viewer clear of his face. His eyes are closed, his head is tilted back against the chair.

STEPHEN MENTAL TRAVELLING.

The house. Day. Stephen is walking up the stairs with a cup in his hands. The light in the house is gloomy, sepulchral. Curtains are drawn to shut out the bright light of day. He comes along the hallway, pushes open the bedroom door. Rachael is in bed, just waking. She half pushes herself up as Stephen sits at her side. Strewn across the bed, papers, books. She is confused, frightened.

RACHAEL: Stephen . . .

STEPHEN: I brought you some coffee . . .

RACHAEL: But I don't understand. Where is this . . .?

STEPHEN: Ssh. It's OK. You're at home. Everything's fine. You've been asleep.

Rachael is looking around the room in astonishment.

RACHAEL: It feels so long . . . I've been away so long . . .

His arm is round her shoulder.

STEPHEN: You were out for a couple of hours.

RACHAEL: It feels like years. Oh God, Stephen, what's happening to me? I'm so frightened. I don't want to be mad.

STEPHEN: Hey now. It was just a sleep. Here, drink this . . .

She refuses the coffee.

RACHAEL: Kiss me . . . I remember now. I was waiting for you, for hours . . .

They kiss. She draws him down with her on to the bed. They kiss again, passionately.

STEPHEN: I love you Rachael. I love you. It's all OK.
She whispers lovingly, possessively, as she unbuttons his shirt.
Then her thin arms are about his neck.
RACHAEL: I was waiting for you . . . and wanting you . . .
waiting for you to come home . . .
STEPHEN: I came as quickly as I could . . . You know it's not
always easy . . .
They kiss.
. . . so easy to get away . . . What was that?
As they begin to make love, there comes a sound from
somewhere in the house. A thump. Stephen half turns. She
draws him back. The sound has reached him again.
There's someone at the door . . .
RACHAEL: Just leave it. Please stay here . . .
STEPHEN: I should go down . . .
He's pulling away. She's trying to hang on, to draw him back.
There's an edge of panic in Rachael's voice. Something
childlike.
RACHAEL: It'll be someone from your work. You'll get
called away. Stephen . . .
He's on his feet.
STEPHEN: I'll come straight back, I promise . . .

STEPHEN'S HOUSE.
WORK STATION. NIGHT.

As Stephen lifts the headset clear, we hear Rachael's voice
still.
RACHAEL: Stephen . . .
He stands and listens. The sound again. From upstairs. He
goes to the foot of the stairs, pauses, then begins to go up,
slowly – up the stairs he has just ascended in his mental
travelling. Rachael's spirit fills the house. He stops at the top
of the stairs. Street light illuminates the floor through a tall
window. The bedroom door is slowly swinging to. There is a
sound of footsteps. He enters the bedroom cautiously. He
approaches the bed, whispers—

STEPHEN: Rachael . . .?

He steps inside the room. A glimpse of the bed – unmade. Then an eruption of movement, a cry of astonishment from Stephen, and a great thud as his body is slammed against the wall, and blinding light as a hand finds the switch. Dean has pinned him against the wall. He has a knife.

DEAN: Been waiting for ya, doc. Must've fallen asleep.

Stephen has raised his arms in surrender. His voice is breathy with shock.

STEPHEN: All right, all right. Put the knife away. Please.

Dean lets go and steps back. But he keeps the knife out.

What do you want?

DEAN: A talk. Downstairs.

He gestures with the knife.

Not too fast. I'll be right behind you.

As they descend the stairs, tight on Stephen who is beginning to make calculations.

STEPHEN: You got past the intruder alarms. That was pretty—

DEAN: Shut up.

They arrive by Stephen's work station. Stephen dreads further destruction. He tries to keep the desperation out of his voice. Dean takes in the equipment on the table.

STEPHEN: Don't be nervous. I'm not going to try—

DEAN: I said shut the fuck up. Go over there. You're working for the Buzzkid Corporation.

Stephen waits.

The hospital told my folks you'd be unemployable after you were sacked.

STEPHEN: Well?

DEAN: We wanted you punished.

STEPHEN: I'm sorry.

DEAN: Still, it's not all bad. My folks lent Danny a lot of money to get through medical college. Now it looks like you're gonna be the one to pay them back.

STEPHEN: Ah, I see. You're threatening me.

DEAN: Yup.

Stephen is moving round towards the fireplace. He raises his

bare hands to show he means no harm.
STEPHEN: Listen, er, Dean, is that your name? Mind if I have a cigarette. You want one?
Stephen takes a cigarette. Leaning against the wall, invisible to Dean, is the baseball bat. Stephen edges nearer to it.
No point my telling you I'm not responsible for your brother's death. But suppose I don't want to give you money.
Grinning broadly, Dean tips the big TV to the floor.
DEAN: Oops.
As the set crashes to the floor, Dean's hand is moving towards one of the electronic boxes.
I'll make a nuisance of my –
His words are cut off as the baseball bat thuds into his stomach at full force. He is completely winded. He drops the knife, and doubles up, fighting for air. Stephen quickly moves to push the electronic pieces out of harm's way. He retrieves the knife. Dean is on his knees, speechless, still trying to inhale. Stephen overcomes the temptation to hit him again. He picks up the phone and dials.
STEPHEN: Police department?

STEPHEN'S DRIVEWAY. NIGHT.

Two patrol cars are in the driveway. Dean is led handcuffed towards an open car door by a patrolman. Stephen watches from the porch of his house.

STEPHEN MENTAL TRAVELLING.

A series of images melt into each other, sometimes fading to grey. Then we might hear only sounds – bells, buzzes, traffic, voices, then the images again, including that of Patrick, the depressive Irishman, with voices murmuring, then laughter, scraps of music, loud sighs. The images and sounds originate from different, unconnected times in Stephen's life, and are highly subjective:

219

Stephen walking away from the Hamonds' apartment building, glancing over his shoulder; an adolescent boy going up on a stage to receive a prize; a mother putting her cool hand on the brow of an ill child; medical students examining a part of a preserved corpse and one of them making a first incision.

Under this, Stephen's voice, far away.

STEPHEN (OS): . . . from all over the place . . . too quick for me to tag them, too strange . . . no effect, maybe the slightest unease . . . move 3 millimetres along the *x* plane . . .

The images fade to a misty greyness, then another sequence begins: The casualty department of a major hospital. A young intern, Stephen, bends over the victim of a traffic accident.

Then, Rachael standing outside her apartment building with a suitcase. Stephen is pulling up in his car. He gets out, strides towards her. His voice sounds younger, exuberant.

Get in the car quick. I'll bring the case . . .

BUZZKID INST. STEPHEN'S LAB. DAY.

Same time. Stephen in the machine, Fred and Bob monitoring, as before.

Fred glances at Bob.

FRED: He's found her.

STEPHEN: We could miss this flight.

Stephen's voice becomes that of the researcher.

Tag this. Woman in doorway.

Then back in the memory.

Leaves at eleven . . . leaves . . . I'm losing it . . .

He opens his eyes.

You get that?

Stephen begins to disconnect himself. He's anxious to get home and barely listening to the two men.

BOB: Sure. But what about the reward sites?

Fred picks up a piece of legal notepaper.

FRED: Yeah – 4 millimetres in the anterior-posterior axis,

between the rostral accumbens and the caudal VTA.
STEPHEN: Yeah, I know . . .
Free of the machine, Stephen comes over to the console to copy the day's 'take' on to disc.
FRED: And then the MFB, where it skirts the hypothalamus. We were going to check out two sites near the midline, one ventral, and the other a dorsal branch . . .
STEPHEN: Yeah, yeah, tomorrow. We'll do all that tomorrow. I gotta go.
He snatches up his coat and hurries out of the lab.

STEPHEN MENTAL TRAVELLING.

A packed auditorium. Night. Stephen is standing at the back. Deeply curious, and a growing pride in this woman who has recently come into his life. On stage, Rachael is coming to the end of her reading. She has the audience in her power.
RACHAEL: . . . But he was asleep and almost smiling, and in the pallor of his upturned throat she thought she saw from one bright morning in her childhood a field of dazzling white snow which she – a small girl of eight – had not dared scar with footprints.
She looks up, a frail, pale figure. She smiles.
Thank you.
On the first wave of enthusiastic applause, cut to –

STEPHEN MENTAL TRAVELLING.

Reception area. Minutes later. Stephen makes his way though the crowd. Admirers are clustered round a table where Rachael is signing her book. The crowd parts, allowing Rachael and Stephen's eyes to meet. His pov: she makes a wry expression. Then we lose sight of her.

221

STEPHEN MENTAL TRAVELLING.

Two hours later. The hotel room. Rachael and Stephen make love. They are enraptured, falling in love. Tight on Rachael staring up at Stephen. Love and distress in equal measure.
RACHAEL: This is impossible, Stephen . . .
He stops her mouth with kisses.

STEPHEN'S HOUSE. STUDY. NIGHT.

Same time. As before, Stephen sprawls in his chair, wearing the headset connected to the electronics. The laptop is within easy reach. We note a tape recorder is running – recording. On the floor by his chair, a half-empty bottle of Scotch. And all around, a rising tide of squalor – remains of half-eaten TV dinners, glasses, empty bottles, ashtrays. A second TV brought down from the bedroom is on the table. The first still lies upended and smashed on the floor. Stephen's head lolls, his arms are thrown back, he moans softly, then louder as he loses himself to the stimulated memory. Then his whole body stiffens and trembles.
STEPHEN: Rachael . . . Rachael!

STEPHEN MENTAL TRAVELLING.

The hotel. After making love. Rachael has gone into the bathroom. We hear the sound of the shower. Stephen rolls over to reach for a glass of water on the bedside table. He accidentally knocks a magazine to the floor. As he leans over the edge of the bed to pick it up he notices a bottle of pills which had been concealed in its pages. He picks up the bottle, reads the label, frowns. He is about to call out to Rachael. Then he changes his mind and pushes the bottle back between the pages of the magazine.

STEPHEN MENTAL TRAVELLING.

A mountain ridge trail. The day after the reading. Stephen and Rachael are out hiking in a high beautiful place. Sunlight, a vast panorama of forest and mountains. They are clambering over rocks. Rachael is excited by her recent literary successes. Stephen is a little distracted.

RACHAEL: . . . so in the end he phoned and I said, Andrew, look, I don't want it in the *New Yorker*, I don't want it in *Vanity Fair*. I wrote it for *Grand Street*, I promised it, he's an old friend. Then there was this silence down the phone, and I could just tell he was thinking of a new approach, and sure enough he suddenly said . . . Stephen, am I boring you?

STEPHEN: No, no. Go on. It's, uh, a whole other world to me this, uh . . .

RACHAEL: Is something bothering you?

They stop, slightly breathless. Stephen hesitates.

Well?

STEPHEN: Why are you taking lithium?

She holds his gaze.

RACHAEL: It's not your business.

STEPHEN: Well, it could be.

He takes her hand.

You could trust me.

Silence. She is looking right into him.

I think you're an amazing woman, Rachael.

She is sharp, defensive.

RACHAEL: And now you know why. It's all down to drugs.

She pulls her hand away, climbs round the rock and walks on. Stephen follows.

I asked you not to expect anything of me, or get too close . . .

He stops her –

STEPHEN: It's too late . . .

– and kisses her.

RACHAEL: Don't . . .

STEPHEN: I want you to trust me . . . tell me about this . . .

She responds, reluctantly at first. Between kisses –

RACHAEL: You're crazy . . .

STEPHEN: That's two of us.

RACHAEL: Idiot.

STEPHEN: Idiot.
She pulls back. Her eyes are filled with tears. She's whispering. In very tight.
RACHAEL: Stephen . . . believe me. It'll destroy you . . .
He draws her towards him, and they stand in the vastness, embracing.

STEPHEN'S HOUSE. STUDY. NIGHT.

Stephen's eyes are open and he has pushed the headset free. It's been a night of steady, morbid drinking. He empties the bottle into his glass, stares into nowhere. Medium shot. The squalor of the room and his state seem confirmation of Rachael's words.

BUZZKID INST. ATRIUM. DAY.

Following morning. Stephen makes his way unsteadily across the atrium towards a quiet spot. It is mid-morning break, and the place is crowded. He catches a waiter by the sleeve.
STEPHEN: Bring me a pot of coffee. Really strong.
Stephen is red-eyed, gaunt, dishevelled. He's losing weight – his clothes hang off him. He lowers himself into a chair, begins to fumble with a cigarette. Immediately Quinn, the young enthusiast, is before him.
QUINN: Hey, I lucked out! Dr Godwin . . .
STEPHEN: Aw shit.
QUINN: John Quinn. Remember me? Mind if I sit down . . .
STEPHEN: I mind.
Quinn is already seated.
QUINN: I've been leaving you messages but I guess you've been busy. We wondered if you'd like to address . . .
STEPHEN: Go away. Please go away.
Quinn laughs nervously and presses on.
QUINN: . . . uh, address this seminar I'm organising on the mind–body problem. I know there's a lot of people who'd love to hear you . . .
The coffee has arrived. Stephen is pouring with a trembling

hand. He speaks gently over Quinn.
STEPHEN: Quinn?
QUINN: – give a neurologist's account of this . . .
STEPHEN: Quinn?
QUINN: . . . old philosophical chestnut . . .
STEPHEN: Quinn. Will you please fuck off.
The young man gets to his feet, smiling painfully.
QUINN: Sure. I mean, I'm sorry. I guess you need to, uh,
look if you'd like to think it over and give a me call I could . . .
*Stephen loses control. He half rises, and shouts at full
volume.*
STEPHEN: Go away! Goddammit, GO AWAY.
*The coffee pot tips to the floor. The atrium falls silent. All
heads are turned. Quinn steps back, astounded. Stephen falls
back in his chair, nursing the sudden shooting pain in his
head. Two waiters hurry over and begin clearing the mess.
Stephen mutters.*
Oh God, leave it, leave it. I just wanted to sit here quietly . . .
*Meanwhile, Butler has appeared. He dismisses Quinn with a
movement of his head.*
Butler sits down at Stephen's side. Stephen groans.
And you . . .
BUTLER: So . . .
He waves the waiters away.
Later. Bring some more. So. How's our pleasure dome?
STEPHEN: Aching like hell.
BUTLER: I was thinking of the headsets and electronics we've
just discovered missing.
STEPHEN: They're safe with me.
BUTLER: Hardly the letter or the spirit of our agreement. In
fact –
Stephen is instantly angry again.
STEPHEN: Listen to me – dah!
*But the pain in his head does not allow it. He forces his
volatile mood under control.*
You want me to find your America – pure happiness at the
throw of a switch. Well, it isn't easy, and it doesn't often
come pure.

BUTLER: That's why we asked you, Stephen.

Stephen sighs, rubs his eyes. The explanation is an effort.

STEPHEN: You're fishing for pleasure. You stimulate a limbic site. That activates an emotion. The emotion lights up networks that code for specific memories. These memories are in no particular place. They're everywhere, they're nowhere, they're in the patterns of firings between neuronal groups. Forget about pleasure, man. You've got yourself a memory machine. The therapeutic possibilities are –

BUTLER: That's for later. The serious wealth is in entertainment. First one in cleans up.

STEPHEN: So, give me a hundred volunteers and five more assistants, I'll do my fishing in the lab here, statistically, scientifically. But if I'm working on my own brain, to protect you from competitors, or the law, I'm doing it at home. My trip, my place.

BUTLER: You've already had one nut break into your house. This prototype cost –

STEPHEN: Fine. Get me a safe.

Butler stands. His tone is cool.

BUTLER: I wouldn't like to think that there are any aspects of your er 'trip' –

He gestures towards Stephen, the state of him, the mess at his feet, – that are irrelevant to this project.

STEPHEN: Everything's relevant.

Butler smiles without parting his lips, and leaves. Stephen nurses his head and closes his eyes. He has succeeded – but only just – in protecting his obsession.

STEPHEN MENTAL TRAVELLING.

These are confused memories. The images are fleeting, fragmentary, the sound echoes indistinctly, the perspectives are disorienting. A slow-motion, underwater feel. It is a wedding picnic by a lake. Late summer, late afternoon sunshine. Dozens of Stephen and Rachael's friends. Smoke

226

from a cook-out. Stephen and Rachael arm in arm smiling, kissing while their wedding guests raise their glasses to them. A child brings a gift, and Rachael, unwrapping it, embraces the child. A friend right by the water's edge, with a camera raised to his face, accidentally steps into an ice bucket. It lodges on to his foot. The friend clowns, hopping about trying to remove it, then topples sideways into the lake. The helpless laughter of Stephen, Rachael and all their guests.

STEPHEN'S HOUSE. STUDY. DAY

As before, Stephen in his chair, with the equipment, and a Scotch within reach. A newly installed steel safe, cemented into the wall, adds to the chaos. This time, dusty sunlight penetrates the scene. Stephen is laughing at the memory – the same loud fall-about laughter that he experienced at the time.

STEPHEN MENTAL TRAVELLING.

The lake again. Fleetingly, we see part of the ice-bucket scene repeated, but in dimmer light. Then we fade through a rapid succession of images – faces, Rachael and Stephen throwing clothes hurriedly into a suitcase; a taxi; an office where the couple are signing a document; a subjective camera hurrying down a flight of stairs ... Until we emerge into sudden brilliant clarity. It is the bedroom upstairs we have seen before. It is flooded with sunlight. There are packing cases. The windows have no curtains. The room has bare boards and no furniture except for the huge bed which removal men are just setting down.

The men have left. Stephen kisses Rachael passionately. He picks her up and carries her to the bed. She takes his head between her two hands and kisses him affectionately on the nose.

RACHEL: Why do you love me so much? It's wonderful, but why me? I don't understand it.

STEPHEN: Fishing for compliments?
RACHAEL: Yup.
STEPHEN: OK. In descending order, because you're light-weight . . .
RACHAEL: Thanks . . .
STEPHEN: I mean portable, and small-eared, juicy, sexy –
RACHAEL: Juicy, sexy. Same thing.
STEPHEN: Well spotted.
RACHAEL: I am not!
STEPHEN: All right, nicely moled. And um, thin-armed, high-browed, thin-skinned, ticklish, skittish, Scottish, Yiddish, thirty-ish . . . and mine –
RACHAEL: ish?
A flicker of seriousness in Stephen's features.
STEPHEN: Mine.
She draws him down to her and they begin to make love. Stephen murmurs Rachael's name, then again, louder –

MENTAL TRAVELLING.
PUBLIC BUILDING. DAY.

– And louder. He is at the top of a mezzanine floor, waving a newspaper, shouting the name. Rachael is at the foot of escalator, looking up at him in bewilderment. Stephen tries to get on the down escalator, but there are too many people in the way. Instead he comes down the up side, taking it three steps at a time, shouting and waving the paper all the while.
STEPHEN: You got it! You made it! You're brilliant! It says so!
He appears at her side, breathless, holding the paper up. The cover of the New York Times *Book Review has a large photograph of Rachael and a headline which reads 'A Strange and Brilliant Tale'. Whooping and hollering, Stephen and Rachael do a whirling dance among the rush hour crowds.*

MENTAL TRAVELLING. HOUSE.
SITTING ROOM. NIGHT.

The room is well-established now with furnishings. Stephen's pov from the door. Rachael is curled into an armchair. The review lies across her lap. She's lost in thought. Stephen approaches, but she doesn't look up.

STEPHEN: Hey. What's up?

RACHAEL: Did you read what they said?

STEPHEN: I skimmed it.

RACHAEL: Well?

STEPHEN: Well, he seems to love your book.

Rachael makes a small sound of contempt and turns away.

RACHAEL: It's a travesty. It's an insult.

Stephen comes closer, kneels by her chair, touches her arm.

STEPHEN: Rachael, come on ...

RACHAEL: I can't believe you didn't read it.

STEPHEN: Let's see.

He goes to pull the paper off her lap. She grips it tight, crumpling a part of it in her first.

RACHAEL: It doesn't matter. You don't have to humour me ...

Close on Stephen. The anxiety in his eyes. He knows the advance signs of the depression stage of her cycle. He summons his patience.

STEPHEN: You got a rave review. People are going to go out and buy it and decide for themselves. It's not important what this guy says ...

RACHAEL: Not to you. I can see that. So let's just leave it ...

He frames her name with his lips, but sound barely escapes them.

STEPHEN: Rachael ...

They look at each other, deeply.

... don't ...

They hold the deep gaze, then they fold each other into an embrace. They are both tearful – with relief, or perhaps sorrow at what they sense is to come. From somewhere far

away a phone is ringing. Stephen looks up. Rachael tightens her grip.
RACHAEL: Leave it. Let it ring.
But Stephen is disengaging. He murmurs apologetically.
STEPHEN: It'll be the lab. Some new results. I have to take it . . .

STEPHEN'S HOUSE. WORK ROOM. DAY.

Same time. The phone is ringing. Stephen pushes the headset clear. Takes his glass, lifts the receiver. His voice is hoarse.
STEPHEN: Yeah?
CAROL: Hi, it's me.
STEPHEN: Ah.
CAROL: I've been thinking about you.
STEPHEN: Uh, who is this?
CAROL: It's Carol. Are you OK? Do you want me to come round?
STEPHEN: No, don't come. Look, Carol. I'll call you soon.
CAROL: Stephen . . . Stephen?
He cuts her off. He takes up the headset, searches on the TV set for a different section of his brain, punches keys on the computer, takes a large pull on the Scotch, sets the tape recorder going and settles back. Medium shot across the room. Stephen in his lonely world.
STEPHEN: Yeah . . . sure, why not? We could both go . . . yeah, drive all night, stay in that place by the river, come back Sunday . . . if you like . . . no, Rachael, it's a great idea. We'll do it . . .
He whoops and punches the air.
Let's go!

BUZZKID INST. STEPHEN'S LAB. DAY.

Fred and Bob with nothing to do in Stephen's absence are playing chess. Stephen appears in the doorway.

BOB: The prodigal doctor!

Stephen is looking worse than ever. He is not eating. His cheeks are hollow. He is unshaved, unkempt. He has the air of an alcoholic in the final stages of deterioration. His manner is distracted, hurried.

STEPHEN: Oh hi. It's OK, uh – carry on. I just came to look for . . .

He is rummaging around the equipment. Fred and Bob go over to him.

FRED: You all right?

BOB: Sit down. Tell us how you are. What's been going on?

STEPHEN: I'm looking for a disc.

Stephen's searchings become more frantic. He can't conceal his querulous desperation.

Work we did on the amygdala, fourth day. I left it right here. One of you must have moved it.

FRED: It's right here with all the others. Hey, you want some coffee?

STEPHEN: Give it here . . .

FRED: We're still straightening out the co-ordinates of the—

STEPHEN: I said give it to me!

He snatches it out of Fred's hand.

Look, I'm sorry . . .

Apology or explanation is beyond him. Stephen hurries out the room.

BOB: Stephen, Dr Brown was asking about you. She came out . . .

Stephen is out of earshot. Bob turns to Fred and shrugs.

BUZZKID INST. DRIVEWAY. DAY.

Stephen hurries to his car. His only thought is to get back to Rachael. He manoeuvres clumsily, banging into another parked car. Then he pulls away hard.

CAR. DAY.

Minutes later. As he drives, Stephen shoves a cassette tape into the car's player. He is a man possessed. He cannot bear to live outside his dream world. Listening to his own voice, he relives the activated memories, mouthing the words, mouthing her answers.

STEPHEN: (tape) Fishing for compliments? ... OK. In descending order. Because you're lightweight ... I mean portable, small-eared, juicy, sexy ...

STEPHEN'S DRIVEWAY. DAY.

Stephen stops the car sharply, runs into the house. He pulls the front door to behind him, but he is in too much of a hurry to notice that it has not closed properly.

STEPHEN MENTAL TRAVELLING.

In the scenes that follow, Stephen's voice over is that of the man in his chair, manipulating the electronics, trying (with less and less success) to avoid the 'bad' memories, and trying to locate, or re-activate, the 'good' ones. In tight on the explosive slam of the bathroom door. Then immediately, Stephen breathless, trying the handle, knocking.

STEPHEN: Rachael, Rachael, open the door. We've got to talk. (VO: Uh ... no ... no)

RACHAEL: I've had enough talking. Just leave me alone!

STEPHEN: Rachael ...

Cut into: Stephen's hand pushing keys on the laptop. A blurry passage of images too rapid to be taken in. Then: a recent memory, seemingly inconsequential, re-examined. It unfolds in dreamy slow motion. Stephen is walking away from the Hamonds' apartment building after his traumatic interview with the dead student's parents. He glances across his shoulder – at a parked car. It is a black sports car with smoked glass windows. Then the same car, another memory.

Stephen parked by the highway, looking back at Butler getting out of his black sports car.

STEPHEN'S HOUSE. STUDY. DAY.

Briefly. Stephen absorbs the significance of this. Then he reaches for the start button of the tape recorder, and then the keys of the laptop.

STEPHEN MENTAL TRAVELLING.

Stephen lying on his back in bed. Rachael tenderly kisses his face. He goes to speak, but Rachael presses her finger across his lips and kisses him again. Her head moves out of shot. Stephen lies waiting.
STEPHEN: *(VO: Come back . . . come back . . .)*
Dissolves briefly into a scene we have seen before: Rachael in bed, Stephen comforting her.
RACHAEL: . . . I'm so frightened. I don't want to be mad . . .
STEPHEN: *(No . . .)*
The computer screen – the cursor dropping down through a list.
In a restaurant. Tight on Rachael. Her face is animated, full of love as she talks to Stephen.
RACHAEL: I just can't wait to get started on this new book.
Cut straight from the restaurant to—
Sudden silence. The house. Rachael's study. She is at her desk. Paper – most of it blank or balled up – is spread before her. She looks wasted. Her hair is lank, she is pale, ill-looking. She's been crying.
RACHAEL: It's all shit.
STEPHEN: Not this, not this . . .
But the scene goes on. Stephen pulls a chair over and sits at her side. He takes her unresponsive hand.
STEPHEN: Did you take your pill?
She sighs and pulls her hand free. She looks away. Stephen

pauses. As the row gathers pace, the angles become tighter, stranger, strengthening an air of unreality.

Try and think back two months . . . You were happy, in love, everyone loved your book, you were excited about the new one. Everything was good. Now everything looks hopeless. But it's a cycle. It's an illness. You've just got to ride it through . . .

RACHAEL: You're trying to crush me . . .

STEPHEN: Sweetheart . . .

RACHAEL: Telling me that I'm crazy, that there's nothing wrong, that it's all in me . . .

STEPHEN: Try and see it as a disease, like measles. Your serotonin is depleted . . .

RACHAEL: Oh my God . . .

STEPHEN: . . . but it'll change, it'll lift. You have to wait it out . . .

RACHAEL: This is science gone crazy. Can't you hear yourself? Yet another man telling a woman she's sick in the head. It's been going on for centuries. But I'm not going to let you do it . . .

STEPHEN: Rachael, listen to me.

RACHAEL: No, you listen. A year ago I was living alone, I wrote books, I was happy. Now I'm living in your house . . .

STEPHEN: Wait . . .

RACHAEL: . . . with your telephone calls, your faxes, your big experiments, your amazing science and I've got no space, no identity, no reality . . .

Despite himself, Stephen loses his temper.

STEPHEN: We bought the house together! You don't answer your calls, you don't like faxes, you've got as much of your own space as you want and you're a big success out there . . .

RACHAEL: I know you hate me, but I'm not frightened of you . . .

STEPHEN: But you're a manic fucking depressive! You're up, everything's great and you love me. You're down, you hate me and it all stinks. You're on a switchback and until you see it, you'll stay a victim of it. And so will I!

The angrier Stephen is, the calmer Rachael becomes. The waif-like face turns to us, the big eyes look right into us.

RACHAEL: Stephen, answer me this. Why is it every time I try to tell you honestly how I feel, you end up shouting at me and telling me I'm sick in my mind?

Stephen goes to speak, and changes his mind and sighs. This is a familiar impasse.

STEPHEN: (Oh God, no . . .)

He picks up his glass but it's empty.

RACHAEL: Could it be you're drinking too much? Is it remotely possible you have one or two problems of your own?

Stephen turns to leave the room as the scene begins to dissolve.

Stephen's hand on the computer keyboard, then the screen, with the cursor flickering over co-ordinates, locations, labels, as he trawls for happier memories.

STEPHEN: (Where are you . . .?)

STEPHEN MENTAL TRAVELLING.

But the images, the memories do not come easily. We see, as before, glimpses of dimmed recollections – the wedding picnic, lovemaking, dancing in the rush hour crowds – but we cannot hang on to them . . .

Come on . . . come on . . .

Then we are in the bedroom. Rachael is in bed, propped up by pillows. Books and papers on the bed. She looks wasted, beautiful. Stephen sits on the bed, dressed to go out, a briefcase on his lap.

Stephen sighs.

I love you.

Rachael's voice is faint, spacey.

RACHAEL: I feel . . . empty. I can't believe . . . that I'm here. I'm not here . . .

STEPHEN: Sweetheart . . .

RACHAEL: I don't want you to go. Stephen, I'm very frightened . . .

STEPHEN: I have to be there. Everyone's counting on me. I'll come straight back . . .

RACHAEL: It's so . . . so black . . . I don't know where I am.

STEPHEN: You're home, in bed, safe.

RACHAEL: But I can't feel it. I can't believe it. Everything's so far away.

STEPHEN: I could get a neighbour to sit with you.

RACHAEL: No! I want you to stay here.

Stephen stands and kisses her cheek. She does not respond.

STEPHEN: Two hours at the most, I promise.

We follow Stephen out the door and down the stairs. He is halfway down when she calls him.

RACHAEL: Stephen . . .

He slows, falters.

STEPHEN: Go back. Please won't you go back . . .

. . . and continues on down. At the bottom he looks up. She's there, in her nightdress, leaning over the banister, the image from his dream, looking wild and lost and pale.

RACHAEL: Stay with me. Please stay with me . . .

He's determined to be firm.

STEPHEN: Rachael, I haven't been in for ten days. If we lose the funding my job goes with it. If you want I'll get Betty to come over . . .

Rachael has slipped away, back to the bedroom. As he leaves he calls.

I'll be really quick.

Stay with her . . . Why didn't you stay with her!

Stephen's fingers punch desperately at the computer keys. The scene dissolves into a brief hiatus of images, until we are suddenly on the walk on the mountain, the day after Rachael's reading. The two are embracing and kissing. In his chair, Stephen, eyes shut, sighs in contentment.

OUTSIDE STEPHEN'S HOUSE. DAY.

Same time. A subjective camera walks into the drive, pauses,

*then approaches the house. A sense of unease in the music cue
– almost a threat. Everything about this approach suggests
the return of Dean. We come up the steps of the porch and
stop before the door. It is ajar. A hand pushes it open. We go
in, across the hall, into the squalor of the work room.
Stephen is lost to the memory of his walk on the mountain
with Rachael. As we approach we catch his side of the
conversation.*

STEPHEN: You could trust me . . . I think you're an amazing
woman, Rachael . . . It's too late . . . I want you to trust me
. . . please tell me about it . . . that's two of us . . .

*While we hear this we have come up close to stand in front of
the computer. The cursor is flashing on the label 'Walk with
R, near Zaca Lake'. A hand comes into shot and scrolls the
cursor down the list, to stop at a set of co-ordinates with the
single title – 'End'. The hand pushes the keys. Stephen groans,
and murmurs.*

STEPHEN: No . . . no . . .

*His hand stretches out towards the keyboard, but it freezes in
place and we hear his gasp, as we cut to –*

STEPHEN MENTAL TRAVELLING.

*The house. Stephen has arrived back from his errand. He
drops his briefcase at the foot of the stairs and calls up.*

STEPHEN: I'm back! Less than two hours!

*Humming quietly – he has been energised by a successful
meeting – he turns to set his keys down on a table.
Something about the quality of the silence in the house makes
him glance up.*

You asleep again?

*Subjective camera. He begins the familiar ascent of the stairs.
Stephen groans.*

I can't do it . . . not this . . .

*He gropes for the computer keys. The hand of the intruder
edges the keyboard out of reach. The intruder whispers softly.
'You have to.' And Stephen is not able to resist now the one*

237

memory he has so far managed to avoid.

He is at the top of the stairs. Across the landing, the bedroom door stands open – as before. We have an angled glimpse of the untidy bed, the books and papers, the hump of Rachael's shape among the bedclothes. He enters the room. She is on her back, utterly still. Satisfied that she is asleep, he walks quietly past the bed to draw the curtains. Light floods the room. We see the image that has haunted him over the years. A fly is crawling across Rachael's face. And her features are too still for sleep.

STEPHEN: Rachael . . .

For a moment time stands still. He cannot will himself to move.

The silence is broken only by Stephen in the chair – his whispered anguish.

Rachael . . .

He raises her eyelid. The pupil dilation response tells him all he needs to know. He picks up an empty bottle of pills, glances at the label. Stephen sits by the bed, in silent shock, clinging to Rachael's hand. The whisper of the intruder floats in over this.

Is she dead?

THE HOUSE. WORK ROOM. DAY.

Close on Stephen. His eyes are still closed. His face is still. The intruder repeats the whispered question.

Is she dead?

Stephen nods. We are in tight on the intruder's hand switching off the computer. The TV screen goes blank.

Tell me. Let me hear you say it.

Tight on Stephen again. A single tear. He manages at last to say quietly, with utter finality—

STEPHEN: She's dead . . .

The intruder persists.

Again.

238

STEPHEN: She's dead . . . she's gone . . . she's gone.
Still tight on Stephen as he opens his eyes. Then his pov. Carol sits facing him, cool, attentive, very beautiful. Stephen pulls the headset clear, struggles up in the chair, seems to see the room for the first time. He's weak.
Thank you.

STEPHEN'S HOUSE. STUDY. DAY.

Half an hour later. Stephen sits with a blanket across his shoulders. The room is in different light – Carol has pulled back the curtains. She brings him a glass of water.
CAROL: How are you feeling?
He breathes deep, searching.
STEPHEN: Like I've been under water for . . . for . . .
CAROL: Twelve days.
STEPHEN: And just coming up for air . . . and I'm very hungry. Carol.
He puts out a hand. She takes it.
You went out to the Institute.
CAROL: You were destroying yourself.
He nods. Then gestures towards the equipment.
STEPHEN: Its irresistible.
CAROL: I can see that—
They turn at a sound. Butler has been watching them.
BUTLER: The door was open . . .
He advances into the room, poised as ever.
I'll be brief. I've come to retrieve the, um, irresistible and terminate our contract. Doesn't seem like you can handle the job – at the personal level.
He goes to the table and begins to disconnect wires and placing the different components in the box Stephen brought them in.
STEPHEN: The machine's too interesting for the entertainment industry, Tom.
BUTLER: Oh yeah.
STEPHEN: And it's never going to work the way you want. You go looking for emotions, you'll always find memories.

239

BUTLER: We've been through all that.

STEPHEN: But it could be a strength. Self-exploration, breaking obsessions, curing phobias, depression . . .

CAROL: Criminal investigations . . .

STEPHEN: Sure. And speaking of which, Tom . . .

Butler has most of what he wants and stands ready to leave. How much did you pay Dean Hamond and his friend to smash up my stuff?

Butler smiles.

BUTLER: Good guess. Five thousand dollars. It was the only way I could think of to get you on the project.

STEPHEN: Criminal act, Tom. Could get you in a lot of trouble, with Buzzkid, with the law.

BUTLER: Sure. If it could be proved.

At that moment there is a loud chunky click from the direction of the table. Everyone looks up, surprised, including Stephen. Then he smiles. He goes to the table and finds the tape recorder. He removes the tape.

STEPHEN: Well, how about that. A confession.

Butler is shaken. He knows he is no physical match for Stephen. He tries hard to appear cool.

BUTLER: OK. Fine. How much do you want for it?

STEPHEN *puts the tape in his pocket.*

STEPHEN: Well now. Not much. You and I'll report back to Buzzkid with the truth – that you can't programme emotions into virtual reality. Then we'll explain the therapeutic possibilities. Hey, Tom. You could actually do some good in the world!

CAROL: *And* make millions.

Butler turns to her.

BUTLER: You really think so?

BUZZKID INST. STEPHEN'S LAB. DAY.

Some weeks later. We are tight on the face of Patrick, the depressive. He is in the scanner, wired up. As before, the face is empty, immobile, void of expression or of the slightest interest in what is going on around him. There is a certain amount of bustle – hands reaching across his chest to adjust the electrode of the ECG. We hear the murmur of voices out of shot. Patrick speaks over them

STEPHEN: Let's run through those co-ordinates one more time. $z-8$, $x-4$, and $y+6$.

PATRICK: I think I'd like to be getting back home now.

FRED: Check. And the movement . . .

STEPHEN: . . . is along the x axis from -4 to -7.

CAROL: 150 mv.

BOB: Fine.

STEPHEN: We're ready to go. OK, Patrick? Perfectly still . . . *The monitors, the crossed lines glowing at the intersection. For a moment Patrick's face remains impassive. Then there is a slow ripple, a delicate unfolding as the features come to life, expression and animation return like warmth, a light comes on in the eyes as alertness and connection take hold, and a faint smile transforms itself into a broad one, and grows into a chuckle. We see now that this is an immensely attractive face, and the voice is warm and melodious.*

PATRICK: You want me to tell you about that day . . . *From the team, a ragged chorus of 'Yeah, let's hear it, you bet . . .'*

. . . because it's as clear to me now . . . it's in front of me now. That evening then we were playing at the Rose and Crown in San Francisco and we were playing reels. It was a good crowd and a few were getting up to dance when Larry the owner came on to the stage and says to me, Jeannie's been taken sudden, I've a taxi outside waiting and you've got to run. And run was what I did and when I got to the ward there was Jeannie, God bless her soul, sitting up, all smiles and the tiny girl in her arms which she put into mine. I held her and looked and she was . . . perfect. Then I heard my name and I turned and there was all the band standing there! And Larry holding out my fiddle and saying, Come on Pat, one for Jeannie and the baby, the Sister says it's fine. And so we played the 'She Moved through the Fair', and Jeannie lifted

241

up her pretty head and sang – ah, it was the voice of an
angel . . .
Patrick sings quaveringly –

> 'As the swan in the evening
> Moved over the lake.'

He breaks off and looks at them.
And all the while the baby slept . . .
   *We look at the team. Fred quickly knocks a tear from his
eye. Bob blows his nose loudly. Ollie clears his throat. Carol
smiles and shakes her head wonderingly. Standing apart are
Baldwin, the head of Buzzkid, and Butler – both clearly
moved. Stephen is rooted to the spot. He takes a deep breath.*
STEPHEN: We'll take a break.

BUZZKID INST.
LAB AND GARDENS. DAY.

*Some minutes later. Tight on Patrick who sits by a window,
gazing out. He is smiling to himself, nodding his head
slightly. Fade up slowly as from far away in the past, the
melody as played by Patrick's band (fiddle, guitar, mandolin,
squeezebox). And then, a woman's voice, sweet and light,
takes up the song. As it swells, we have Patrick's view of the
gardens and we see what is making him smile. In sunshine,
Stephen and Carol are walking among the flowers, talking,
laughing, delighted in each other's company. They pause to
kiss as we hear –*

> And she came close beside me,
> And this she did say,
> It will not be long
> Till our wedding day.

Fade to Black.

The song continues with end credits.

ENDS.

Bernard O'Donoghue

LONG WORDS

I can't remember what enterprise it was
We were breaking to each other
That made Denis John give me the word:
'My grandmother' (I knew her: a woman
Forever at her prayers) 'says
The longest word in the world is
Transcranscriptiation.'

So far I haven't found one longer than it,
For all my browsing in the Dictionary.
'Though I didn't go to school myself',
The old people were very fond of saying,
'Still I met the scholars coming home.'

THE DEFINITION OF LOVE

It's strange, considering how many lines
Have been written on it, that no one's said
Where love most holds sway: neither at sex
Nor in wishing someone else's welfare,
But in spending the whole time over dinner
Apparently absorbed in conversation,
While really trying to make your hand take courage
To cross the invisible sword on the tablecloth
And touch a finger balanced on the linen.

A young curate of a parish in West Cork
Was told his mother was seriously ill
And he must come home to Boherbue
(In fact she was dead already; they had meant

To soften the blow). He drove recklessly
Through mid-Kerry and crashed to his death
In the beautiful valley of Glenflesk.
This was because he fantasised in vain
About touching her fingers one last time.

Matthew Singh-Toor

SQUIRREL MAN MAC

Dear Anand,

I'm writing this as I sit in Brockwell Park, near to my flat in Brixton. The sun is shining and it's unusually hot for the beginning of May. The park is quite beautiful, with huge old oak trees and shrubs, and remarkably tame squirrels which come right up to you.

Happy birthday for March. Sorry I forgot to send a card – unforgivable, I know, as we share the same birthday. I've shown your photo (copy enclosed) to my parents, and they both agree we look like twins. I thought your mother and aunties were exaggerating when I was in Sowhaddhi Khas, but since my return home the resemblance has appeared stronger to me every day. It's strange how one's perceptions change.

Please thank your family again for their hospitality in my moment of crisis. I'd assumed I'd have some relatives, however distant, in the village and I'm still not convinced they *have* all moved away. Maybe they got wind of who I was and were worried I was after my grandfather's old land. In any case, I don't know what I'd have done if you hadn't put me up. It was wonderful to finally see where my father was born, and you and your family made me feel as if I really belonged in the village – despite the lack of blood relatives to greet me.

Anand, actually I didn't write the above in Brockwell Park at

245

all. I *did* sit there this afternoon, on a bench, with my pad and pen, intending to write to you, but I couldn't concentrate; it was too chilly. I know I said it was hot for May but I must have been dreaming of the Punjab again; wishing I was still there with you.

I go to the park quite often. It spreads over a small hill, which is good to climb to get away from the hustle and bustle of South London. Living in Brixton can get you down, what with all the traffic and tension, and people knocking their shoulders into you the whole time. There's a big old house on top of the hill – I'm not sure what it's used for now – and lots of benches where I can sit and think, or try to write!

I really liked the poems you sent. The colours you describe are so evocative, so different from those of South London; all those yellows, browns and reds, of earth, dust and clay. They reminded me that, whilst in India, one of the few things I really missed was the lush green grass that blankets Brockwell Park. Don't worry, I won't send you an ode on the subject – I'm no poet! I haven't forgotten you quoting Tagore and Tennyson with equal ease, as I sat on the side of your bed and blushed at my ignorance of both.

I braved the cold for three hours this afternoon, before returning to my flat to start this letter proper. It was worth it for the wildlife. The squirrels are, as I mentioned, remarkable. They're not like the ones in the country, where my parents live, nor like the ones you get in India; these squirrels are like miniature elderly people. They scuttle along the metalled paths on their hind legs, their tiny fists clenched and twisted back, as though with arthritis. They're quite brazen – they march straight under whichever bench you're sitting on and gaze up at you through the slats; black, rabbit-dropping noses twitching, whiskers quivering. Squirrels are supposed to use their ears to detect danger, but the ones in Brockwell Park use them to listen to your breath and your heartbeat. They're not interested in people's food though; they never go after crumbs, although once or twice, from the corner of my eye, I have caught them imitating me as I've bitten into a sandwich or sausage roll. I'm sure I've even heard them giggling.

Dear Anand,

I'm writing to thank you and your family for your hospitality during my visit to Sowhaddhi Khas. Your mother and aunties said we looked like twins and I feel that I have found in you a true brother. Imagine, if my grandfather had not transported my father to England, we could have grown up side by side and I would speak both Punjabi and English, like you, and share your extensive knowledge of both Asian and European history and culture.

It's funny; we're so close spiritually, yet neither of us has the slightest idea what the other is doing at any given moment. I could be anywhere: in my flat; visiting Buckingham Palace; or eating fish and chips at the top of Blackpool Tower. Actually, Anand, I'm sitting on a bench on a hill in Brockwell Park, Brixton, and the weather is glorious; very hot for May.

I do so love this park; I've come here often since moving to South London. My flat is spacious and comfortable, but it can be rather gloomy to pass a spring afternoon in the basement of a Victorian terrace. And the wildlife in the park is a marvel; the squirrels are completely tame and virtually climb into your lap.

Do you believe in telepathy? It's a strange question, I know, but I have felt on several occasions since my return from India that I was seeing the world through your eyes. One night, in a dream a few weeks ago, I found myself down at the ghat, by the Sutlej, cleansing myself at dawn. I was alone, but I was alone in *your* body. I know how alike we look, but it was definitely *your* body; slightly shorter than mine, the muscles more compact. I felt completely at ease, scooping up handfuls of water, watching the droplets splash down my, or rather your, stomach and thighs (I'm embarrassed to mention it now; it brings to mind all those Bollywood sari-drenching scenes!). And then there was another instance, not a dream this time, when I was sitting here, watching the crows in the oak trees, and suddenly I felt that I didn't belong; that the sun, though shining brightly, was freezing cold; that the passers-by were all bloated ghouls, their skin too pale or too black. I don't know; maybe I'd somehow linked up with you, crossed brain waves. I could smell your skin for hours afterwards.

Anand, I really am not a very skilful correspondent. I could certainly never match your elegant turns of phrase; you'll reap the rewards of your Dehra Dun education for years to come. I have a small confession to make – I didn't write the above whilst sitting in Brockwell Park at all. I did intend to – the sun was shining brightly this morning and it was very warm for early May, so I made myself a packed lunch, climbed the hill and sat on one of the benches at the top. But I had to leave before I'd even started eating, because something upset me.

My flat is fine for writing. I haven't got a desk or table in my room, but the bed is comfortable and I can lean my back against the wall. There's the tiniest bit of damp, but you'd expect that of a basement flat, and the woman in the room above, Miss MacLeod, can be a little noisy, especially when she uses the payphone in the hall. Of course, it would seem small by your standards, and I don't have any servants, but that's a cultural as much as an economic difference, I'm sure.

I expect you want to know what upset me in the park, but I'm loath to tell you, in case you think me odd. 'What a flirt!' you must be thinking.

My father, by the way, has a photo of himself as an infant, in which he's standing in front of my grandfather's house in Sowhaddhi Khas. Maybe I could send you a copy. You might recognise it – it's very impressive; Moghul architecture I think, with a hint of Byzantine. I seem to remember peacocks on the lawn, and a waterway. Of course, this would have been before Partition. He still has a gardener, a cleaner and a cook, in Buckinghamshire. Or rather, he has a gardener, a cleaner and a cook *now*; it took him years of hard work to get where he is in this country.

It was stupid really; nothing to get upset about. I took my sandwich box from my rucksack, removed the lid, picked out a Marmite sandwich and lifted it to my mouth. And at that precise moment a flock of crows floated down from the oak tree above and landed on the metalled path, cawing idiotically. They hopped about, all facing the same way, and I wasn't sure if they were looking at me. Then a wave of pigeons descended, and another, and another, interspersing themselves between the crows; all looking in the same direction. And then, to complete the tableau, ten or twenty squirrels scrambled down the tree trunks and scurried in amongst the throng, which was by now undulating like one single louse-ridden beast.

Were they after my lunch, I wondered. I put my sandwich back in its box and sealed the lid. I considered moving to another bench, but wavered. Yes, the creatures' behaviour was disturbing, vile even, but somehow I felt flattered, and very warm. Did they want something from me? Were they really all looking at me, expectantly; waiting for me to provide for them?

Of course, they weren't. They were looking to one of their own kind. There was a rustling from the holly bush to my left, and a piece of bread came flying through the air. It landed in the middle of the throng, precipitating a pitched battle; a blur of beaks, claws and vicious little needle teeth.

I pictured him, then, standing behind the holly bush – a dirty old squirrelman with mangy fur, stinking of damp and faeces and urine. And then, as I expected, he emerged in his dirty old squirrelman's mac, a red-and-blue-striped shopping bag in each hand, stuffed with stale bread, acorns and monkey nuts. He grinned his disgusting Pied Piper grin as he passed me by and the hordes hopped and scampered after him down the hill.

I sat in silence. The park is never silent; there are always crows cawing in the trees, and the hum of traffic far below. But I sat in silence. It had all been a terrible misunderstanding, and there was nothing for it but to forgo the sun and take my lunch, my pad and my pen back to my flat.

I sat in the kitchen, which was empty – I share it with the

house's other occupants, along with the bathroom, but they were all out. I didn't mind at all.

Dear Anand,

Sorry it's taken me so long to write; it's difficult to find the time and the words. Thanks for your letter, and your hospitality in Sowhaddhi Khas, which I would be glad to return should you ever visit London (there would be no problem with the sleeping arrangements). You must thank your family for their kindness during my stay. I fully expected to lodge at my grandfather's old house in the village, or at the very least with one of his cousins, and I was genuinely surprised that nobody had any recollection of him or his land. Please pass my regards to your mother, who listened so patiently to my story and was so tireless in her inquiries around the locality. I honestly felt like your twin brother by the time I left, and remember with much affection the farewell your aunties gave me at the bus stand. My cheeks ache for their tender pinches and petting. Does your mother want her tiffin tin back? It's quite a talking point in my flat.

I'm sitting in Brockwell Park, Brixton, as I write, on a bench at the top of the hill. It's a beautiful spring day, scorching for early May, though nothing like the heat of the Punjab of course. The wildlife here is breathtaking. There are pigeons and crows and squirrels, all of which are happy to hop on to the bench beside you and eat out of your hand. Come summer, the peacocks and humming birds will fly over from Hyde Park and there have been a few recent sightings of the elephant and tiger that escaped from Gerry Cottle's Circus last Christmas. Perhaps our worlds are moving closer. I read an article in *Nature* magazine the other day, suggesting that the earth's temperature is evening out and we can expect uniform tropical conditions within the next fifty years. Just imagine, in many ways it really would become irrelevant where exactly on the globe one was born, and settling in a new country would involve so much less time for readjustment.

I don't want to speak out of turn, Anand, but I'd like to reassure you about something. It's hardly worth mentioning, but I did notice that, during my stay, your mother and aunties favoured *me* slightly, and it made me just a little anxious for your feelings. Certainly there was much talk of us looking like twins, and it was great fun swapping clothes and horsing around, playing tricks on the servants, but you can't have failed to notice all those stray comments about my stature, the superior quality of my attire, the fairness of my skin and my likeness to this or that film star. I must admit, I lapped it all up and found the attention flattering. But I always believed you were really the more handsome, the better educated, the wittier and more sophisticated and, dare I say it, the more desirable of the two of us. Whatever advantages over you I may appear to have amount to very little, and I could not bear for your self-esteem to have suffered as a result of my visit.

On a lighter note, the most wonderful thing happened before I began writing. I mentioned the charming wildlife in the park to you earlier. Well, now it really has excelled itself. As I polished off my picnic of ciabatta bread with Emmenthal, Gruyère and sun-dried tomatoes, wave after wave of pigeons, crows, magpies, cockatoos and eagles swooped down on to the metalled path before me and hopped blissfully from foot to foot, chirping and cawing all the while. And the source of their delight? A lovely old man, who stepped out from the holly bush to my left, a wicker basket full of millet, grapes and French toast on each arm. Clad in a top hat and morning suit, he tossed handfuls of food to the excited birds, which thronged merrily behind him as he skipped down the hill.

This certainly brought a smile to my face. London teems with the most delightful array of benign eccentrics. I believe this old boy is one of a growing band of pensioners who deliberately flout the Capital's prohibition on the feeding of birds. One old lady even went to prison for it. And good for her, I say. What's wrong with a little individualism and imagination in these dreary times? Some of these bureaucrats should think long and hard about what makes this nation so singular!

Anand, I've just read the above back to myself and have realised that some parts of my letter are not strictly true. I'm not actually sitting in Brockwell Park. I'm sitting in the kitchen of my flat. It's a shared kitchen and it's easier to write in here because, during the day, the only other person in the house is Miss Ella MacLeod, who spends her whole time either banging and screaming up and down the stairs or shouting at people down the payphone on the wall outside my room. I don't mind; it's warmer in here than in my flat, or room – whatever you want to call it – which has no heating. It does have its own sink though, and a lock on the door. You'd probably be a little shocked, if you came to stay, at the lack of verandas, Persian carpets, manicured lawns and VCRs. But I'm sure you realise how much more expensive accommodation is in London than the Punjab, relatively speaking.

It's strange; you probably don't notice when my letters are slightly inaccurate or fanciful and, to be honest, I can't see that it matters, as long as I give you a reliable overall picture of my life here in South London. I *did* go to the park earlier today, and watched an old man feeding the crows, pigeons and squirrels for an hour or two. He's always hanging around the benches at the top of the hill, in his shabby green mac. There's an outhouse there – the gents toilets – which he pops into quite often; old men's bladders being what they are.

Anand, the time I spent with you and your family in Sowhaddhi Khas really was the most affirmative and pleasurable of my life, and I don't wish to appear rude or ungrateful, but one or two incidents have been preying on my mind. They're probably entirely inconsequential but, given that our two hearts beat virtually as one, across pasture, ocean, jungle and desert, I'm sure you'd hate me to withhold anything.

Do you remember the day of our picnic, underneath the Gandhiji memorial? It was the first time I'd seen your entire family assembled, and I was quite overwhelmed by the number of aunties, uncles, cousins, nephews and nieces sitting resplendent in their silk saris, suits and salwar kameezes (a gathering of my own clan involves a sombre evening alone with my mother and father, around the old oak table in their gloomy dining room). Overall, the day was highly pleasurable, with delightful food and company and your Uncle Mahesh's moving ghazals, but I was a little disconcerted by some of your younger cousins' behaviour. On a couple of occasions I gained the distinct impression that they found their amusement at my expense; imitating my walk, my accent, my way of eating. They were never so impolite as to do this directly to my face, but I do know what I saw from the corner of my eye. Furthermore, I noticed that when I faced them directly, they fell suddenly silent, staring intently at the dusty ground. I am not an unduly sensitive individual, and would usually take such youthful high spirits in my stride, but I was further disturbed by your aunties' reactions. I am sure they saw what was going on but, rather than issuing some mild reprimand, they flashed a look of amused disdain in my direction, then turned back to their sisters, with whom I am convinced I heard them giggling.

I really do not want to press the point, and I am naturally cautious of relating anything that might threaten the intimacy of our relationship, but I do feel the issue of your family's attitude to me goes a little deeper than I have so far suggested. There is, Anand, absolutely no doubt in my mind that my grandfather once owned the largest, most luxurious house in Sowhaddhi Khas and that his gardens and farmland were amongst the most envied in District Ludhiana. He had countless servants, owned Rolls-Royces and Harley Davidsons by the score, and I understand he frequently entertained prominent politicians and film stars. I once saw a photograph, at the back of a drawer in my parents' bedroom, that proves this categorically, and I'm sure my father must have dozens more stashed away. I am therefore slightly bemused at your family's apparent ignorance of my grandfather's status and even his very existence. True, your mother and aunties listened patiently to my descriptions of the house, grounds and various of my distant relatives, and said they would make inquiries around the village, but they treated the whole matter so lightly and with such an air of benign condescension that I am not quite sure what to think.

It's strange; the old man in the park has never smiled at me, or even looked me in the eye. I see him almost every day, as I while away my hours on the benches at the top of the hill. But, although we've never acknowledged one another formally, I think it's fair to say we have established some kind of relationship, or rapport. We are obviously each aware of the other's presence and we respect one another's space; never sitting together on the same bench, or even crossing paths. So, yes, I think it would be fair to call our deliberate lack of interaction a form of communication.

He's actually more interested in the park's wildlife than its human visitors, and is always producing some titbit or other from the pocket of his mac: bacon rind for the blackbirds; worms for the robins; dead voles for the crows. He has two particular favourites; a couple of squirrels he sometimes spends an entire day watching, as they make their long circuits of the park. Imagine it, Anand; me spending hours watching an old man on a bench watching a couple of squirrels!

Technically speaking, they're not squirrels at all; they're squirrel*men*, although only the old man and I seem to realise this. The young mothers with their pushchairs and the young men in their tracksuits see only the silver-bristled backs and foppish tails, but the old man and I look longer and harder and observe their tiny, erect pink nipples and beady black eyes, and their thick members, half-swollen, making their groin-fur bulge out and drag along the ground. It can be quite a hypnotic sight. They're there all day, every day, pounding the paths that criss-cross and encircle the park; gargantuan haunches driving their squirrelman legs like pistons.

The funny thing is, although the two squirrelmen are the old man's favourites, they don't hold him in the slightest regard. I've seen him try any number of treats to attract their attention – acorns, nuts, carrots, toffee, crème brûlée, fifty pence pieces – but nothing has ever tempted them. Perhaps this is what keeps the old man going; the dream that one day, as one of the squirrelmen thunders all the way from the bottom of the hill to the outhouse at the top, his fancy will be caught by the offer of a tasty morsel and, for the first time, he will turn his shiny, aggressive, lustful eyes on the old man and lash out his tongue, whipping the treat from the palm of his hand. I would love to witness this. It would feel like a victory. The old man might even turn to me, look me full in the face, and beckon me to his bench to celebrate.

Dear Anand,

Thank you for all the letters, cards, telegrams and gifts you have sent over the past months. I'm sorry to have taken so long to reply, but it has been quite a task assimilating the marvellous yet shocking revelations made to me during my stay in Sowhaddhi Khas. The good news is that by a remarkable twist of fate I shall soon be returned to your warm embrace. But more of that later.

Where are you as you read this, Anand? Sitting on the veranda, sipping chai and toying with your usual breakfast of toast and devilled quail's eggs? Or are you in the back of the bumpy old Ambassador, dreaming of the afternoons we spent on the divan in the marquee? Wherever you are, I want you to close your eyes and picture my return to my father's house in Buckinghamshire.

I hurried there straight from the airport, in my crumpled safari suit; my heart pounding, my mind ablaze, even after the eight-hour flight. Dear old Reynolds, my father's retainer, opened the huge oak front door, stooping and beaming from beneath his mop of salt-and-pepper hair. As he ushered me inside, the hounds bounded up to me, skidding on the polished parquet and yapping with joy. I fussed over them briefly, treating them each to a mint imperial, then strode past the Old Masters that line the hall to my father's study, my chin set firm with resolve. There, I rapped on the door, quite manfully, and awaited his summons.

He had not changed. Can you picture my father, Anand, in his metallic blue dressing-gown and emerald silk turban? His wiry grey beard down to his waist, his mottled face cracked with dark lines, and his soft brown eyes set back into two crevices. He cocked his head, smiled and uttered the word – 'son' – which time and again has spirited me across the Afghan rug into his powerful arms. He kissed my forehead and my eyes, then, sensing the change in me, held me away slightly and asked for my news.

I told him, Anand; I told him your mother's story, *our* story, and I watched him dissolve to a silky puddle of metallic blue and emerald green at my feet. Afterwards, as he sat hugging his knees, rocking back and forth, he begged my forgiveness. He said he knew he had committed a crime against God in separating a pair of twins and that not a day has passed he hasn't cursed himself for it. He said he has never stopped loving your – our – mother and that he hates himself still for not fighting harder to convince his family and hers that their mutual devotion was stronger and more worthy than any ancestral feud. And then, Anand, a huge tear fell from his eye and he bellowed to the chandelier hanging from the vaulted ceiling that blessed was the day Parvinder Singh's twin sons were reunited.

So why, you must be asking, has it taken so long for me to relate to you our father's rapturous response? Have I been selfish, or overly cautious? A little of each, I suppose, in addition to a profound need for solitary contemplation, which could be satisfied only within the confines of my simple, whitewashed cell in Brixton, and here in the tranquillity of Brockwell Park.

Think of it, Anand – we two have grown from the same cleft egg. Our DNA is identical. We each comprise the same matter. Yet, before we could even focus on our mother's kohl-rimmed eyes, we were wrenched apart, each to grow up oblivious of the other's very existence, but each tormented by an inexplicable, aching sense of loss. Certainly our parents have wronged us; it was cruel of my father to allow me to believe that his wife – that brittle ghost-like woman who has always flinched from my touch – was my natural mother. And you will find it difficult, I am sure, to forgive our true mother and her family for maintaining to you the myth of our father's death. But, in these past months of meditation, I have come to discern in the midst of all this pain and tragedy, furled tight beneath the petals of a thousand lies and secrets, the essence of a miracle: you and I, Anand, are one person; a single man who has been blessed with two entirely discrete lives. And now we have the opportunity to bond once more, to heal the cleft, and encompass in one mind the cultural knowledge, the spirit, the individuality, the *being* of two. We are, I believe, the way forward.

Do you remember the look on our mother's face as I climbed the steps to the aeroplane, ready to depart the Punjab? The hot wind whipped across the runway, pressing her silver-threaded sari to her bosom, and her eyes implored me to write quickly and tell her of our father's reaction to the momentous news. Well, you must share this letter with her now, and set her heart at rest. You must tell her that the time to hide our origins, the time for shame, is over.

And what of the future? When will we be united once more? Here, as I indicated at the beginning of my missive, the hand of fate has intervened most extraordinarily.

As I write, I am sitting on a bench high up on the hill in Brockwell Park. It is a beautiful day, very warm for early May, and the metalled paths are thickly blanketed with cherry blossom. A few petals have even found their way into the hair of the charming old man sitting beside me, whom I have come to know as the Coach, and upon whom my tale hinges. He must be about sixty and, in his tweed jacket and cravat, has the look of a benign but eccentric uncle. We have just finished our lunch of pâté de foie gras, crackers, strawberries and champagne – quite a change from my regimen of oatcakes and water during these past months of reflection.

The Coach and I spoke for the first time last week,

although we have been engaged in a mutual pursuit for far longer. Every day, since the beginning of March, we have whiled away our afternoons on the benches outside the teashop at the top of the hill, watching two of Brockwell Park's greatest living athletes. These two Adonises, in their Umbro shorts and Adidas trainers, spend hours pounding the paths that criss-cross and circumscribe the park. They are tireless, driven – pausing only to visit the outhouse by the benches – and they communicate little; primarily by locking their steely eyes with those of passing strangers. I myself have now been introduced to them formally, but I still think of them by the names I invented earlier in the year – Dark Crop and Mousey Crew – which describe the attractive colour and style of their hair. With summer's early arrival, they have peeled off their Kangol sweatshirts and vests to reveal smooth, well-defined pectorals and biceps and, incredibly, each passing day marks even greater development of their mighty thighs and calves.

Throughout March, as we sat on our benches, the Coach would often turn from the athletes to me, his eyes glistening with the most intense kind of admiration. By the end of the month I recognised something else in his gaze; an unmistakable pride. Then, on the first Monday in April, he moved from his customary bench by the privet-lined path leading to the outhouse and came to share my seat. There we sat, nibbling our oatcakes and monkey nuts, our hearts thumping with excitement at the display of physical perfection and sporting prowess before us. And then, one afternoon last week, just as the two athletes gained the top of the hill, from opposite sides, the Coach turned to me and asked if I would care to join the three of them in the teashop. Imagine my surprise! And imagine my greater surprise when the Coach informed me, over Viennese whirls and Earl Grey tea, that Dark Crop and Mousey Crew were to represent England in the World Speedwalking Games in the Punjab in June, and that whilst he could confidently coach and chaperon them, they really needed an interpreter – someone fluent in Punjabi – and could that interpreter possibly be me?

I dropped my teacup, Anand, and the whole room – no, the whole park – fell silent. The sun disappeared behind a cloud, and I looked around me; at the coach, at Dark Crop, at Mousey Crew, and at all the other customers sitting, mouths agape, in their blazers, boaters and organza dresses. Every pigeon, crow, squirrel, peacock, giraffe and elephant in the park seemed to emerge from the undergrowth to press up against the teashop's glass windows, awaiting my reply; looking to me to save the day. And then, Anand, the sun re-emerged, poking a golden finger at my shattered cup, revealing beauty in the broken Willow Pattern, and I cried that yes, of course I would travel with the Coach and his charges to the Punjab, that I would be honoured to share with them my historical, cultural and linguistic expertise, that my father would join our party, that we could all stay for as long as we wanted with my mother in Sowhaddhi Khas, and that finally my twin brother and I would find peace as our two worlds merged irrevocably into one.

I shall not attempt to describe the roar of approval that went up from the teashop or the ensuing scenes of jubilation, except to say that the streets of the Borough of Lambeth, South London, have not witnessed such joy since the Queen's Silver Jubilee, 1977.

It is raining hard now, Anand – it has been raining for as long as I can remember – and I will not lie any more. Ella MacLeod has just smashed the phone receiver against the wall in the hall and slammed the front door behind her. Her slippers will be soaked already. It is raining so hard that the drops ricochet straight back up from the pavement.

I sat at the top of the hill for three hours this afternoon, in the rain; a fog of wet leaves and earth in my nostrils. The old man was on the bench opposite, and between us we had the park covered – three-hundred-and-sixty-degree surveillance. We haven't spoken in all these months, but we look each other over quite openly now. He is bald, with a thick white moustache and whiskers. His nose and cheeks are ruddy with burst blood vessels, his eyes are grey and watery, and the liver-spotted skin of his forehead is flaking away. Sometimes he produces a crust of bread or a monkey nut from the pocket of his mac, for the squirrels, which climb up on to the bench to eat from his hand.

Two of the park's other regulars, whom I've come to know as Skinhead One and Skinhead Two, were there this afternoon, and the old man and I watched them compulsively, as usual. They are of average height and build. They wear trainers and blue jeans or combat trousers, and green nylon bomber jackets. They are unremarkable. But there must be something about their gait, the confidence of their cold stare, that compels other men to track them down, to follow their trail. They must have some strange power, something inborn, something the old man and I lack, that makes us less than them. Why else would we crave their acknowledgement? Why else would we sit and watch, hoping, hoping, hoping?

My parents visited yesterday. They didn't stay long; they didn't even take their coats off. My mother stood silently in her stilettos and mink, staring at my Indian Tourist Board poster, while my father paced the floorboards, testing the windowsills and walls for dust and grime with the finger of his leather driving glove. I made some tea, but they held the cracked mugs suspiciously, and drank not a drop. My father told me he had business in Croydon and they really must press on. I walked them to the front door and, as I shook hands with my father, his thin smile twisted to a grimace and he said he had hoped that with my education and all he had invested in me, I would amount to something more than this. Then he turned and left, and I made to kiss my mother's cheek, but she pulled away and squeezed my hand. I watched the BMW glide down the street then opened my fist and found a five-pound note inside.

I hope you will not think the less of me, Anand. It would have been nice to meet you – it would be nice to be somewhere warm – and should you ever visit South London you are more than welcome to stay. But this will be my last letter for the time being.

I trailed one of them around the park this afternoon; I'm not sure whether it was Skinhead One or Skinhead Two. I tried to imitate his walk and posture, keeping ten or twenty feet behind, and each time he paused to survey the park's other occupants I attempted to catch his eye. But not once did he acknowledge me; in fact, after an hour or so I suspected he was speeding up, to throw me off his scent. Eventually we arrived at the top of the hill and he disappeared down the dark, privet-lined path leading to the outhouse. I loitered outside for several minutes, my pulse racing, feeling a little sick. Then I took a deep breath and followed him inside.

They were both there, Skinhead One and Skinhead Two, standing at the steel urinal, and for a split second, as my heart jumped, I connected with their look of brutal, brackish lust. Each was staring at the other's engorged penis – stroking, squeezing, tugging; pulling back the foreskin. Then the thick stench of disinfectant and stale piss tore into my nostrils, and they were zipping themselves up, smirking to each other, almost giggling as they walked out of the gentlemen's public toilets, straight past me. I rested my head against a cubicle door for a few seconds, staring at an old NF logo scrawled in biro, and waited for my own penis to stop throbbing; for the blood to quieten in my ears. Then I returned to my bench, opposite the old man, who smiled at me as I resumed my watch.

Skinhead One and Skinhead Two were on opposite sides of the park by now, treading the metalled paths, dictating the order of things with their steely gaze.

Dear Papa,

Sorry I haven't been in touch for so long. I'm writing to ask you to stop forwarding my mail to Brixton. There have been three consecutive weeks of sunshine now and, although it is only the beginning of May, I thought it time to move out. My room was, to be honest, dingy, dusty, depressing and damp, and one of the house's residents belonged, quite frankly, in a mental institution.

As I write, I am sitting on a bench high up on the hill in Brockwell Park, which affords a fine, clear view of South London, and possibly beyond. The grass is dotted with women, men and children of every race and creed; dozing, reading, playing volleyball, or simply gazing at the sky. Beside me are my possessions: three dustbin liners full of clothes, a sleeping bag, my toothbrush and my Encyclopaedia of Indian Mythology. So, you'll be pleased to hear, I'm well set for the summer and no longer a burden on either the State or the taxpayer.

A short while ago, Papa, I visited the gentlemen's public toilets, which are situated at the end of a little privet-lined path next to my bench. They really are a disgrace, with cubicle doors hanging off their hinges, toilet bowls stuffed with waxy paper and faeces, and a red-tiled floor flooded with a quarter-inch of urine and disinfectant. Yet, despite the stench and squalor, these conveniences have, in the few minutes just past, witnessed one of the most unexpected and affirmative experiences of my life. Do not be shocked, Papa, and do not throw this letter down; I want to guide you through this step by step.

Papa, listen – my plimsoll made a quiet splash as I stepped over the threshold, attracting the attention of the old man standing at the urinal. I see him all the time in the park, sitting on the benches in his shabby green mac. He grinned as he turned to face me, revealing two crowded rows of yellow teeth and, as I headed for the cubicle, he shook his penis with a slightly exaggerated action.

I always use the cubicles, Papa, like you told me when I was little; I always keep myself out of sight. But today I didn't lock the door; I left it slightly ajar and the flesh of my buttocks and thighs quivered as I pissed into the brown-stained bowl. When I had finished I stood still for a minute, listening to the plips and plops of water falling from pipe to cistern. Then I heard the urinal's automatic flush roar to life, and yanked hard on the chain in my cubicle.

The old man must have timed it to the second. As I pulled the door fully open and raised my eyes to the sink, I saw before me his thick penis and plump testicles, hanging from his fly like shiny wet fruit. Then, in the blink of an eye, he scooped them into the palm of his hand, tucked them away, zipped up his trousers, and turned to face the grimy mirror above the wash basin. He was quite masterly – in precise control of what and how much I saw. And then he just stood there, washing his hands, grinning at me from the mirror; inviting me to action.

There is, Papa, in the top left-hand cupboard of your wardrobe, an old shoe box. You took it down to show me once, when I was six or seven, and I've crept into your bedroom many times since to look inside. It contains an iron discus, attached to a bracelet, a small steel dagger and a sandalwood comb. I remember you laying them out before me on the carpet, then putting on an old pair of shorts and letting your long black hair down from your turban. You told me these five things made you a Sikh; a Singh; a lion. Then I clambered on to your back and screamed and giggled as you carried me around the house on all fours, up and down the stairs, twisting your head around, roaring at the floor, the walls, the windows, the ceiling.

I could have despised the old man easily, Papa. I could have kicked his brittle legs from under him, smashed his tired skull against the porcelain; he is a *dirty* old man, after all. But his grin was full of excitement, his eyes watery and gentle, and he was looking straight *at* me – not away from, not through, but straight *at* me. He warmed me, Papa. So, I shuffled up behind him, making ripples in the lake of piss and disinfectant. I laid my head on his shoulder and kissed the back of his wrinkled neck, and he closed his eyes and moaned lightly, and I wrapped my arms around his waist and pushed my hand down the front of his trousers. He led the way, then, back to the cubicle, where I twisted my supple limbs around his dry, papery ones, and unbuttoned his shirt to press my face into the warm nest of coarse white hair and scaly flesh.

After we had finished – hands sticky and pungent, shirts buttoned over cum-spattered stomachs – he stroked my cheek, whispered his wheezy thanks, and made to leave the cubicle. But I stopped him; grasping his bony shoulder and kissing his cracked lips, tracing my tongue around his teeth and gums. Then I took his hand, squeezed it tight, and we left the men's public toilets together, to sit on our bench and bask in the afternoon sun. I've no idea where he is now – he disappeared into the undergrowth a few minutes ago, to forage for I don't know what, but I'm sure he'll be back.

Perhaps, Papa, you could visit me, if you happened to be passing. I know you have business contacts in Croydon, and Brockwell Park is virtually on the way – just off the A23. You could bring the cardboard box from your wardrobe. You could bring Mama too – I would love to show her around the park – and we could have a picnic: French sticks and La Vache Qui Rit; Hula Hoops, Wagon Wheels and Tizer. I could even invite the old man. He *will* reappear from the undergrowth, I'm sure.

There is, Papa, absolutely no doubt in my mind that Granddad once owned the largest, most luxurious house in Sowhaddhi Khas, and that his gardens and farmland were amongst the most envied in District Ludhiana. I once saw a photograph of you standing on the veranda; there were peacocks on the lawn, I'm sure, and row upon row of Rolls-Royces and Harley Davidsons, proudly polished by the servants.

You could dig out that photo, Papa; it might be on top of the wardrobe in one of your dusty suitcases, or lost in a stack of yellowing forms. Then we could sit in a circle on the grass – you and Mama, the old man and I – and you could explain to us how it felt to stand on the veranda at Grandad's house in District Ludhiana, Punjab, India, on that day, when you were a child. I'm sure it would help me, Papa; I'm sure it would help us all.

Listen, Papa.

Listen, Papa: it would make our summer complete.

Ben Rice

RAMONE

I

Always lift a skull with both hands.

They come back to me,
These instructions from my
Dead uncle Ramone.

Big, heavy, Ramone.

Let me excavate him.
Let me ease him out of the grave.

II

Let me think of him clasping my head
And brushing the hair from my eyes

As if it is earth. The wonderful size
Of his fingers as they take hold of my jaw.

You scrape away the soil from the exterior,
Then cover with layers of aluminium foil,
Put it in polythene foam in a container
And then repack with acid-free tissue paper.

It's easy but you have to be thorough, see?

III

Umpteen stories my guardian whispered me
About who he'd turned up; how he'd find skeletons

Lying all warm in the clay, or just the fragments:
Happy their souls were in heaven.

One or two were *even older* than him.

And some of them *looked like they were copulating,
They were so close.*

Some of them were *tiny scraps of enamel.*

IV

*You have to be careful when lifting.
Or the ribs will crumble to dust.*

Ramone could tell me all about it
Now I was old enough.

It was like he was making a song
Out of old vertebrae

As he hitched me up on his back
And I swung on his collar bone.

And I worshipped the ground my Uncle Ramone
Dug in; he brought toothpicks home,

Plasterers' leaves and lollipop sticks
Which sometimes had jokes on.

V

I learnt them by rote.

The one about cremation pits,
About pyre debris and carbonised seeds.

I'd stay up late most nights
With my head full of coprolites,

With intestinal parasites,
Or a decaying patella.

What else do I remember?

That epiphyses look like small stones.

That remains of children are often confused
With small animals like rabbits and dogs.

That they are fragile as anything.

That bones of infants and adults should never be
Bagged together.

JIM

The night was close and it was time
To be putting up a bivvy;

There was a clearing to the west
Beside some bluebells; I found it.

There was shelter from the wind
And a curve of silver birches around it.

The grass was dry as a tortoise.

There was a small apple tree.
The moon wasn't up quite yet.

It was as safe as it would ever be,
We were tired as we would ever get.

There was a stream nearby,
And there were logs that could be chopped,

And Jim said: *No. We ain't stopping here*.

And everybody stopped.

Nobody breathed.

And then I said: 'Jim. Why not?
We can put up here for a night
And duck out by dawn. Easy as pie.'

And Jim looked round and said: *It don't smell right*.

And all you could hear was nothing

Until Jim spat on a nettle
And his saliva fizzed.

Then he slid out his knife from the sheath.
He picked up a windfall.
He looked at it hard.
He slashed it twice. He said:

Wherever this fucker lands
We make our base.

He leant back.
And hurled his arm across.

But the apple caught a branch, or something,

Because it rolled back straight
To the same place.

And I said nothing. And the others: nothing.

And there was a look on Jim's face
Like he wanted to stab me twice
And hurl me into the bracken.

Adam Thorpe

SAWMILL

THIS WAS HOW Mason lost his arm.

He told me about it himself in the sweep-out from Mahongo, after the Mba rebellion spilled down from the mountains. Those were gorilla rather than guerrilla mountains, as a matter of fact. Big hairy creatures with liquid eyes – very cautious, only violent at the last resort – lived in there amongst the big leaves and liana. The peaks were in cloud most of the time, and the ground underfoot squelched on the lower slopes, where the rifts and folds were full of fog and a heat clammier even than Mahongo's. Then you'd get keen types going up in a T-shirt and almost freezing to death at night, soaked to the skin by a precipitation that was chill and perpetual.

From my window you could see the peaks beyond the forest, rising up into a lid of cloud. I'd found an old copy of Stanley's book on the Congo in the Club's cupboard, and read what he had to say about equatorial Africa (copying out the long words I hadn't heard before: I was educating myself). He said the light was solemn and frigid, and made the bush look flat, as if the equator's sun knew no angles, shining down on the mid-belt of the planet through a gauze of dust or of moisture. He said it made the bush look merciless, primal, pre-human. I couldn't see this; to me the light was part of the difference that Africa made to me. She made me grow against the harshness and the luxuriance of her, and the light was both those things. I mentioned this once to the DO's assistant, when the show was on the road and passing

270

through Mahongo; he was an educated chap, and reckoned that Stanley saw in Africa what he couldn't face up to in himself.

'What's that?' I asked, still in my eager period.

'A total lack of human sympathy. Complete egotism. An unpleasant streak of sadism.'

I nodded. That was the first time I had ever thought of Stanley as anything but heroic. But Africa does that to her white visitors; it draws out of you what you had never even looked at back home.

That's why I'm not so sure about Mason's story any more. It sounds like a justification, a type of excuse. But I'll tell it to you anyway, because I've started.

Mason was by now the manager at our newest sawmill. He was in his forties. He'd taken a long time to get to this position. He'd come out very young – at least twenty years before independence – as a mechanic's mate; turning bolts, greasing gears, steel-brushing rusted bits. This kept him busy, as metal no sooner touches this climate than it starts to corrode. He was already a drinker, and spent most of his free time down at the English Club in Kasa, the next stop on the tooth-loosening dirt track coming south out of Mahongo. You know what they say about us: wherever there's an Englishman, you'll find a garden; wherever there are two Englishmen, you'll find a club. Mason started this club with Jack Mole, the sawmill's chief engineer. They both hailed from Matlock, by sheer chance, and had been brought up two streets from each other without knowing it. That club was a kind of glorified Scotch Club, no more than an old dilapidated shack from the coffee-growing era with some tatty old wicker-chairs they'd filched from somewhere: but it was legendary all the way to the coast for its conviviality and high stakes on the gaming table. It was finally closed by orders of the sawmill's manager, after Mason had lost his young *bibi* to Jack Mole at bridge. The manager could stomach money being gambled, but not people – not even pagans, because he was a young, up-to-date type. Mason's attitude was as cold and hard as Stanley's: these people were there to be used, and if they weren't used they were in the way. One day he struck a black worker several times over the head with a bamboo cane for some minor infringement, and the worker sued him, because suing people is as normal as eating out there. Mason was moved to another sawmill, nearer Mahongo, owned by the same company. Because this was a bigger affair, he was quite happy.

Why wasn't he sacked?

Because he was never sick, never wobbly one week out of every month, like the rest of us; took twenty minutes off for lunch to our two hours; could repair anything that moved, even without the necessary spare parts (which were usually sent out late or got stolen on the way); and never lost a certain cheery grin, even in the rainy season. Now and then, when something finally got to him, he would crack – disappear for a day or two with a couple of bottles of Scotch, or get violent. To the company, that was better than the sluggishness, the gloom and the nonchalance, the plop-plop-plop of the mind rotting down, that afflicted the rest of us half the time.

I was the company's junior clerk, at the time Mason was transferred. Gleaming wet behind the ears, fresh from a bank in Chepstow, I was already training locals to take over my job. It was a strange era: there were all these nationalist movements, tribal movements, peasant movements, communist movements and so forth, which we were told was part of the process towards self-government. It felt like anarchy to me, and I feared what would happen when we left. But the clever university-types kept quoting the UN Charter of '45 and rabbiting on about democratisation and such things at parties (when they weren't fuming about something or other), so I shut up.

The company had its concession off the Government, which was by now an Executive Council with an African prime minister and ministers, so we had to go along with the general policy. We assumed that this concession (and we had it for thirty years) would be transferred intact once proper self-government had happened; there was so much virgin forest at this time, it felt like we were nibbling at its hem. There was room for everyone. Felling the bush meant clear-felling for farming-land: it was all part of the civilising process. We were helping the natives; even when a road was cut, it had squatters either side of it, cutting a mile deeper in to plant their millet. We didn't throw them off, but we took the timber. What I can't stand about ecologists is their hypocrisy: do *they* leave the brambles and nettles standing in their back gardens? Five thousand years ago, Britain was a great wodge of forest from end to end; the trees started at each cliff-edge, and met in the middle without a break. One great wood, as dark and humid as the rain-forest, if not as hot. God knows how it was ever cleared with nothing but antler-picks and brawn. Getting rid of a big tree, roots and all, is one of the hardest things a man can do, even with a caterpillar tractor and a donkey-winch. They got rid of millions, and it was just as wet then as it is now, so they can't have fired them. Perhaps they had Mason.

Whatever, without that great feat our island wouldn't be where it is now. And who are we to deny those fruits to Africans? If most of the areas we cleared out there weren't, in the end, farmed, but left for the rain to wash away, was it our fault?

After spending seven years on that sawmill, ending up as its chief mechanic, the miracle happened: a brand-new site was established seventy-five miles west of Mahongo, where the forest had more than its fair share of ebony, mansonia, yellow-wood or West African teak, red-heart, and some big mahogany. There were no villages in that sector, to speak of. And Mason was appointed manager.

He was the only one who could take it on. The place was in a gloomy rift on the lower slopes, teeming with tsetse, and shrouded most of the time in fog. It was too wet to do any kiln-drying, let alone air-drying, and some of us wondered why they couldn't just pull out the logs and have them sawn down our way; but the powers-that-be decided that they would be trucked out of there as boards. Later, I learned that the whole project was Mason's idea in the first place, shared with a visiting director (Bob Clifford, I think) over a beer in the Club late one night. Mason had driven over there one weekend, on a recce, and had climbed up above the mist. He could see the mahoganies sticking up out of the white, rolling sea like the grey masts of drowned ships. It was a beautiful sight, he said: he felt like he'd stumbled on gold.

Real gold – and diamonds – were being stumbled on, deeper into the interior; but we were timber men. The mining men were different. They were saggy and stubbled, spending their time scratching about in the dirt (or ordering others to). There was a pecking order, and timber came above gold or diamonds, and those came above rutile or manganese. That's the way we saw it, anyway. There is nothing in the mining line to compare with a big tree slowly crashing down out of the sky, letting the sun in like a blade.

All Mason's men were black, and pagan. He liked it that way: he could boss them about, rib them, chide them in the way he reckoned they understood and appreciated. They were good, well-trained men, because Mason had learned his stuff off the Canadians – huge, hard-drinking lumberjacks the company hired in the early days to teach the ropes. He not only practically built the place single-handed, it was said, but hand-picked his team. Keeping the Christian ones out also kept the missionaries out. Mason's view of missionaries was unprintable.

But his real secret, I reckon, was to keep his cheery grin glued to his face, whatever – even when he was screaming at someone. You know what the Africans say about the crocodile? They say it's the only animal that smiles when it kills. They called Mason *Pa Croc*, informally. But Pa is a term of respect, and the croc is worshipped when it's not being speared or shot, so Mason liked his nickname. Even his teeth, on the odd occasion he came down to Mahongo and met me for a beer, seemed to have grown bigger and yellower.

The timber that came out of there was stupendous: it was all the lorries' suspension could do not to crack under its weight, but that was partly because it was still green. He liked to drive the odd lorry himself, to Mahongo; then he'd hand

over to the white tough perched next to him, who'd take it all
the way to the company's big air-drying yard on the coast,
next to the port at Korondi. They were incredible, those
drivers: hulks who'd keep going twelve hours over roads
more pot-holes than surface, splattered head to foot in
copper-coloured mud or caked in dust (depending on the
season), arriving at the port with a thirst for beer and whores
sufficient to knock a sailor out of the running, plunging into
the thundering ocean for a wash then sleeping in their cabs
under the coconut-palms like babies. We trusted them purely,
even as we feared them. Mason knew some of those old
trucks from his earliest days, and liked to have them banging
and jolting under him occasionally, the timber stretched out
for an infinity behind his neck. Mahogany and red-heart and
mansonia and ebony, barked and sawn and gleaming under
their chains, smelling sweet and rich and full. Our own two
operations (I was head clerk for the whole circuit, by now)
were pulling out saplings in comparison. Mason's team were
clear-cutting up a valley said to be the haunt of a giant gorilla
twenty feet tall. Looking at what came bouncing on the back
of those Fodens down Mahongo's main street, I could well
believe it.

'It's like the nicest, fattest, softest *bibi* you've ever had,' he
said to me one time, under the crooked fan at the Union Jack
Club. His big, red face (the only brown he ever acquired was
off the trees' juice) shone with pleasure as much as perspiration. There were leaves in his hair, thinned and paled from
the bright ginger mop even I remembered, and the hairs on
his forearms were white with sawdust. He's a completely
satisfied man, I thought – in a land of chronic frustration,
sickness, and resentment. Africa doesn't wear him down: it
plumps him up. He draws her into his squat, square body,
and feeds off her greedy juices as mosquitoes feed off the rest
of us. (I never knew him once to get bitten by anything except
the touring DO's pet spaniel.)

I smiled, and asked him how, without real women, he kept
the team happy up there in that God-forsaken place. He told
me he'd introduced a recreational pursuit from Derbyshire

pubs – the Derbyshire pubs of his youth, I suppose. There were lots of forest rats in the sawmill camp, like there'd been lots of rats in Matlock, big ones from the barns. You fastened a live rat to a hook in the middle of a round table, giving it just enough run not to slip off the edge. Someone tied your hands behind your back. The spectators then laid wagers on whether you could kill the rat inside so many minutes, using nothing but your teeth.

They kept the rats in cages, up in the sawmill. This classified them as pets, and somehow appeased the more fearful pagans, who were afraid they might be haunted by the rat's spirit or double or whatever. Every Saturday night they had a rat massacre, he said, and everyone's mouth was bright with blood. They drank beer, but not too much. A drunk man would have his nose bitten off. You drank enough to give you courage. Mason said that his name, Pa Croc, was more than justified by his performance.

'Do you have any fights between the men?' I asked, feeling a little shaken.

'That's the point of it,' he said. 'Keeps us happy and peaceful all week, like a lengthy bash with a top-quality whore. Takes the lid off.'

My own experience of the whores in Mahongo or on the coast was slight, but if it involved a bed you were lucky. By now I had a native girl, a *bibi*, so my seedy days were over. She was exceptionally beautiful, to my mind, and her skin was more indigo than black; she stayed in a hut behind my shack of a house and came to me at night. If it had been acceptable, socially, I might have married her. But I was keen to move up in those circles and had my eye on a colleague's sister, who'd come out to visit him recently. She was called Gillian, and was as white and cool as the inside of a cucumber, which for some reason made my blood-pressure rise in the romantic way. We wrote to each other, anyway, and she was impressed by my long words, words like 'assiduously' and 'attenuating' and 'antithesis' (I logged them in my pocket-book, until the ants got it). I took her out to the films on my two-yearly leaves, just about getting to the petting stage – but she didn't know about my *bibi*. She married someone called Dudley Baugh in the end, when I was about to come home and propose with the help of a malachite brooch set in freshly-minted gold. When I heard, I chucked it into the smelly creek where the mangroves start. Propitiation, they call it.

It was from my *bibi* that I heard the story of Mason's arm, that's why I mention her. I had got her brother a job as a cook up in the camp, and he eventually told her the truth. If it wasn't for certain other facts, I'd have assumed it was an ordinary accident: limbs, or bits of limbs, were lost like shillings on Club Bridge Night amongst the sawmill operators. In those days, we were more lax about safety regs, I suppose. It was all part of the harshness, the luxuriance, as fever and the bloody runs were. I'd been hit by malaria five times, despite being careful with the chloroquine, and I looked older than my thirty-odd, by now. The joke went that you lost weight twice in our company – once with fever, and once by having a bit lopped off, so you had to make it up with your belly. Another joke: this worker sits too close to the head saw and loses a buttock. Big Chief Barney 'Barking' Soames (the top man at HQ for years) comes up just after and wonders why the feeder's stopped running. The manager says: 'I'm getting behind with my orders.' We thought up lots like that over our beers and whiskies, but those are the only two I can bring to mind, at present.

Odd reports were coming out of Mason's mill. For a few months, the logs and planks had diminished. One week had passed without anything at all, and then a truck had arrived with a few lengths of poor-quality, warped *musonga* banging about on the flat-bed. The driver reckoned that there were still enough big trees left in the rift to keep a saw busy for years, and that the forest track was in as good a condition as any track can be expected to be in a wet equatorial belt. But the machinery was in poor shape – at least, the head saw, the main circular one, kept breaking down, the feeder repeatedly jammed, the generator expired twice while he was there and even the gas cylinder in the kitchen-house had blown up (my *bibi*'s brother was unhurt).

I asked him how Mason was taking this.

'Badly,' he replied. 'His cheery grin's still on him, but I think he's going to crack.'

'Why do you think he's going to crack?'

'He told me to fetch him a white goat. It's got to be white. All the goats up there, the ones that haven't been eaten by leopards, are black-and-white or brown. Funny voice, he had, when he said it. Like he was somewhere else.'

This was certainly *not* a sign that he was about to crack, if the mechanical faults were sabotage, as we reckoned they must be. Mason knew what he was doing: he was appeasing the gods and spirits of the forest he was cutting down – in other words, appeasing his own men. All our sawmills had been through this fairly messy business, before they started operating properly, or when a big saw was replaced. The BOB, or Bloody Old Baptism, we called it. An albino goat was tied on to the feeder and fed alive on to the saw. To hear the poor animal bleat like pity as the feeder jolted it along, and then explode into blood and gore as the saw's teeth met its stomach, made me feel sick, frankly. It didn't even have time to scream. When I first came out, the DO would stay away from the ceremony. Now, with all this Africanisation business, he'd feel it incumbent on him to attend, his immaculate whites far enough away not to get spotted. The DO's pretty little wife came once, and surprised us by taking a photograph instead of fainting. 'A fascinating traditional custom,' she called it. I called it barbarity, but not to her face.

The albino goat was sent up after a couple of weeks of official faffing about (YCHA, or You Can't Hurry Africa), and then there was silence. I was asked to pay a visit, as the circuit clerk in charge of accounts and a personal friend of Mason's. I should have looked forward to it, but I didn't. I wasted a couple of days when my works Land Rover broke down after fifty miles and had to be towed back by a passing truck. The road was pretty bad – it was mid-May, and the first big drench had hit us – but the Land Rover made it a second time. What was worrying us was that Mason should have been sending down all the green stock he'd pulled out for the last two months, before it started to warp and the summer downpour made the road impassable, at least for laden trucks. Instead, there had been next to nothing since January.

I arrived in a more than light drizzle, and actually felt chilled. I hadn't realised it was so high above sea-level. The valley stretched away and up like a fold out of Hell: coppery-green gloom, full of writhing mist, a great ruck in the moss that was the far tops of a million trees so high that it made you giddy when you were underneath them, looking up. I thought of big black gorillas skulking unseen in there, and shivered under my umbrella. Running across the puddles to the main block – no more than the standard long tin shed on a concrete base – I thought I saw something white skipping about beyond the head saw's housing. Well, if he hadn't sacrificed the goat, the spanners would go on being dropped in the works. But I couldn't spot a single worker. Not one. The place looked abandoned. This actually frightened me in some way. I'd expected to come up here into a welcoming bustle and screech of activity. Instead, there were soggy hills of sawdust, countless strewn branches, and rain-blackened logs casually thrown around the place, along with some green slabs and boards that were starting to writhe, they were so moist.

It looked as if something really extraordinary had happened: Mason had gone to seed.

I would have been surprised if he, of all people, had started this place with a team of pagans without baptising it in the native manner, but the ceremony hadn't been reported and none of us had been notified, let alone the DO's office. It had been going great guns for two years, this mill, until around January. The head saw was the original one. So it should have been. Even this climate couldn't do much to that principal item of equipment, if it was kept properly oiled and greased – and all ours sharpened and cleaned themselves on the wood. These were the thoughts going through my head as I found the shelter of the main block. But if that white glimpsed thing was the goat, they didn't add up. Nothing added up – but that was not an unusual situation for Africa, even for the chief clerk in charge of accounts. As long as Mason hadn't run off into the bush, or been carved up by the insurgents who were already active, so we were told, a hundred miles to the north of here, I'd presumably have the adding-up done for me by the man himself.

I couldn't find him.

The generator was still happily humming, which reminded me of the German helmet I'd found rocking by the chess-board during our lot's advance through Normandy some ten years earlier. So I radioed HQ.

'I know it sounds what you might call preposterous, but I can't find Mason.'

'Can't find him?'

'I think he might have gone bush-happy for a bit. He's done it before. The trouble is, there's no one else here but the albino goat. If he does come back, he'll have to hire a whole team and recommence.'

HQ were both furious and heartbroken, of course. By the time I'd made it back with a raging fever that sprang on to me halfway along that bloody awful road, all sticky clay and brackish puddles brimming into rivulets you could drown a kid in, they were elated. He'd radioed at dusk, just as I was staggering into the mission hospital on the Mahongo road for a shot. (I'd driven, there and back, in a single day, one hundred and fifty-five miles, give or take a pot-hole the size of my bed.)

He'd cleared up a sticky matter, he claimed. Or he was about to clear it up, in a couple of days, at dawn. There was no question of getting another team: his team were all there, present and correct. HQ probably doubted the tightness of my screws for a moment, even before they knew the state of my temperature, because they double-checked with him that the place had been left empty. He agreed that it had, but only for the day. If the timber wasn't all delivered by the time the storms were on us, and the road was a stream (if there was a road left at all), he'd offer his resignation.

I'd sweated out my malarial bout (brought on by the camp's chill, I suppose), by sundowner-time the following evening, but was still a touch wobbly when, a couple of days later, the rumour circulated in the office, confirmed in the Club, that Mason had been brought into the mission hospital with his arm cut off at the elbow. A rough tourniquet of oily wipes and a bandage of same had saved him from bleeding to death, but he wasn't in a fit state to be talked to after the bone-rattling journey in one of his own little bush-wagons, thrashed nigh to its component parts by a terrified chief mechanic. The oil had acted as a disinfectant (Mason was legendarily careless about his medical equipment, and had nothing more than a packet of Elastoplast and some Epsom's beyond the resident stack of chloroquine), and he was up and about within a matter of days. He was pretty jolly, given his trauma and permanent handicap, but his cheery grin had changed to a sort of knowing smile. It made me wonder if he hadn't got his own supply of hashish. He hadn't had that sort of quiet knowingness before: a cheery vigour, yes, and what the supply manager at HQ referred to as Mason's Mania (meaning an incredible ability to work in torpid heat without wiping one's brow, let alone dropping – usually the first sign that the 'bitch' had got you, and you were about to go bonkers), but not that deep sort of knowingness, not that eerie kind of quiet smile.

Sure enough, even before he was back at his post a week or two later, the timber started rolling in. By the time the rains were playing the devil's tattoo on our tin roofs ten times over each week, the bulk of it was stacked in the kilns and my accounts were looking very rosy, thank you. Now, I assumed that Mason had done something really extraordinary: I assumed – and my version took the Club by stealth, rather than storm, so I had it told back to me by seedy old bores like Bill Price the cocoa trader, or 'Ambling' Ambrose from the manganese-ore outfit past the scruffy lean-tos on the edge of town – that Mason had baptised the blade with his own blood, had sacrificed his own limb. Incredible as this seemed to anyone who didn't know Mason, my version was mostly met by modest nods from those who did. It turned him into something truly legendary.

Then my *bibi* received a visit from her brother just before Christmas (all the workers had a couple of weeks' leave a year), and my version was proven quite dull, compared to the reality. By cobbling together her brother's account, and dovetailing it with Mason's own story (told to me while fleeing Mahongo in poor old Ambrose's Humber Snipe), I've reached a pretty reliable explication that adds up in all essential details.

This, then, is how Mason lost his arm.

There was a huge grey mahogany in the centre of the valley, easily the tallest, reaching up for the light and, once there, carrying on for another few floors so it ended up towering over the rest. It was the big cherry, was how Mason put it. It was the big prize, one for the timber-trade's record books. It made you giddy just looking up at it, and took two minutes to circle – running. There was a snag: the locals – there were a few pigmy-like locals, scattered about in the hills, in their tatty little clusters of huts, without even a loincloth to their name – told one of the workers that this tree was sacred to them. Mason had clear-cut right up to its outlying branches. Everything was ready: the chains, the saws, the ropes, the vehicles, the grabs, men, the lot. He'd heard rumours, of course, for some weeks, that there might be a lot of palaver if he cut this particular tree, but he'd been confronted by this nervous type of superstitiousness before, and had overridden it by a mixture of guile and sheer white-man's will.

Then the locals appeared from the trees. They had their sorcerer with them, dressed in a devil's mask that came down to his knees, who actually spat through the mouth-hole at Mason before going into this mad, wild dance around the mahogany. The workers fled, and since the pigmy types were armed with poison-tipped arrows, Mason retreated too.

He waited a few days, clear-felled right round the tree and

for a mile into the tangle beyond – and then offered his men a deal: if they cut the mahogany, he would protect them with his own magic. He produced a wad of greasy old pound notes from his wallet and waved them in their faces. Greed vied with superstition, and greed won (as it always does). Of course, he had to add to the cash-till magic with a touch of indigenous stuff, some home-made mumbo-jumbo involving a strangled cockerel and mashed palm-leaves and milk, but it was the extra pay that did the trick.

Very early, just before dawn, the air still chilly and the mist just stirring from the ground or the air or wherever it comes from, the team crept out to the big tree, tied the chains and set the teeth of the biggest two-man handsaw against it. Not using a mechanised saw was Mason's wheeze; he didn't want to be a poison-quilled porcupine. But just in case the locals noticed the tip thrashing about, or a sudden absence of their 'steeple' (as Mason himself described it), he set a few workers about as guards, clutching rusty old Lee Enfields sent up from the company store.

The double handsaw squealed and squeaked, others took over, it jammed, Mason fixed the problem without even swearing, the tree moaned and groaned and shivered, then fell down with the most colossal crash that made the ground bounce under their shoes like rubber. Its resident bird-life fled in great flocks, leaving only a few multi-coloured feathers floating down. What seemed like a hundred screeching monkeys had leapt as it fell, finding no nearby branches and so mostly breaking their necks – or finding a softer landing on some of the workers, who screeched likewise, picked themselves up, and fled. Caterpillars, moths, spiders the size of plates, armies of ants – these all spilled out in an instant panic, causing consternation among the men. A little bush-baby was picked up, petrified with terror, clutching Mason's thumb with its miniature mitts. (He kept it as a souvenir, but it died a couple of days later.) No locals appeared, however, and the tree was cut into lengths, to be hauled away.

The saw jammed. The chains broke. The biggest caterpillar tractor steamed to a stop. A donkey-winch somehow slipped into a swampy patch, bubbling under for good. By twilight, in a dense rainy fog, only one section had made it over the clear-cut's churn of mud to the stack. The next day, a bolt behind the gang-saw flew off and practically brained one of the mechanics. The feeder jammed on a perfectly ordinary load of red-heart and then, when started up again, smoked like a charcoal fire. Three of Mason's best workers were suddenly crippled by yaws, and the chief hauler appeared to have yellow jack. The camp overseer was bitten by a green mamba and was only saved by prompt action from his boss. Then the gas-bottle blew up, setting the kitchen alight, while my *bibi*'s brother was stirring the *fu-fu* in the yard. On the third day, the generator clicked and gave out, plunging the camp into darkness. The paraffin lamps were extinguished in a bone-chilling downpour at midnight, some actually losing their glass to thermal shock. The black clouds broke dramatically and revealed the most enormous full moon above the nearest peak, which loomed in the shape of a vast and hairy man – a gorilla, Mason thought, complete with gleaming eyes from some effect of moonlight on the canopy's leaves, or the rocks beyond the tree-line.

The workers knew what it was, of course. But you can't put a felled tree back. As Mason himself said, it's like sticking back a limb, or going back in time. Two, three, four centuries, perhaps more. He found himself waking up at night, sweating like a pig behind his mosquito-net, out of a real corker of a nightmare involving spiders, leopards, and gorillas with devil-masks. A storm cracked over them like the sky was a giant nut, and blew the tin roof off the saw-housing; the tin roof beheaded the camp mongrel and embedded itself in the mahogany log. Lightning lit up the scene and workers claimed to have spotted blood flowing from the log's bark and rippling towards them.

Basically, the whole site was a seethe of panic. Mason's very good in these situations: he offered to cleanse the place with a sacrifice. His resident medicine man consulted his oracle and reckoned that only the flesh and blood of something white would do. Mason nodded benignly and ordered up the albino goat. The goat arrived but on spending its last night in the compound, mysteriously acquired yellow patches on its flanks. The other resident soothsayer consulted his grains again and reckoned that only something black would do. The first agreed (he must have been in a bad way), and added that this something would only be found in the forest. Mason is a great layer of traps as well as an excellent hunter, and gambled that he could come back with something suitable. He went out to where he had set them a couple of days before, followed by the whole team, who were by now convinced the place was full of spirits intent on their destruction. That was, then, the day I arrived and found the mill and the camp deserted.

In the first trap they found the paw of a mongoose. It was blackish, but neither medicine man would accept it as satisfactory. In the second there was nothing. In the third, set quite deep into the uncut gloom, there was a small, black, hairy lump which whimpered. It was a young gorilla – not much more than a baby, caught by its foot. The workers reckoned it had been delivered by the mother, in obedience to the forest spirits, or the ghost of the mahogany tree itself. They were eager for their pounds, of course. The resident sorcerers nodded excitedly. It was black, and might be the child of the giant hairy man, who was in turn the mountain's child. Mason looked up, through a slash in the canopy, at the peak. A rare ray of sun had lit it. Its dark, bare crest had turned golden. He carried the whimpering bundle himself back to the camp.

'If I hadn't had to wait until the stipulated dawn, I'd still have the one to go with him,' he said, waving his right hand about, when he was telling me all this.

The Humber had stopped in a cloud of dust caused by a stream of trucks and mammy-wagons temporarily snarled up in our mass exodus. People were clinging to the sides, or on top of bundles and suitcases and other people where logs or cocoa-sacks usually went, or gossips on their way to market. Mason leaned out of the window to shout: great barrel chest, hairy shoulders, singlet black with exertion all the way down the spine. I suddenly found him repulsive – maybe because I was moving up in the world, and wearing a club tie even at the worst of times, which was now. I was fleeing Mahongo with nothing more than a spare set of clothes and my accounts books on the back-seat, but I had donned my tie. That back-seat was where Ambrose had had his heart attack in front of the Friendly Stores just the day before, when someone a few yards off had fired the old German cannon at the mountains. Now he was trussed in a sack in the boot, for God's sake, already smelling to high heaven. (We hadn't wanted to leave him there, to be kicked and mauled, and we couldn't find the time or the spades to bury him up in the cemetery.)

We got going again. I was waiting for the horrible climax. I like gorillas. I like baby animals. So the thought of a baby gorilla sliding towards that big saw made me want to throw up, frankly. Mason didn't like animals in the same way as I did. He only liked their skins.

All that night, the baby gorilla whimpered. It didn't sleep: its eyes stared at Mason mournfully in the glow of the paraffin, and Mason stared back. He talked to it, in the end. He tried to explain. It wiped its mouth and held its injured foot, which Mason had dressed and bandaged as if it was his own. The creature whimpered and clung to a blanket in the corner of the room.

'Funny thing was,' Mason said, 'it didn't *accuse*, if you know what I mean. It didn't *accuse*. It was just frit. It didn't blame me for anything. It understood, see, the whys and wherefores of life. Dog eats dog. And the other way round.'

I snorted at his familiar joke, realising in a flash Mason's true secret: he was terrified of being blamed for anything. Anything. It was his one great weakness, but he'd turned it inside out, into a strength.

The next day, they tied the baby gorilla to the head-end of a heavyweight log of yellow-wood at the top of the feeder-table and started the rollers going without a hitch. Things were already beginning to function normally, in anticipation. Mason was hoping, for the first time in his life, that something would go wrong with the head saw, but it didn't. It started circling smoothly and cleanly, building up speed in that majestic way, inevitable somehow, like the roll of the planet on its diurnal round and so on. The baby gorilla, just clear of the rollers, was moving slowly and steadily towards the saw's teeth, almost as if it was dragging the log behind it. The workers watched in a semicircle, some of them close enough to be splashed. This was very big medicine. This was the biggest medicine any of them had ever seen. Then, from out of that glossy little bundle of black fur, those eyes peeped and found Mason's own. Huge eyes, liquid, much bigger than a human's. The creature was five feet from the spinning metal, by now; the eyes carried on gazing at him, as they had done all night in his room.

What made Mason run forward at that point was that the thing didn't know what was about to happen to it. It might have been on its way to its mother, for all it knew. That's what the eyes told him: he was delivering the most innocent of innocents to its bloody awful end.

He grabbed it about a foot and a half away from the table and hung on. The workers were shouting at him. The rollers of the feeder slipped a bit then pushed the log against Mason's weight and strength. He'd somehow lifted the animal a bit but the rope tying it was biting into its fur and flesh as the log inched forward. It was crying out now, in pain from the rope. Mason screamed for a knife but no one could hear him over the saw's screech. The big log's tonnage was too much even for him. He held the baby gorilla tight and watched the rope on the feeder inch forward and fray against the spinning blade. The instant he felt it give, he yanked the animal away and dropped it on the ground. There was blood splashing and spurting over his boots and over its fur. He swore and screamed from sadness more than horror, but the baby gorilla looked up at him, got to its feet, and clutched his leg. There was nothing wrong with it at all.

He saw a hand and forearm on the ground, being pissed on by golden sawdust as the log carried on through. The arm's elbow-end was emptying its blood into the mud, like a tipped jug. It was a white arm. His own arm shot to where its partner should have been, hanging at his side, and found a mess of stump.

'Like putting your fingers into warm porridge,' he said. 'Like, if you were being a bit original as a kid, and playing up, you put your fingers into your oats of a morning. I don't remember much, after that. I found myself in my bed. First thing I asked was: where is it? Na arm cut off, some idiot said. No, I mean the gorilla, the little hairy boy. Dat small-small beef done be over deer, they said. He was, too. In the corner. Right as rain. We had a gingerly cuddle, he and I. Apart from his tics, he were like a big black teddy, only softer.'

'What did you do with him?'

'He was called Small-small, by the time I got back. Having the time of his little life. Stayed with me a bit, until he was old enough to be delivered back to the bush. Sad day.'

'You were trusting. I mean, of your men. Lamb to slaughter, I'd have thought.'

'I had said to them: if anything happens to this little man, while I'm away being mended, you no get your dash, dat clear? I thought they'd have another go at laying this curse, you see. Oh no, they said, na small-small beef done be safe too much, Pa.'

'That amazes me, Mason.'

'It did me, too, until I passed the head saw, with all that blood on it. My blood. Pa Croc's blood.'

He was quiet for a bit, then he said:

'Big medicine for a big tree, see. Dog eats dog. And the other way round.'

'Not quite, Mason,' I replied, smiling at him through the red swirl kicked up off the road by the fleeing populace. 'Not quite. Not that time. Most times, but not that time.'

I expected him to turn round and edge his mouth into its usual grin. But he stayed looking straight forward, with his mouth turned down, the skin of his face veneered in dust.

Propitiation, I thought. Propitiation.

Well, we're all in need of it, at times.

Oliver Reynolds

SONNETS FOR HELEN

You are French. You're fourteen with long red hair.
  As we make love
In a Louis Quatorze chair, all you wear
  Is one black glove

And a silver chain singing at your neck,
  Jingling sunlight and air
As we sway to Putney on the top deck:
  'Deux allers à l'Homme Vert.'

Les Champs-Élysées is the Fulham Road.
  Our bus fills with the crack
Of myrtle branches on the roof, their fragrant load
  Of incense and arrack.

We've brought Valentine's Day to November.
  London's asphalt orchard
Reflowers again as I remember
  My name for you: Orchid.

Mme de Maintenon, the past is now,
  Blaze and ember
As indivisible as Camembert and cow,
  January and December.

Quand vous serez bien vieille, I'll still call.
  My collar furred with snow,

My stick canoodling with yours in the hall,
  I'll be ardent, if slow.

We'll take tea, then each other, by the hour.
  You are the pliant girl
I keep in la Rue de la Tombe-Issoire
  (Every swine has his pearl).

The bus snorts, shudders, stops dead in its tracks.
  Looking down we could swear
As the sun dapples us with dots and flecks
  The road is a river.

Our conductor speaks: 'It's not the Thames or the Seine
  Or the light playing tricks.
Look at it now, and then never again.
  It's the Styx.

Here's your change.' He puts pennies on our eyes.
  It starts to rain.
'Plus ça change . . .' is French for 'Surprise, surprise.'
  I blink, in vain.

Blubbing like kids, all the passengers stand.
  We remove our berets.
Tears sprout on our cheeks – cataracts of sand,
  Tell-tale berries.

You're English. You're my age. Your hair is brown and short.
  I take your hand.
After rain and river, blindness and sight,
  We reach dry land.

I am drenched with memory. Time and place
  Are this night,
This bed and the smell of tea-tree oil on your face.
  You turn off the light.

Silver charms whisper – your Star of David
  And your lucky turtle.
Then whiffs of heaven ... I must have drifted ...
  Eucalyptus ... Myrtle.

Michael Dibdin

LOVER PIE

(Amant en croûte)

This age-old dish is admittedly time-consuming, but for sheer satisfaction and that personal touch this is a case where the end amply justifies the means. Most of the work is in the preparation, and those for whom time is at a premium – or who are just plain squeamish – may prefer to leave this to a professional.

Slaughtering

According to tradition, the lover should be stuck in the throat during the act of sexual union. These days, however, many people will prefer to avoid the suffering this may cause, not to mention the mess, by shooting the victim with a small-bore rifle while he or she is taking a shower. As in the traditional method, the carcass is thus stripped and ready for butchering, but with the added advantage that it can be bled and skinned with a minimum of fuss and bother.

Butchering

For detailed instructions on this complex and fascinating subject, consult the section on pigs in any reliable text on animal husbandry. The essential difference is that our carcass needs to be not just scraped but skinned. The basic steps are:
1. Bleeding (set aside about a pint)
2. Skinning
3. Hanging
4. Jointing

Preparation

Having slaughtered your lover, prepare a stock. For this you

will need:
  The skull, split
  The skin
  The hands and feet (set aside the nails)
  The lungs and intestines, thoroughly cleaned
  The bones
  1 cup fat, rendered
  1 pt blood
  A bouquet garni
  Salt and pepper to taste

Over high heat, burn the meat in half the fat, together with the bones and skin. Transfer to a stock pot, add the blood and seasoning, cover with cold water and simmer slowly for 4–5 hours partially covered, skimming off the scum and bile as it rises. Strain and reduce to a quarter of its volume.

While the stock is simmering, sauté the remaining meat (except for the heart, brain, liver and kidneys) in the rest of the fat. Leave to cool, then chop finely and pack into a large pie dish. Make a ring in the centre with the raw diced liver and kidneys. Within it, place the heart and brain, whole.

Moisten the meat with the reduced stock and cover with a lid of puff pastry. Decorate the rim with the finger and toe-nails and set the eyes together at the centre. Bake in a moderate oven until the pastry is crisp and golden-brown and the eyes feel tender when pricked with a fork.

Serving

Traditionally, red wine is served with a male lover and white with a female, but feel free to experiment – there are no hard and fast rules in these matters! Should your lover have been born in a good year, a particularly thoughtful gesture is to wash him or her down with a fine claret or Sauterne of that vintage, decanted a month in advance and served piping hot with a maraschino cherry.

The pie itself may be eaten either hot or cold, squatting naked on the floor moaning 'I love you madly oh my love you'll never know how much I love you I could eat you up my darling I want you inside me right now every last inch of you,' etc. Tear any remaining food from the dish with your hands and smear it liberally about your body. Then stick the rifle up your arse and pull the trigger.

Serves one right.

Michael Hofmann

LEWIS HOLLOW ROAD

The walls – sloping like a tent's – of pre-slathered
   plasterboard
depending from a single great beam, the slushy track
   outside a bobsleigh run
negotiated by the neighbours' four-wheel drives at odd
   hours,
the black metamorphic bulk of the treetrunk through the
   night,
icicles dripping and growing and shrinking and forking
   like Tirpitz's beard,

the outside in in the form of quills and feathers and
   stingray bones and pine cones,
Indian burial chamber bric-à-brac, the six-foot rattler in
   the mudroom,
a Spanish guitar and a Dustbuster hanging together like a
   yellow-grey Braque,
the alphabetical books at rest on many shelves and the
   unsleeping regard
of Auden and Burroughs on postcards, the sacred monsters
   of the place,

gods of incompatible religions, ourselves under a couple of
   blankets,
one of them notionally electric, sometimes knotted
   together in brief sleep,
as often each hugging his edge of the bed, lying three or

four bodies apart,
wrestling with ourselves and our doubts and miseries, and
   you asking,
awkwardly, unexpectedly, à propos of nothing much: 'Do
   you think I'm real?'

NIGHT TRAIN

In the half-compartment
set aside for the handicapped
I crossed my feet on the battered
fire-extinguisher,

the grandfather, maybe,
of my shaken can of County
foaming at the widget,

and sat remembering the dowdily
glaring train back from Guildford,
feeling parched and let down
after our reading,

the series of benighted stops
where no one got on
– much less got off –

at one of which, at least,
I put it to you, not joking,
though you weren't to know that then,
that we might elope together

somewhere in Wild West Surrey,
wo sich die Füchse gute Nacht sagen,
before we could reach

Suburbiton and Esher
Welcomes Careful Drivers,
the sporting meccas
of Wimbledon and Twickers,

the windows of the jolly poly
where you worked behind the bar
in a thriftstore bronze dress

and short back and sides,
chronically undecided
between Venus pandemos
and Jeanne d'Arc.

Philip Kerr

FOUR REVIEWS IN SEARCH OF
A BIOGRAPHY

THE EGYPTIAN
by Tom Emlyn

(Times Literary Supplement)

Moses: a Biography by Jonathan Joseph, Aitken & Niven, £25, 720pp

Jonathan Joseph is the author of an acclaimed history of Jewish intellectualism, *Three Hundred Years of Solitude: Jewish Thought from Spinoza to Einstein*. But his latest book, it seems to me, has quite comprehensively undermined this earlier work with the assertion that Moses was not a Jew at all and that those distinctive features of Israelite religion that appear with him were borrowed from the religion of the ancient Egyptians.

This is not to say that somehow the intellectual contributions of figures such as Marx, Freud and Wittgenstein are negated as a result of what appears in Dr Joseph's book; however it is my impression that he has done nothing less than call into question three thousand years of Jewish tradition that, on the evidence of his previous book, helped to shape their thinking.

Moses is nonetheless a remarkable achievement. Relying on sources as diverse as Manetho, Josephus, Herodotus, Frazer, Freud and Ranke (the bibliography in this magisterial biography is nearly fifty pages long), Joseph has constructed a life that is as vivid as if Moses' widows (he had several wives in addition to Zipporah, the daughter of a Midianite shepherd) had granted the author access to all the man's private papers. It is fair to add that much of what appears in the book is based, by Joseph's own admission, on a considerable amount of guesswork; but this is guesswork of such an impassive, sophisticated variety that one quite yields oneself up to his attempt 'to reconstitute things (without neglecting any clue or hypothesis, no matter how remote)'. Indeed his devotion to the search for what can reasonably be described as truth is such that he examines every source almost as if he were a detective.

Hitherto, most of what we knew about Moses came from the Pentateuch (the first five books of the Old Testament), the Talmud (the compilation of Hebrew laws and legends), and the Koran, as well as the work of the native Egyptian historian Manetho that was subsequently transmitted by the Jewish historian Flavius Josephus. Dr Joseph occupies the first half of his book 'deconstructing this received, almost Hegelian myth of Moses' with a textual rigour that would have been worthy of Barthes or Derrida; and, having arrived at 'a transcendental, value-free knowledge of what can be agreed about history's first recorded revolutionary', Joseph then sets about reinterpreting the 'signs' that constitute the life of Moses in the light of what is now known about Egyptian monotheism.

'There is no doubt,' says Joseph, 'that monotheism was a tenet of Egyptian religious faith 2,500 years before Moses and quite possibly even longer. Much of the polytheism that was practised was purely symbolic; and many of the Egyptian "gods" were comparable to the pixies and fairies of Christian nations.'

The source and head of all the gods in Egypt was Ptah, 'the One Spirit God, the Eternal Heart or Mind, self-created, self-existent, without beginning or end.' Only this lofty concept was rather hard for the working-class Egyptian to grasp. Few outside the priesthood could ever have understood it at all and, gradually, Ra, the Sun God (created by Ptah), was allowed to succeed Ptah as the King of the gods. Ra's physical body, the solar disc itself, was the god Aten. Ptah also created Amen, who was both Spirit and Matter. Despite all this, for a long while names mattered little to the ordinary worshipper and, however the god was addressed – be it Ra, Amen-Ra, or Aten – it was always the One God, the Sun God, that the Egyptians had in mind.

While the majority of people came to prefer the worship of anthropomorphised fetishes instead of 'One' (Dr Joseph holds this to be analogous to the modern Christian cult of saint-worship), there were some who remained faithful to the idea of the One God whose symbolic energy was manifested in the rays of the sun. Among these devotees of the cult of Aten were a group of Hebrews dwelling in a northern Egyptian province called Goshen. According to Dr Joseph (and indeed, Sigmund Freud before him) these Hebrews worshipped a volcano-dwelling God called Yahweh. Joseph's thesis is that at some time during their sojourn in Egypt, these Hebrews came to identify Yahweh with the Sun God Aten. 'According to the Egyptian priests, Aten had first appeared on top of a mountain and this was the reason why the pyramids were built, as symbols of the sun's arrival in the world. It could not have been difficult for the Hebrews to have reasoned that Aten's mountain might just as well have been Yahweh's volcano.'

The Aten cult saw the zenith of its popularity with the accession of the Pharaoh Amenhotep IV who renamed himself Akhenaten in honour of his god. A period of religious fundamentalism ensued with Akhenaten attempting to destroy all the other Egyptian gods, especially the god Amen. The restoration of a pure Spirit God was popular with the priestly class, among whom Dr Joseph numbers Moses. But these religious upheavals were not welcomed by the mass of Egyptians and resulted in Akhenaten's deposal. With the removal of Akhenaten, the so-called heretic Pharaoh, the old popular cult of Amen was restored and the pendulum of persecution swung in the opposite direction. Joseph argues that it was the Hebrews' stubborn devotion to the cult of the One God, Aten, which caused them to be singled out for especially harsh treatment. ('And the Egyptians made the Children of Israel to serve with rigour: and they made their lives bitter with hard bondage' Exodus 1.13, 14.) Religious freedom, Joseph suggests, was the main motive behind the Exodus.

But who was Moses? And where did he come from? The suspicion that Moses was an Egyptian has been voiced often enough from the earliest times (Josephus) up to the present. Recently there was even a scholarly attempt to prove that Moses and Akhenaten were one and the same person. Like Freud before him however, Dr Joseph argues the case for Moses as Tuthmosis, the son of a Pharaoh – in all probability, Amenhotep III. But whereas Freud drew back from being more specific about Moses' origins (perhaps at the request of certain Jewish scholars), Joseph states his belief that Tuthmosis was the Kheri Heb, or High Priest of Egypt, and second in importance only to Pharaoh himself; and, that the Children of Israel were chosen by him rather than by God, because of their faithful adherence to the One God, Aten. In Deuteronomy 6.4, Moses says 'Hear O Israel: the Lord our God is one Lord'. Now the Hebrew word for 'Lord' is 'Adonai' or 'Adon' that is also the equivalent of the Egyptian word 'Aten'.

The author provides many such etymological comparisons and for my own part I could have wished that he had reserved the bulk of them for an appendix. The same goes for the exhaustive list of theological similarities which he draws between the god of the Egyptians and the God of the Hebrews. (Perhaps the most interesting of these is the similarity between the Egyptian creation myth and that in the Book of Genesis.) But I cannot in all conscience cavil too much: the cumulative effect is a very persuasive case for a shrewd piece of eclecticism on the part of Tuthmosis.

That he carried it off so well should hardly surprise us. As Kheri Heb, Tuthmosis would have been well-acquainted with all the mysteries of the ancient Egyptians and, as such, a powerful magician, not to mention a good psychologist. The best part of Dr Joseph's book is his description of Tuthmosis the Magician and his ability to impress God's will upon the credulous. It was no accident that Tuthmosis brought down a variety of plagues upon the Egyptians with the aid of his ebony rod. The symbol of the Kheri Heb's authority was his rod and this was also the symbol for 'god'. The Kheri Heb also possessed the art of writing, itself a magical achievement. Who better than the Kheri Heb, says Joseph, to 'receive' the Ten Commandments and to write them on tablets of stone? Joseph suggests that these would have been written in hieroglyphs, which only the priests could read. Moreover, it was commonly accepted that the priest or magician could, by means of touch, endow certain stones with magical power which, says Joseph, might help to explain the power of the Ark of the Covenant. (Joseph describes how the Ark was in reality the Barque of the Sun-God, Aten, in which he sailed across the sky.)

One of the more fascinating aspects of Dr Joseph's analysis is the comparison of the events described in Exodus 14, when the God of Tuthmosis performed his most spectacular feat, parting the waters of the Red Sea, and the magician Djadamankh who, a thousand years before Tuthmosis, used spells to divide the waters of a lake into two parts. Joseph explains how a similar 'trick' was still being performed a thousand years after Tuthmosis, by the Pharaoh Nectanebus, using a tank of water and some wax models of his Persian enemies.

Of Dr Joseph's biography one can say with total confidence that it is extremely unlikely to be surpassed, at least in my lifetime, although whether or not there will be some who could wish it to be suppressed remains to be seen. For my own part the result of his exhaustive endeavours is a triumph and – like all first-rate scholarship – enormously enjoyable.

Tom Emlyn's eighth novel, *Night and her Train of Stars*, has just been published by Viking

HOLY MOSES!?
by William Balowe

(Observer Book Section)

Moses: a Biography by Jonathan Joseph, Aitken & Niven, £25, 720pp

Question: who was the most influential Jew in history? Jesus? Marx? Freud? Moses might well be a candidate: after all it was his laws that have helped to shape the destiny of the Jews for over 3,000 years. Except, according to Jonathan Joseph, Moses wasn't a Jew at all. He wasn't even part-Israelite: he was an Egyptian, the son of Pharaoh, an adept magician, the High Priest of Egypt, the sometime King of Ethiopia, and, after the Exodus, murdered by his ungrateful and idolatrous followers. Not even his name was a Hebrew one, explains Joseph:

'"Moshe" is an extremely rare, not to say unique name in early Hebrew. "Mose", on the other hand, is an extremely common part of many compound names during the New Kingdom period of Egyptian history, and means "child". Mose was routinely suffixed to the name of an Egyptian god such as Amon, or Ptah. There are several theophorous names in the list of Eighteenth Dynasty kings which start with the name of the Pharaoh Ahmose. In all probability the man history calls Moses was Toth or Tuth-mosis, after Thoth, the Egyptian god of wisdom.'

Jonathan Joseph's *Moses: a Biography* is very much a book of our iconoclastic (some would say nihilist) times and within such a limitation it is a very good book indeed. It claims to be a biography since biographies – particularly the controversial ones (as indeed this one promises to be) – sell in large numbers. Of course it is nothing of the kind. To my mind a true biography must retain a chronological pattern that is associated with history. The problem with a subject like Moses is that it really is impossible to separate myth from history with any certainty, especially when one considers that even the historians are in the myth-making business (Herodotus and Josephus are two notoriously mythologising examples whom Joseph quotes extensively).

For all that, Joseph is scrupulous in admitting when he is being speculative, when historical; and his journalist's instinct is alert to the kind of provocative comparisons that help to elevate the book above the ordinary and which are almost enough to overcome one's uneasiness about this kind of biography:

'Tuthmosis,' writes Joseph, 'was the greatest Egyptian in history until Gamal Abdel Nasser toppled King Farouk, established a Socialist Arab state and nationalised the Suez Canal. The two men had much more in common than hitherto has been allowed.'

The book contains many other equally impertinent but, taken as a whole, ultimately persuasive comparisons. For instance there is the author's assertion that far from being chosen by God, the humble, sheep-herding Israelites were originally moved to celebrate their having been chosen by a Prince of Egypt and that this became 'the foundation for the myth of iconophratry'. Ritual circumcision, fasting, not to mention the design of the priestly garments, were all borrowed from the Egyptians, says Joseph; while most of the plagues which Tuthmosis called down upon the Egyptians were simple conjuring tricks or natural phenomena. (During the annual period of the Inundation, the Nile waters would turn red with river mud which had the appearance of blood, to say nothing of killing all the fish.)

As to the cause of the Exodus itself, Joseph maintains that it was the last chapter in a religious reformation such as that which divided sixteenth-century Europe, and that the 'Protestant' Israelites quit 'Catholic' Egypt in search of religious freedom. 'In many ways, it was a journey analogous to that of the Pilgrim Fathers who fled England and then sailed from the Netherlands in order to escape religious persecution in a New World.'

What makes all these parallels especially interesting is that Jonathan Joseph is himself a Jew, although by his own admission he is neither a believer in God nor in Zionism. In the book's conclusion he states that

> by providing rational explanations for many of the curious phenomena we find described in the Pentateuch it was not my intention to obstruct religious belief. Indeed it is my earnest desire that this book will help to foment a greater understanding of the religio-cultural history that is common to both Arab and Israeli and, as a result point the way forward to peaceful coexistence. For God is still God whether he be called Allah, Amen, Aten, or Yahweh. It makes no difference that the God of Israel was also the God of the Egyptians before them. No one nation has a monopoly on God.

(To underline this point – and just in case the Christians were beginning to think they had got away scot-free – Joseph analyses the similarities between the theology of Thoth and the opening verses of St John's Gospel.)

It might make no difference to enlightened, atheist souls like Joseph whether God be called Allah, Jehovah, Eric Clapton, or old Nobogod, but the recent history of that unhappy region, the Middle East, demonstrates that it makes a lot of difference to Jew and Arab alike. While I feel glad that I live in a society in which Jonathan Joseph is free to publish this book, I suspect it is quite possible that it may yet have a resonance quite beyond its own importance.

William Balowe's biography of Saul Bellow has just been published as a Faber paperback

KARL REICHMANN

(The *Guardian*)

Moses: a Biography by Jonathan Joseph, Aitken & Niven, £25, 720pp

At first glance this book might be seen as the literary expression of the Mosaic law against the making of images. For, as in the story of the Golden Calf (it was more probably made of bronze), Jonathan Joseph has taken the image of Moses (inevitably one thinks of Michelangelo's magnificent statue in St Peter's) and 'burnt it with fire and ground it to powder . . .' Well almost. It's not that the author questions the existence of a character named Moses. Far from it. But as one who is himself a Jew I find he questions everything that one had ever been taught about him.

The truth about Moses, says Joseph, is that he 'was not so much a prophet as the first in an apostolic succession of intellectuals who have offered their fellow man a certain view of the meaning of life – a succession that descends as far as Marx and Freud'.

Born the youngest son of the Pharaoh Amenhotep III, Tuthmosis (as Joseph suggests we should learn to call him) was 'instructed in all the wisdom of the Egyptians and he was mighty in his words and deeds' (Acts, 7, 22). Joseph interprets this verse from the New Testament as early authority for his thesis that Tuthmosis was brought up in the Egyptian priesthood and became deeply learned in the magical rituals of Isis, the great magician goddess. Joseph further argues that the extent of Tuthmosis' knowledge of the cult of Isis is evidenced by the close similarity which exists between that cult and the Mosaic construction of the Tabernacle, the precepts he organised concerning offerings, the accoutrements of the Tabernacle and the official dress of the priests.

Joseph also tells us that the Ten Commandments and Mosaic law in general were borrowed wholesale from the Egyptian *Book of the Dead*. Even the Mosaic injunction against the eating of pork was, explains the author, a legacy of Egyptian religious practice: Ra cursed the pig after Set assumed the form of a black hog to tear out the eye of Horus. Animals were always important to the Egyptians and their numerous cults came to dominate religious belief as early as the pre-dynastic period, i.e. at least two thousand years before Tuthmosis. Bulls and cows were held in the greatest honour and their worship was common in Egypt. In all likelihood, explains Joseph, the golden calf fashioned by Aaron out of molten gold was in reality a bronze figure of the bull-calf god Apis, an incarnation of Osiris, an example of which is to be found in the British Museum.

'It was quite natural that the Israelites should have made a calf,' says Joseph, 'although worship, at least as we understand it, would not have been their primary intention.

Thinking that they had been abandoned by 'this Moses' they thought to seek the guidance of an oracle, the most popular version of which was the Apis bull. Inquiries presented to the image would, it was believed, have found their reply through children who, taken possession by the spirit of the god, would have prophesied what was to become of the Israelites. That Apis was just one of a number of gods to be brought out of Egypt by the Children of Israel may be confirmed by the words of the prophet Ezekiel (20, 8); and a continuing devotion to Ra, the sun god, can be seen in the story of Balaam's Ass (Numbers, 22): an ass was one of Ra's favourite personifications.

The impetus of Joseph's argument is hardest to withstand where it deals with the circumstances of Tuthmosis' birth, as described in the second chapter of Exodus. The author starts off from the premise of Otto Rank and Freud 'that almost all the prominent civilised nations . . . began at an early stage to glorify their heroes, legendary kings and princes . . . in a number of poetic tales . . .' Heroes such as Cyrus, Romulus, Sargon of Agade and, Freud believed, Moses. We are most of us familiar with story of how Moses' Levite mother hid her son from the genocidally-minded Pharaoh and laid him in a basket made of bulrushes that she placed among the reeds at the river's edge, 'a story,' writes Joseph, 'that echoes the earlier Sumerian story of King Sargon, who was also discovered in the rushes of a Mesopotamian river bank'.

Freud argued the case for a 'legend' created among the Jewish people designed to turn the Egyptian Moses into a Jew. But Joseph takes a step back and examines the legend itself in the context of Egyptian myth, specifically the myth of the god Osiris.

Osiris, son of Ra, ruled Egypt with his queen, the goddess Isis. But his brother Set was bitterly jealous of Osiris and resolved to kill him. He made a marvellous sarcophagus and tricked Osiris into lying inside it, whereupon Set nailed it up, sealed it with molten lead, and set the coffin adrift on the Nile. Knowing that the dead may not rest without their funeral rites, Isis set out to find her husband's corpse. This had been cast up on the shores of Byblos and became a magnificent tree, enclosing the coffin and Osiris within its trunk. The King of Byblos, admiring the tree, had it cut down and used it as a pillar to support the roof of his palace. When Isis found this out, she presented herself at the King's court, ingratiated herself with his Queen and engineered her appointment as nurse to the young prince. Eventually Isis persuaded the King to allow her to cut open the pillar and take away the body of Osiris. Only Set discovered where Isis placed her husband's body and tore it into many pieces which he then scattered throughout the land. Isis built a boat of bulrushes and once again set out to search for the body of Osiris. From which time forth, the Nile crocodiles would never molest a reed boat because they thought it carried Isis on her quest. The legend has it that Horus continued to seek to avenge Osiris and when he shall finally have vanquished Set, then Osiris will return to earth and reign once more as king in Egypt.

The similarities should be obvious without detailing Joseph's painstaking and scholarly comparisons. But not the least of his evidence is that the bitumen and pitch supposedly used to bind the bulrushes of Moses' basket, although common enough in Sumeria, were substances unknown in Egypt until Ptolemaic times. In short, Joseph argues the case for not one but two legends: the first legend, created by the Egyptians in order to turn Tuthmosis into Osiris, perhaps with the purpose of contesting the Egyptian throne; and, following the failure of this attempted *coup d'état*, the second legend created by the Israelites in order to turn Tuthmosis into a Jew. Tuthmosis' sister Miriam, in all probability an Egyptian high priestess of the cult of Isis, represents the goddess herself. There was nothing new in the Israelites' appropriation of the Osirian myth, comments Joseph, and he points out that it is virtually identical with the Greek Persephone myth. As to the wanderings of the Israelites in the wilderness, Joseph maintains that this was a simple allegory of the difficult passage of Osiris through the underworld.

My own sense of personal journey through Dr Joseph's book has proved equally problematic. While I accept the sincerity of Joseph's introductory asseveration that, unlike Freud whom he here paraphrases, he has 'no wish to deprive a people of the man whom they take pride in as the greatest of their sons', I find that I have gained in knowledge only what I have simultaneously lost in religious persuasion. The fact of the matter is that by having his prophet brought so close to scrutiny, I find that God has quite evaporated and now I feel rather like a small boy who has been cruelly told the awful truth about Santa Claus.

Doubtless Joseph would argue that we should never put truth aside in favour of national or religious interests. That is real freedom of speech, in which freedom's limit is not the sacred and since it is a principle to which my life has been committed I will say that Joseph's book has changed my life. But because it is not always pleasant to know the truth – it offends just as often as a lie – I will add that only time will tell if his book has changed me for the better.

Karl Reichmann is an *Extraordinary Fellow of Churchill College, Cambridge*

MOSES THE LAW GIVER
by Aylssa Ayer

The *Independent*

Moses: a Biography by Jonathan Joseph, Aitken & Niven, £25, 720pp

There is something in this excellent book to offend nearly everyone. Jews will doubtless be offended by Dr Joseph's persuasively argued thesis that Moses was an Egyptian sunworshipper, polygamist and that some time after the incident of the Golden Calf he was murdered by the Israelites (the real reason why he never entered the Promised Land). Muslims will most probably be insulted by the propinquity the author alleges exists between ancient Egyptian monotheism (they worshipped the 'One' god, the sun god Ra) and Islam's fundamental declaration of faith that 'there is no god, but God.' Christians will perhaps take rather longer to work up a head of steam against Joseph's argument that 'the idea of a Christ was only ever meant to be a substitute and successor for Moses' and that 'the mythical circumstances of Moses's birth and death were the prototype for those of Jesus'. Freudians will work themselves into a state at Joseph's suggestion that, in writing his monograph, *Moses and Monotheism*, Freud backed away from making the conclusions at which Joseph has now arrived. Egyptologists will feel a sense of irritation that a comparatively peaceful backwater of academe is now a Red Sea of angry division between those who support Joseph's theories and those who disagree with them.

Speaking for my own irreligious self, what I find most offensive about the book is Joseph's unswerving affirmation of Moses' greatness. While I can accept the comparisons he makes with other great 'revolutionaries' such as Martin Luther and Nasser, the fact remains that Moses was not a very nice man.

For a start there is the principle of *lex talionis* which underlies all of Mosaic jurisprudence and continues, even today, to plague legal systems everywhere. For instance, in the United States, the people who are usually most in favour of executing condemned murderers are those people who live by their Bibles and frequently quote – usually incorrectly – the infamous text from Exodus which says 'life for life, eye for eye, tooth for tooth, hand for hand, foot for foot, burn for burn, wound for wound, stripe for stripe.' (21, 23–25).

Then there is Moses' attitude towards homosexuals: 'If a man lies with a male as with a woman, both of them have committed an abomination; they shall be put to death, their blood is upon them.' Those same lunatics who maintain that AIDS is God's vengeance on homosexuals (in the face of all the evidence that it is primarily a heterosexual disease) are those same people who quote that text from Leviticus on the subject. Nor was Moses any more tolerant of nudity: nakedness, says Moses, 'is a shameful thing'. And his discrimination against the blind, the lame, hunchbacks, dwarfs, people with itching diseases, or men with crushed testicles – none of whom were to be allowed to offer bread to God (Leviticus 21) – quite takes your breath away. The old boy even took a harsh view of people who get themselves tattooed (Leviticus 19, 28).

Much of this 'Torah', or teaching, was of course, the basis of the Talmud and, when it is considered that Talmudic Law (upon which much existing Western jurisprudence is still based) lists 36 capital offences and 207 flagellable transgressions, one is left with the distinct impression of Moses as the Ayatollah Khomeini of his day. It is even arguable that it was the Children of Israel who declared history's first 'holy war', when they sought to capture the land flowing with milk and honey that was Canaan.

To a woman there are two things that make Moses an offensive being. The first of these was the elevation of patriarchal custom to tribal law which enabled women to be treated as chattels and which was designed to make the priesthood exclusively male. This was best characterised by the primitive, misogynistic fear of menstruation. Leviticus 12 is full of nonsense about the uncleanliness of women and rituals for their purification, all of which quite misses the point about menstruation. A woman's periodic discharge is essentially a regenerative system. Sloughing off blood and disintegrating endometrial tissue is the uterus's way of purifying itself and no amount of male nonsensical ritual on the subject is about to improve on things. Moses was the world's first sexual fascist.

And then there is Moses' violent opposition to all wizardry and witchcraft: 'You shall not permit a sorceress to live' (Exodus 22, 18). It was this biblical injunction which was to be the basis of all European witch trials from the Middle Ages until the early eighteenth century and which cost the lives of hundreds of thousands of people, most of them women. For all that, I am quite persuaded by Dr Joseph's impressive evidence that Moses was himself a trained magician and that, following the Exodus, his strict injunctions against sorcery were designed to protect his own monopoly of magic. 'Despite the Mosaic rejection of sorcery,' adds Joseph, 'even a cursory examination of those sacrifices and ceremonials that are exhaustively detailed in Exodus and Leviticus reveals that these are magic rites pure and simple.'

Georg Büchner wrote in *Danton's Death* that it was no good trying to shift the blame for things on to God since God no longer existed, and man had become responsible for his own destiny. To my mind this book shows where much of the blame for two thousand years of sexual superstition and intolerance belongs: squarely on Moses' shoulders.

Aylssa Ayer is the author of *Of Mense and Men*, Chatto & Windus, £15.99

313

Kathy Lette

A DAY IN A SWINGING LONDONER'S LIFE

FOR MOST MASOCHISTS, a quick thrashing with a bit of wet lettuce in Soho will suffice. But not being a member of the Tory Party, *my* greatest feat of masochism is reading one of those 'A Day in the Life of a Swinging Londoner' columns. Invariably, some not just name-, but place-dropping member of London's Celebritocracy is boasting about her high-powered, action-packed day, beginning with breakfast in bed – I'm not talking the cold cuppa and soggy Weetabix *I* always get. (Hey, between that and the muesli, it's the lesser of two weevils.) Oh no. For *her* it's oven-warmed *pain chocolat* and a single red rose, presented by an adoring spouse as the brace of children (the heir and the spare) frolic joyfully around the family hearth in Hampstead.

Naturally this is followed by a breath-taking itinerary of jogging, static cycling, yoga, meditation and bread-baking before dropping the children off at 'Baby Mensa', pausing on route to pick up various prizes for literature, followed by lunch at the Ivy with Melvyn Bragg, Tina Brown and a couple of Captains of Industry.

A hurdy-gurdy of high-profile It Girl parties at Nobos and champagne-saturated book launches à la Groucho have to be endured, before co-cooking a gourmet feast over which hubby and wife quote a fair whack of love poetry to each other, inspiring them to execute chapters six to nine of the Kama Sutra before falling into a deep sleep.

Hello?

Sleep deprivation is a torture in some countries of the

314

world. This is because *it works*. I'd confess to anything . . . although with a six- and a four-year-old, there's nothing to confess to. The highlight of my day is retrieving the guinea-pig from the depths of the blender. That's why I became a mother. I just couldn't resist the glamour of it all. Have been woken at dawn by my miniature insomniacs for as long as I can remember.

7 a.m., abandon 'A Day in the Life of a Very Big Fibber' to make breakfast. I don't so much eat breakfast, as wear it. My progeny are going through a stage where they think food is a decorative option. It's like dining with Henry VIII. Within ten minutes, they've trashed the kitchen with rock-star style.

Food-facials cement-rendering to our features, we then set about Doing Fabulously Creative Things With Finger Paints. By mid-morning I am so bored with making science labs for Doctor X and his Street Sharks out of old shoe boxes, I'm tempted to grow a yeast infection for a change of pace.

According to American *Vanity Fair*, London is swinging again. For a fleeting moment I consider venturing out to sample the world's hippest metropolis, but taking into account IRA bomb scares and gale warnings (the sky has been a grey duvet for as long as I can remember. 'Where were you on the night of December 1st till March 29?') and the fact that all my friends have tested positive to allergies to Ninja Turtles and nappies – this is a society, don't forget, which keeps its dogs at home and sends its children off to high-class kennels called Eton and Harrow – and suddenly I'm feeling all swung out.

'Where do roads end?' and 'How do eyebrows know to stop growing in the middle?' demand the rug-rats, stereo-phonically. 'Where does wind blow from?' 'If God made us, who made God?' My Nietzsche impression is interrupted by a clipboard-clutching dish-washing-liquid researcher who wants to know what kind of mother I am. I stare at her blankly. 'A working mother?' she prompts, patronisingly. Now there's a tautology.

'No,' I snap, slamming the door. 'As in *Theresa*.'

In the short time it takes me not to win a free sample of

dish-washing liquid, my daughter has decided to go for gold in the Projectile Vomit Olympics. Just to add the icing to another fun-packed London day, the washing machine breaks down. Dripping in drool and stool, I search for my little boy who has gone suspiciously quiet. This is because he's now put the guinea-pig down the toilet and flooded the bathroom.

Deprived of his fun, my offspring gives me one of those 'hey, I gave you the best year of my life' looks. The sort of look which suggests a future career in publishing, starting with his sequel to *Mommy Dearest*. He spends the afternoon convincing his convalescing sister that her Rupert Bear slippers are going to savage her. I comfort myself that things could be worse, they've yet to take up the descant recorder.

Five paint bomb fights, one hepatitis injection (well, wouldn't you? After giving mouth-to-mouth resuscitation to a guinea-pig?), seventy-six orphanage threats, a dressing-down from my card-carrying Islington feminist friend (I was caught screening a Thomas the Tank Engine video. There's one female engine called Daisy, who's frightened of cows and has eyelashes which, when she blinks, look like a couple of tarantulas mating) and ninety-five choruses of Old MacDonald's Farm later (what kind of noise does an armadillo make?) – I'm just adopting the foetal position and trying to remember what my name is ... when the phone rings. It's Petronella or Henryella or something-or-other-ella, asking me if I'd like to be interviewed for 'A Day in the Life of a Swinging Londoner'.

'Well ...' I hear myself purr, 'it invariably begins with breakfast in bed – complete with oven-warmed *pain chocolat* and a single red rose – presented by an adoring spouse, as a brace of children frolic joyfully around the family hearth ...'

Andrea Levy

DEBORAH

DEBORAH LIVED IN my flats at number forty-six, on the ground floor next to the drying room. It was a long way from where I lived which was on the same floor but round the bend in the balcony. If I looked out of my bedroom window I could see into Deborah's. When the wind blew, the curtains of her flat usually flapped out the top of the open window and fluttered around – knocking against the bricks, billowing up, waving in front of the windows above. As the curtains blew you could catch a glimpse of all the beds that were squashed into the bedrooms in Deborah's flat. Nobody ever really knew how many there were in Deborah's family. Some said twelve, others said fourteen. And Deborah, when I asked her, said it depended on whether her dad was home.

After our church harvest festival, the vicar would bring Deborah's mum some of the baskets with the fruit and tins of beans and biscuits that we had all collected. 'Why don't we get any?' I asked my mum. 'Because they need it and we have it to give,' she would say. But Deborah always told me, 'In my house, Coca-Cola comes out of the taps, not water.' And I told my mum and asked if we could have that too. But she said, 'Don't go believing what that girl says. Deborah is a liar.'

Deborah could have a pretty face. Sometimes at school when they made her wash it in the little basins in the toilet, you could clearly see her pale blue eyes with their dark outer ring, and her pink cheeks that could puff up into a smile like a hamster storing nuts. Her teeth were white and small and stuck out in the front because, when no one was looking, she would suck her thumb. And when she spoke, her tongue hit her teeth and made her sound like a baby. She had little rings of grey cotton thread through her ears where they were pierced. 'It keeps me holes open,' she told everyone. ''Cause I lost me gold earrings.' Her socks always looked the same – grey that once was white – one up, one down, with most of the fabric sliding inside her shoe, revealing the back of her ankle and heel which was always crusted with black dirt. Her left shoe had a buckle and strap that worked, but the right one flapped open and when she ran fast she had to hop to keep it on. She wore dresses like all the girls did, but Deborah's waistband was always too high and the first two buttons on the back of her dress never did up. And Deborah smelt. She smelt of behind my bed where there were speckles of black on the wall. She smelt of milk going off and old shoe-bags in the cloakroom at school and the bottom of the bin after you'd tipped the contents down the shute.

Deborah came to my front door nearly every day. 'Can Fern come out to play?' she'd ask. Sometimes my mum would look down at her and say, 'She can't come out today, she's got a cold.' At which Deborah would say, 'Well, let us come in then.' And my mum would say, 'No, she's ill.' Deborah would put her hands on her hips, 'Let her come to the door then.'

'No! Fern is not well. You understand me?' Mum would then have to shut the door. But Deborah would lift up the letter box and shout down the hall, 'Fern, are you coming out to play?' While my mum tutted, 'The cheek of that girl!'

There was a woman who lived upstairs, on the first balcony, over the pram sheds. Her name was Mrs Wheeler. She had hair that looked like yellow candy floss, whipped-up and piled on top of her head in a style called a bird's nest. She stank of perfume and we all used to hold our noses when she went by and say, 'Poo, I can still smell it,' after she'd been gone for ages. She used to come on to her balcony and ask one of us kids to go on an errand to the shops for her. She was always doing that and someone would go and buy her a tin of peas or some potatoes. When you brought them back she'd give you sixpence for going. But she never let Deborah go for her. 'Not you,' she'd say when Deborah would step forward with a grin on her face. 'I've given you money before and I never see nothing for it.' Deborah would stop smiling and shout back at her. She'd shout, 'Shut up, you silly old cow! Go and get it yourself, you lazy old bag.' I was always shocked at Deborah's cheek to grown-ups. But it made me giggle and we'd all laugh in the porch. Except no one could earn a sixpence after that.

Deborah cheated in games. She stuck the ball down her knickers in 'Queenie-eye, Queenie-eye – who's got the ball?' She always moved in 'Peep behind the curtain', and would push you hard and say, 'No I never,' if you complained that she did. When we played the game where you take a step forward if the letter called out is in your name, she always won. Because she said she had loads of middle names that had all the zeds and exes that no one else had. But she made them up – the Zaza's and Lexy's. Everybody knew it because they weren't even real names. And when we played shows in the porch with everyone standing up in turn and singing *Bachelor boy* or *How much is that doggy in the window*, Deborah, on her go, would just get up and show everybody her knickers because she couldn't sing and didn't know any songs.

But she was really good for some things. She could make herself go all floppy like a rag doll. So on Guy Fawkes night we made her the guy. We put one of those cardboard masks that you buy from the sweetshop over her face. Then we sat her outside the gate of the flats and waited for people to come past. 'Penny for the guy,' we said. And everyone looked at us impressed, 'That's a good guy,' then gave us money for Deborah. But then this man insisted on sticking the money into the guy's mouth. And Deborah had to suck a threepenny bit. She jumped up spitting and screaming, 'I've swallowed thousands of germs. I'm gonna die.' She wouldn't do it any more after that. 'You do it now, Fern,' she said. But no one could get as floppy as Deborah.

She could get back your ball from anywhere. If someone hit it over the wall into the gardens of the houses, Deborah would take a run at the wall, scamper over it and disappear for a few minutes. Then the ball would be thrown back and Deborah would climb back after it. And if someone shouted, 'Oihh you,' Deborah would stick her two fingers up at them. She could go over railings, walk along walls. She could jump all ten of a flight of steps without having to hold the banister. She just threw herself off, landing on her hands and knees. Scraped hands and bloody knees never bothered Deborah. 'It don't hurt me. Nothing hurts me,' she'd say. And she'd show you her scabs if she liked you.

I didn't really want to play at Deborah's – her house smelt. And Deborah's mum's stockings hung down from her knees, and her legs were fat and white and had blue lumpy lines all over them. She wore her slippers in the street and was always shouting. We could hear her in our flat even when the telly was on. 'There goes that woman again,' my mum would say. But Deborah said, 'I wanna show you something,' and I hoped it was the tap where the Cola comes out.

Kenny just followed us. He was always doing that. 'What you doing – where you going?' he asked us. He walked two feet behind me and Deborah with his hands in his pockets, kicking at imaginary stones.

'Get lost,' Deborah told him. But he just looked around then said, 'Where you going – what you doing?' and carried on following. Kenny was much younger than me and Deborah, that's why he followed us. His mum lived on the third floor and his dad drove a motorbike at weekends. Kenny was a little kid who wore short trousers and was useless at throwing a ball – he'd aim it forward and it would go behind him. He wore glasses that had a grubby pink plaster over one of the lenses because he had a lazy eye. And he was ginger and cried if you called him carrot.

'Let us come?' he said. So we let him because he didn't have anyone else to play with.

There was no one else in at Deborah's. She took us in her bedroom – the room with loads of beds. There were clothes everywhere. Shoes, knickers and socks where pillows should be. Dresses and trousers all over the beds, hanging off and spilling on to the floor. There was a coat on a hanger that was hanging from the curtain rail – big and dark in the window like a stranger you shouldn't talk to. The curtain was orange and ripped at the bottom with a safety pin through the hole to keep it together. The wallpaper was green – little green flowers all over the room. And there were black footprints up high on the wall. The light socket in the centre of the ceiling didn't have a bulb in it, but had lots of black flex and leads attached instead. And the flex and leads were strung over the room like a Christmas decoration of spider's legs.

'Are you going to show us the Coca-Cola tap?' I asked her.

'It's not working,' she said. 'Look, I've got something else to show you.' She pointed to the wall over a bed. Just above where the pillow should have been there was a little picture torn out of a magazine with jagged edges up one side, stuck on the wall with Sellotape. It was of Pinky and Perky. Two pink puppet pigs dressed as if they were going away on holiday, in sunglasses and flowery shirts.

'That's mine,' Deborah said. She jumped on the bed and pointed, 'That's Pinky and that's Perky.'

Kenny started to laugh. 'Is that all you've got?' he said looking around.

'Let's see the tap anyway,' I asked her again. But Deborah said, 'Do you want to see my bum?' She lifted up her dress and pulled her knickers down. Kenny put his hand over his mouth. 'Oh you're dirty.' He began to giggle but went up close and put his head right next to it.

'Let's see your bum, Fern,' Deborah said, as she pulled her knickers back up.

'No.'

'I'll show you mine,' Kenny said. He turned round, pulled down his trousers and pushed out his bottom. It had ginger freckles on it. Then he pulled his trousers up again quickly and began jumping up and down laughing. Deborah stuck out her bum again, holding down her knickers and twisting round like she was dancing. So I showed them mine. And they were quiet for a second as they looked at it. Until we all began to laugh. Kenny jumped on the bed and started jumping up and down.

'Let's see Kenny's again,' Deborah said and she grabbed at Kenny's trousers. But he held on to them. Deborah pulled hard and they came down. And Kenny pulled them up again.

'Let's see yours again, Fern,' Deborah said. But I said, 'No.'

'Oh go on – I showed you mine.' She got on the bed and began jumping with Kenny.

'Let's play something else,' I said. 'Haven't you got any games?'

Deborah jumped off the bed and landed right on me, her face next to mine.

'Fern, do you know that milk comes out of women's tits when she has a baby?'

Kenny was still jumping – getting higher and higher waving his arms in the air.

'Everybody knows that,' I said.

'You know how they get it to come out?' Deborah carried on. Kenny started singing, 'Tits and bum, tits and bum,' in time to his jumping. I didn't answer her. But she said, 'You have to have your nipples pierced with a pin.' I put my arms across me and screamed, 'Do ya!' and decided never to have a baby.

'Yeah, my sisters had it done. How else d'you think it comes out? They put a pin in it and the milk comes out.' Then Deborah put her warm hand right over my chest with her fingers spread out and her palm right over my nipple. She breathed bubble-gum breath into my face and said, 'Shall I show ya!'

But Kenny had jumped so high that his arms hit the electric leads that were coming out of the light socket. The light socket pulled out of the ceiling and sent down a shower of plaster and dust all over the bed and clothes. In a second things were crashing down all over the room. A light smashed on to the floor and the bulb broke and made a tinkling sound. Something else I couldn't see went thud. We just watched it all happen like in a film when a ghost is about. In the end there were just two metal pointy wires coming from a hole in the ceiling and the black flexes and leads were over the room.

'Kenny, look what you've done,' I shouted. And Kenny said, 'I never did nothing . . . I never touched nothing . . . I never . . . I never did nothing.' But his face screwed up like he was going to cry.

'You better get your mum to fix it, Deborah,' I told her. But Deborah started to shake. She stood in front of me with her legs shivering and her hands trembling like she was cold from coming out of the swimming pool. 'We'll tell her Kenny did it. It wasn't you. Or get your dad – he'll fix it,' I said. Deborah started to scream, 'No! No! No!' She was looking all around her and crying, 'No! No!' She held her hands between her legs, jiggling up and down and screaming, 'No! No!' Kenny started to giggle at her.

'It's all right, your mum'll fix it,' I told her. But she threw herself on the floor, right at my feet. She lay flat for a second then she wriggled like an insect under the bed. Kenny knelt down to see where she had gone. 'She's crying under the bed,' he said and started to laugh. 'She's a scaredicat. She's gone under the bed.'

I knelt down and looked. She was squashed against the wall, shaking, with her thumb in her mouth, making little whimpering sounds like a dog.

'Deborah. Come out or I'm going home,' I told her. But she wouldn't move. 'I'm going home,' I shouted.

And I left. I left the room with the plaster and the dust and the black electric leads like spider's legs. And I left Deborah under the bed with Kenny in his short grey trousers on his knees pointing at her and saying, 'She's a scaredicat. She's under the bed and she's crying. She's a cry-baby.'

It wasn't until much later that I saw Kenny and Deborah again. I was playing two balls up against the wall. It was the furthest I'd ever got before dropping the ball but there was no one around to see. I was on to 'one two three and twistsies'. Then I saw Kenny coming out of the drying room and I dropped a ball. He didn't have any clothes on. Nothing. No shoes, no socks, no short grey trousers. He didn't even have his glasses on. He was completely bare. I could see his willie. Dangling between his legs like a little slug – bouncing up and down as he ran from the drying-room door. It made me laugh but I put my hand over my mouth so he wouldn't see. I watched him run along the balcony, his mouth open as if he was screaming but with no sound coming out. He started to move backwards then forwards, left, right – like he didn't know which way to go. And as he ran, his willie kept bobbing up and down. Then Kenny was crying. He saw me and held his arms out to me like a baby, running towards me, wanting to be picked up. And as he got closer I could see that all over his white skin were red slashes. As he got closer I could see that some of them were bleeding – oozing blood. Some of them were raised, some were raw, some of them had blood coming from them in long dribbles. He was striped with them, over his legs and arms and chest and face. And his eye, the lazy one, was roaming around in its socket – slowly moving from one side to the other.

I didn't want to touch him – I wrapped my arms around me and stepped back as he came close. That's when I saw Deborah coming out of the drying room with a grin on her face and in her hand she was holding a black lead – like a spider's leg but one with spiky metal ends.

'Go to your mum, Kenny,' I told him. I pointed the way. He turned round and ran towards the porch. I followed him up the flights of stairs. I followed behind him, listening to him crying and watching his white bottom – slashed and raw pink – slipping from side to side as he lifted his leg up each step.

His mum screamed.

Everyone wanted to know where Deborah was. Kenny's dad wanted to know. Neighbours who stood at open doors wanted to know. Mrs Wheeler from her balcony wanted to know. My mum wanted to know.

'Where is she, Fern? When did you last see her? She whipped that little boy. Where is that evil girl?'

And the shouting started outside Deborah's flat. Kenny's

dad roaring and Deborah's mum yelling, 'If it was her I'll kill her – when I get hold of her I'll kill her.' The police were called and mingled with everyone who'd come to stare. And Kenny was taken away in an ambulance.

It was me who found her. She was sitting in the top porch, round the block, where we hardly ever go except when you don't want to be found in hide-and-seek. She was sitting in the corner, humming, with her knees up and her cardigan pulled up over her head and down in front of her face. She was sucking her thumb and rocking lightly backwards and forwards. And coming out from between her legs was a small trickle of piss that crept slowly along the ground.

Marina Warner

NATURAL LIMITS

'ELEVEN THOUSAND VIRGINS?'

'Yes, eleven thousand, absolutely.'

'The whole population of Cologne can't have been as big as that, then. You said the fourth century?'

'Oh, far less. Think of it: a palisade on a muddy river bank, a smoking encampment, and perhaps a paved road. There wouldn't have been much more, then, in the *Colonia Agrippinensis*.'

'So the murderees would have outnumbered the ordinary inhabitants?'

'You're being literal-minded, *cara*.'

'And every one of them was killed?'

'Every single one. Brutally murdered. Chopped and split by the Hun. Like so much firewood. Memling painted it as a kind of pre-run of the slasher movie.'

'Not everyone, in fact. There was one saved.'

The chevrons of Bettina's eyebrows sharpened in surprise at the young man's interjection.

'Rudi, I didn't know!' She urged him on.

'She escaped by playing dead. Then afterwards she felt great remorse that she had not been martyred with the others.'

But Rudi missed the chance to elaborate further, because their turn came to choose from the heaped display of sausage and other cured and treated meats in the delicatessen where they had been waiting.

'This is the not-to-be-missed German cultural experience, not those old, dusty and – how do you say – sick legends,' said Rudi. Candace detected a stint on the East Coast in the accent of Bettina's new PA.

The differing sheen of glass, of marble, of tiles, swam with liquid highlights as in a Dutch still life in the cooled shop interior; some of the counters were barrows, and had striped awnings with gay dagging to match, others were sparkling crystal and chrome display cases as in expensive cosmetic departments; all were piled high and heavy, with bundles of root vegetables still attached to bouquets of top growth greenery, and authentically engrimed. Though indoors, the stands were disposed haphazardly, to create the semblance of a street market; the assistants wore bright aprons with posies and frolicsome baby wild animals on them.

Rudi pointed to a pale pepper-dusted salame and turned to Bettina for approval.

She nodded. 'You choose enough for the three of us tonight. Make it a feast!' But she looked at the crimson, inky, veined and roseate pilings of cold cuts and sausage without enthusiasm. 'I leave you to the *wurst*, Rudi – we'll find some salady stuff meanwhile.'

'I mustn't eat too much,' said Candace, helplessly fixed on the spectacle of the massive charcuterie breakwater. 'It's all very well for you.' Bettina was wearing green silk shantung trousers with black piping down the sides, which her mother had made up for her from material which she had bought in Hong Kong. 'The excess of it. Who eats all this?'

Bettina's eyes, which were childlike in their roundness, tilted up at the corners when she was amused.

'Haven't you seen them – everywhere? The munchers, the feeders . . .' She chomped with her jaw. But she stopped, worrying for her friend, who for a moment had looked stricken. Candace was certainly heavier than the last time she had seen her, and puffy in her face and neck. From drink? From clandestine eating? Or from quiet secret crying in the night? From doing all of these?

Bettina put her hand on Candace's arm. 'Come, the

327

vegetables and the fruit are very good here.' She spoke English rapidly, with an Italian intonation; the magazine she published was printed in Turin, and her life and work there had blurred the German in her voice. 'They leave the earth on for effect, to make you believe in their extra naturalness. Then you're happy to pay more. But at the same time it works, the taste is better. *Vedrai*, tonight with Gervase, we'll have a wonderful picnic: carrots and olives and tomatoes and cheese and everything that's good for you. With champagne or schnapps.'

'You're bringing some?'

Rudi nodded 'I have put some bottles in the boot.'

'And besides,' Bettina carried on, 'you'll see that Gervase will have some too. He has an appetite under his cool, controlled exterior. He's a kind of a magician, and magicians have to experience everything in order to ... deepen their knowledge. When we were younger, Gervase and I, before he went to live at Hollen, we tried to eat a toad together once. He said it was a species famous for possessing in its epidermis a certain substance, an antidote to all poisons known. He said we would never suffer from the effects of pollution again. He was always making big boasts like that. He managed a little piece. But I didn't have the nerve.'

Bettina and Gervase were together one whole summer in the early seventies; there are still photographs of events they staged in various galleries here and there.

'But the whole point of this, Candace dear,' she said, for she caught Candace's anxiety that she would be intruding on a lovers' reunion, 'is that you and I will have some time together, with no one else, no phone calls, nothing, and I want to hear *everything*.'

Bettina Strahler never seemed to be running things; her manner was attentive, as if she were keen to follow others' directions and take instruction. But this was only a feint. If it weren't hard to compare people to dogs without sounding derogatory, thought Candace, Bettina was like a beautiful pointer, with enhanced sensitivity in her ears, her nose, those delicate pricked arches of her brows, the tips of her fingers and the tips of her toes; yet she succeeded in being in charge. She was almost always subtle about it; yet Candace could think of no one who could create such quivering bright loops of energy around her as she moved.

When Bettina telephoned from Basel, Candace had risen to her suggestion, to make time in both their busy lives to be together, because, she told herself, she had to learn to be grown-up, and she needed a friend to convince her. It wasn't that Bettina was an obvious exemplar for growing old. But in the matter of growing up, she could learn so much from her, Candace decided, because she's instinct with vitality, she's gifted at staying alive, and keeping hold of life. And that means she has understood limits, that she has grasped them. She doesn't smoke, any more; Candace couldn't give up. Something eludes me, she thought, something precious and good about life itself. Like a child who won't eat because she hates the breasts growing on her thin ribbed chest, I can't make myself put away that childish thing, that flirting and courting of glamorous Mister Death, in his biker's leathers, with his smouldering eyes, his smouldering fag, his dirty finger-nails. So it had become her New Year's resolution, her opening herself to facing change, to entertaining the thought of daily yoga, of twenty-four lengths weekly, of a polyunsaturated fat-free diet, a bathroom exercise bicycle, an office trampoline, nicorette blister packs, manuals of hiking trails, and catalogues of outdoor protective clothing made of ever more evolved fibres to resist wind and sleet and sun and salt, such as she saw in friends' living rooms, in magazines and papers, and through the blindless windows of street-level gyms. But still she couldn't overcome her repugnance for these attributes of proper grown-upness, and adopt even only one of them.

Familiar faces that are now dead smile at me, she acknowledged, from the obituary pages more often than I expected; and acquaintances I thought far older than I am turn out to be several years younger, and there they are, gone to their long home. In the English papers they don't tell you what they died of; in America, where the topic of health has driven out other ways of seeing and everything has become either a hazard or a benefit, the obits close with the brief, melancholy envoi: of cancer of the bowel; of the ovaries; of the jaw; of AIDS-related complications. Tom (*your* Tom, as he used to say with heavy and hate-filled irony) keeled over with old age. He had almost everything. I got so sick of the list. But it was fundamentally old age. Used up. He had been used up for years.

Bettina had said, 'Come and join me, I am going to visit Gervase Mendoza in Cologne. We can travel together. You know, he has become very interested in death. And interesting about it, too, I think. Everyone should be, but we are all shy and awkward and our tongues go dry and our lips go thick when the subject arises. Artists can still deal with it better. Gervase is a new Grünewald: miracles and disease, together; angels and pustules; demons and rainbows. This metaphysic is still somehow in the German psyche; he has inherited it.'

Grünewald. A new Grünewald. Will he help me seize hold of death, Candace asked herself. Understand what had happened, to Tom. That it will happen to me? Unless.

Tom's white-grey crunchy bits unburned in the handful of dust. Like the bonemeal scattered round the roots of roses in the spring. I must organise a ceremony, she resolved. Some friends, somewhere he enjoyed. A spattering, a mulch, then something growing in his memory. Something inscribed. *In Memoriam Tom Wendle. He loved this spot.* She used to get choked up reading such remembrances on benches in the park. You can only read them when nobody's sitting there, and this conjures the ghost very effectively. The thermos flask, the newspaper, the eyes looking up at the view: he loved this spot.

I am trying to understand this, thought Candace Parris. I am trying not to join him. I am trying to learn to want to join him and the others later, rather than sooner.

She could see Bettina was thinking of asking her to write about Gervase Mendoza for *Balcon*, her impeccably-designed, trilingual art quarterly; or perhaps conduct a conversation. She was running a series of such exchanges, and had provoked much comment: in London, Candace had heard young pv crawlers in the latest geek polyester chic and lemon yellow haircuts exclaiming at them. Most recently, she had published a trialogue between the Oldenburgs (Claes and Coosje) and Rachel Whiteread; before that, there had been tapes made with Louise Bourgeois and a Russian artist Bettina was supporting.

They walked out into the cold Cologne shopping mall, the winter biting small stars into the paving stones. At a square where a Romanesque church showed its wartime losses in restored walls of slub concrete, they stopped and went in. While Rudi was finding the sacristan, Candace and Bettina wandered into a side-chapel, frescoed with the legend of the massacre in High Gothic: the anonymous artist had a feel for fashion, for every one of the hundreds of individualised tendril-haired maidens, as she fell under the executioners' savage attack, was swathed in beautiful, rich drapery, with rills of lace and silk undergarments swirling from brocade gowns, and perfect shoes, square-toed in the latest court style contemporary with the artist and the original audience.

The sacristan was ready for them now, Rudi came to tell them. A man in his fifties, dressed in a green felt hunting jacket with antler horn buttons was waiting by an armoured door which was buckled from age, bolted and padlocked; when he unfastened the hasp, a narrow Gothic arch was revealed, with a dark wooden inner door.

He found the light, but it was dim, and the smell of the chamber reached them before they could make out its contents, as of an old apple store that has been forgotten, so that all the sweet aroma has turned to wrinkled, webbed, pickling must. It was hard at first for Candace to see what she was looking at. The bones in the roof of the Chamber were assembled in festoons and swags, so that they weren't recognisable at all as belonging to bodies, but appeared some variety of baroque plasterwork. But then the vaults became legible, and she realised that the martyrs had all been jumbled and shuffled together as in an elephant graveyard or the grimmer heaps of victims from genocidal wars: in the vault, praises were written in the long bones and the forearms for the slanted shorter strokes of the letters: a femur for the upright on the T, a pair of tibia for the V of Virgo: *Ave Ursula, virgo praedilectissima. Deo gratias. Requiescat in pace.* There were armouries Candace had seen in the guard rooms of grim old castles like Windsor, which display weapons in similar analytic patterns, but here the rosettes were made of shoulderblades, not bucklers, and the starbursts of clavicles, not scimitars.

Bettina whispered to her, her eyes mischievous, 'Pious ladies did it all. Like pokerwork. Or that Victorian way of making straw pictures, you know. The V&A has some.' She gestured stitching with her fingers. 'In the tedious dark winter evenings . . . think of the deep pleasure; think of the *frisson*.'

For days, for weeks, for months, they must have worked, thought Candace, looking at the tiers of shanks and fibulae, as they pushed the bones around until they struck a design they fancied, then hooked them in place with silver wire, before hoisting the finished tray on to the ceiling.

They were not lacking for materials: it must have been the largest boneyard anyone had ever seen when they came across it in 1155, during the building of the medieval city walls.

'So you think it was a bit like cuddling up with a horror movie at a teenage sleepover?' asked Candace. She thought of her friends' daughters, in a blissful kindle, shrieking and squealing at some monster foaming green wax from fanged jaws. 'The Cologne Ladies' quilting bee assembling eleven thousand dead women's bones?'

'Yes, if you think kids are trying to look Death in the eye and tell him, "No go, my friend." But come over here!'

Bettina beckoned her over; she was tapping the walls where reliquary heads were stacked in niches, some of their pretty young faces painted pink and white, some mask-like, golden. Candace joined her, and peered in through the gilded baroque oculi that divided the niches. Inside each one, lavishly veiled in dust, there were skulls, shelf upon shelf.

Candace was silenced; then she whispered, in tones as subdued as felt appropriate: 'Bettina, it's weird, weird and gruesome. Why?'

'Why did they do it? Or why did we come? Because Gervase's work is rooted in Catholic cult and ritual practices like this, and the form they take here. No carnival joking, no capering and thumbing your nose here; no singing and dancing, no Mexican Day of the Dead. The cult of death straight up. "Death is a master from Germany." You know, the kids in Berlin are writing that on the walls now.'

The killing fields of Cologne. Inside each oculus Candace could see the empty eyes of one of Ursula's band looking back at her, blindly, of course. Cézanne's great charnel portraits of his last years.

The guide was explaining something to them. They took it in turns to translate for her:

'Ursula was English.'

'She was?' exclaimed the visiting Englishwoman on cue.

'Yes, an English princess. Something like your Princess Diana.'

'And so were most of her handmaidens.'

'Your compatriots,' said Rudi. 'You feel at home here?'

'Ursula had been betrothed to someone by her father, a pagan. But she refused to marry a pagan.'

'Of course.'

'Instead she sailed away in a boat for a year or two – with all her train.'

'A flotilla,' said Bettina. 'Ten ships, a thousand virgins in each. They made landfalls, spectacular landfalls, on the way. In Brittany, in Flanders. Then they sailed here, up the Rhine, and came face to face with the masters from Germany.'

Bettina began talking again to the sacristan; at her prompting, he unlatched the golden perforated screen that covered one part of the wall opposite the altar, and there, inside, were rows of skulls, like an anatomical specimen collection made during the rationalist vogue for palaeontology, for evolutionary research and brainpan measurements. But Candace saw that each of St Ursula's companions was

visored, so that their deep and empty eyes swam above a
purple mask as if over a yashmak; thick with dust, of course,
the trimmings of gold lace gimp tarnished; after so many
centuries since the ladies' industry had adorned them, they
still displayed a baroque luxury. The sacristan in his hunting
jacket took one off the shelf and held it out for inspection.

'Esmeraria,' he said. 'Saint Esmeraria. She was Ursula's
first cousin, noble-born, like herself . . .' He paused, holding
the skull under Candace's nose, as he nudged Bettina to
translate. She did so, and he picked up the head again. 'They
played together as children, and she stepped in front of a
spear to defend Ursula, crying, "Heavenly Father, I come to
thee with gladness in my heart!" She was a Precursor, she was
to Saint Ursula like John the Baptist to Jesus.'

He was warming to his topic, and walked up to the high
altar of the chapel and picked up a glass vitrine, in which
another visored skull was ensconced.

'Here is Saint Ursula's head.' He held out the relic in its
glass dome to Candace.

Bettina said, 'You may hold it if you wish. It's a privilege.
He can see you are a serious person who will understand.'

The sacristan urged her to accept his proffered treasure.
The expression in his eyes was solemn, even slightly alarmed,
as if he were defying his own better judgement.

'You know, she is the patron saint of migraines, because
she was decapitated,' said Bettina. 'Make a wish.'

'Bettina!' Candace protested, receiving the glass box with
some reluctance. 'You're such a pagan. A prayer, that's
what's called for. This isn't a birthday cake.'

She took it, and looked at the cracks in the skull where the
plates of the cranium were stitched together as if hemmed
by a sewing machine. There was a round hole in the forehead; a wormhole? The same hand-embroidered visor covered her jaws; otherwise, she realised, all these skulls would
have grinned and gaped like ghouls on a fairground ghost
train.

Then she saw that, in contrast, the reliquary heads on the

shelves beside them were showing their rosebud or gilded mouths.

And every one of them was smiling.

The skull in the case was making her feel very peculiar; queasy, and light and out of scale. Not least because she couldn't grasp why she was consenting at all: Here I am, she thought, in this gaudy charnel house, my Yorick no more St Ursula than a stage prop, a nameless ghost's skull in my hand, the ruin of some forgotten Roman from a jostling, phantom population murmuring at me through matter that's no more alive today than . . . what? Than a stone, a busted plastic bottle, a dented tin can, refuse, rubbish, there was nothing of Tom left behind in those scraps of ash and bone; nothing. He's only alive in my memory and in others', and even if memory is made of chemical spurts triggered by grey matter, it's certainly got to be less material than this box, this skull on a pillow.

'It's made me feel rather sick,' she admitted, sucking at the cold air outside once they had left the Golden Chamber and St Ursula's Church.

They walked back to the car in the side street where Rudi had parked it. Bettina was smiling.

'You're so perverse,' said Candace. 'You Catholics.'

'But you were fascinated, weren't you?'

Bettina was sitting in the back; she wanted Candace to see the view, though there was little in view from the autobahn except the flat winter fields dragged into a uniform puddled grey as they drove by.

'I didn't exactly like it. And I don't understand. For me, the dead no longer exist. At least that's what I believe with my rational mind.'

'The rest is voodoo. I know. Tom, Allen, my friend Judith who committed suicide in the river last year, none of them exist any more. At least not materially. But it's hard to let go of the idea of getting through, isn't it? Touching those bits that were once . . .'

Candace protested, 'You sound as if you believe those

bones really are what they're claimed to be. It's preposterous. How could you?'

'Gervase will make it clear. But you don't have to write anything, not unless you want to. It's just, you would do it – well, you would do it perfectly.'

There was a moment of quiet; the winter trees streaked by.

'By the way, Rudi,' said Bettina. 'Tell us about the only one who survived.'

He was pleased to be brought in; he gave a chuckle.

'It wasn't for long. She was choked to death by her mother-in-law a few years later. So she was able to get together with the others, in heaven.

'But she didn't get to be a full Virgin Martyr, I guess.'

The monastery where Gervase Mendoza lived was a disused bottle factory. Over the last three years, he had gradually filled the long central space of the factory floor with exhibits; the upper gallery, where the manager's office and other administrative areas had been, now contained his private apartment and the guest bedroom.

He came to the door as soon as he heard the car. He was wearing a cassock; the black cloth was rusty at the cuffs and hem, and stained with plaster and paint and glue and resin and other materials he was using. His tense eyes were the kind that look as if they're lit up from behind, like an advertisement for a painkiller. He kissed Bettina three times, saying her name, slowly, as if he heard such a name for the first time. His hand when he shook Candace's was chapped; his manner almost absurdly formal, as if he were receiving her on an official occasion: 'I am glad you have come to the Museum of Likeness and Presence; please will you sign the visitors' book. I am afraid that if I don't ask you to do it straight away, I shall forget in the excitement of your company.'

The table contained a small rack of postcards, and a flat glass-topped tray in which a few objects were displayed. 'Museum Replicas,' said the label. Candace noticed an enamel pin brooch of an eye, encircled by what looked like flames.

They presented Gervase with the wine and bag of supplies for their meal; Bettina arranged for Rudi to return the following morning.

They stood together in the entrance to the museum for a while in silence, looking ahead, into the exhibition area.

After the passing of this awkwardness, Gervase handed out acoustiguides, and showed Candace how to tune in to the English translation.

'You will find it very easy to follow. This version takes only half an hour. I haven't yet completed the fuller account. I am composing it now. It will take much longer. For those who like to let their minds wander . . .'

The Museum of Likeness and Presence began with a peepshow: through a pinhole, you could see a tiny piece of fabric, set into what looked like a lump of rock crystal, which had the effect of magnifying it, as if it were an ancient incised gem too small to see with the naked eye. Music played on the acoustiguide, with choirboy sweetness; Gervase's voice, speaking softly, perhaps to lighten his accent, explained, 'The swaddling bands of Jesus were brought to Germany by the second of the Magi, King Melchior, whose remains still lie in the cathedral of Cologne, in a magnificent reliquary that comprises 1,436 cabochon stones of Hellenistic date, mostly originating in Asia Minor and other parts of the ancient Greek empire. Melchior, who was over a thousand years old (longevity was in the family, as it still is in some parts of the eastern Steppes), presented the swaddling bands to the grandfather of Carolus Magnus, who preserved them in a precious coffer that is only opened for one day every two years. However, the Museum of Likeness and Presence was able to locate a piece of the miracle-working cloths that Melchior had kept back for his own use. It was handed down in the female line of the family of the Gräfin Adelheid von Kreuzeningen who was gracious enough to donate it in her grandmother's memory.'

Candace unlatched the device in her ear, and went to find

Bettina, who was listening in front of another vitrine in which was coiled a rope, with some miniature white roses growing beside it from a seeming fissure in the earth that covered the floor of the showcase.

Bettina forestalled her, pointing: 'The rope which the famous fakir something-or-other-Nandy used to climb up to heaven in the year seventeen hundred and something,' she said. 'He always left behind him an elusive scent of roses. So we have the flowers.'

Candace giggled. Then she noticed that the roses weren't real. They were so delicately rendered, almost tremulous, that they must have been cast from the real thing by lost wax, and then painted, or enamelled.

Gervase Mendoza had worked before as a restorer; Bettina had done the same course in fine art conservation techniques in Rome in the early seventies, and they had been friends since then, as his international reputation as appropriation artist and culture guru grew. Recently he'd established his Museum of Likeness and Presence, his *wunderkammer*, his cabinet of curiosities, and visitors were beginning to make the journey into the countryside near Cologne in greater numbers. It remained a mystery how he survived; the entry charge was nominal. But then he truly lived like a monk, as he claimed to do.

'The thing about Gervase now,' Bettina confided, pausing her machine and moving them towards another case, 'is that he will never depart from the role he's assumed. The likeness he presents is the truth. He wants you to believe that there's nothing else lying veiled behind, and in many ways there isn't. However much you try to make him – to talk normally, to talk about what he's doing, what he's exactly up to – he won't. I don't even know any more if he thinks he's playing, or not. He'll tell you he's in charge of a small, little-known museum of sacred icons and relics, he'll insist that he was appointed by his order, and there's no more to it than that.'

They were now looking at the flaming enamel eye, the original of the replica in the museum shop.

Bettina turned on the tape again and fixed the earpiece; Candace did likewise.

'The eye is the lucky jewel,' said the steady, accented voice. 'Found in the brow of the toad when the princess in the fairy story lost her golden ball down the well and he retrieved it for her. Some say it is the pineal eye which experiences the wonders which the eyes of the body cannot see.'

Bettina touched her on the arm. 'You see that is the clue. Gervase always had a thing about toads.'

The cabinet contained some more predictable items: a unicorn horn, a stuffed mermaid like many found in animal specimen collections of the seventeenth and eighteenth centuries; a curling, crumpled horn that had grown from the forehead of a certain Magdalena Duckers.

Candace remembered those freak shows of her journey through the States many years before, 'Ripley's Believe It or Not!' in which Houdini's stunts were reproduced alongside bearded ladies, the Most Gigantic Amethyst ever mined, and the slippers of the Chinese Cinderella (two and a half centimetres of flowered satin).

In an aquarium some cone snails were crawling over tiny pebbles: Gervase's commentary explained that their venom produced such a deep sleep that the victim would appear to be dead, and that certain celebrated resurrections may have occurred after an unsuspected encounter with such a snail. The creature's method was to stun any obstacle with its slime.

'This is true, I think, by the way,' said Bettina. 'And these are real snails.'

'I don't think so,' her friend replied, keeping her eyes fixed on the moving forms. 'The pattern of their movements repeats. Watch. But how's it done? With magnets? With electronics?'

'The method is part of the mystery, I guess. Gervase is rocking your deepest sense of stability, undoing your bearings in reality. He wants you to know wonder again, and in that way to see God. That's the point, like it or leave it.'

Candace no longer wanted to cry out against it; or at least that wasn't the only response. She wanted to laugh. She was laughing. It was a funny feeling, loose and wild, and the image of a kite passed across her mind, at the moment when the child flying it lets go, and it bobs away, jerking in the wind and gaining height till lost to sight.

Gervase accepted the picnic Bettina had brought, and indeed, it seemed as if he would have overlooked the question of eating altogether if they had not appeared; he took pieces of sausage and tomato and he drank Bettina's champagne, rather obediently and frugally. But the stubborn consistency of his play-acting – if it was play-acting – made him flat company; it reminded Candace of visiting heavily sedated friends in hospital after a crisis; she was soon floundering about for a topic that would crack his apparent automatism. Bettina had infinite patience with artists and their idiosyncrasies, it was part of her job, she said, and however obdurate their pretence or their mask, she remained interested. But she was alert to Candace's need for comforting, and so she soon announced that they were retiring, and drew Candace off early to their cell.

Neither woman had yet lost her parents; so they were still someone's children, and for this reason perhaps, they were able to sit together like children on the thin mattress, tipped towards each other by the sagging chain-link hammock of a bedstead, and Candace smoked and dunked the butts in the wash-basin when she'd finished. Bettina talked about the friends she had lost; and the loved ones. She made it possible for Candace to think, to speak, to face their absence with her. We have lost so many, thought Candace, but somehow this hasn't taught me to accept what's coming and change my ways. Bettina's eyes searched out that space in the middle distance that is also somehow that recess of memory deep in the back of the head where the lost loved one can be made visible, still moving, still talking; her vision became wings for Candace, that she could fasten to her ankles, to her cap, so that she too could follow. She may be as incapable of being sensible as I am, Candace was thinking, but she doesn't evade the issue or pretend the worst hasn't happened: one form of blindness doesn't, in her case, throw a cast over the whole of her sight, as it does with me.

'I didn't go to Tom's funeral,' she finally confessed. 'I was ready, I was dressed, and then I couldn't make myself. The undertakers telephoned afterwards. I was so ashamed. They were calling to make an appointment to deliver the urn.'

She was able to admit it to Bettina, her terrible failure. Her denial, as a therapist would call it. Bettina knew; friends had told her. Candace herself had rung her, late one night, and left a wandering message on her machine.

Candace was saying: 'But the last time Tom and I slept together was 1986. And that was a mistake. I never considered myself attached. Not really, not properly. But I turned out to be, you know: "A little more than kin and a little less than kind."'

Bettina put her head on one side and one of her delicate eyebrows contracted. 'Why are you reproaching yourself? Tom could have been having a joke: it sounds like one to me. To send you his jar . . .'

'Urn.'

'Urn, of course. *Urna*. A kind of comic revenge of the discarded lover. The sort of prank you get in low Italian fables. Boccaccio-style misogyny.'

'For what?'

'For sleeping with him in the first place; or, for not sleeping with him since 1986. I don't know. I never sleep with anyone now. It's too complicated.'

'I don't either. But not because I've made up my mind not to. I'm cursed with heterosexuality.'

Bettina threw back her head with laughter. 'You should be happy about that – the fires not dim yet!'

The sound of feet shuffled down the gallery towards their door, followed by a tap and Gervase's voice calling: '*Liebe Bettina!*' Bettina's eyes danced over her hand as she smothered a laugh.

'Gervase! At this time of night!'

Candace tried to straighten herself; to run a brush through her hair, brighten her lips and cheeks.

'Come, I have something to show you!'

'We're coming,' Bettina sang out. 'Just a minute.'

He took them along the gallery, now lit only by the glow above the doors of their bedroom and from the frosted glass windows of the manager's former office cubicle, his closed apartment's antechamber.

'Your eyes will soon become accustomed to the darkness, and you will see better.'

Gervase reached for Bettina's hand; she gave Candace her other and the three of them seemed to tiptoe through the darkness of the museum's central nave. At the far end, in a new glass box, was the shape of a head apparently made of gold, for its edges flared, though the rest of it was black. As they got closer, they still couldn't pick out any features, and when they were standing almost with their noses to the glass, there was nothing in the case except an oval glow suspended over a small cushion made of plum velvet.

'Bettina, and you, too, Bettina's dear friend, you are the first to see the greatest treasure the Museum of Likeness and Presence has been fortunate to acquire. Just keep your eyes steady, as if looking through the case, past it, not trying to pick out anything in it, and you will begin to see something.'

In the dark, Gervase's low, stilted speech made Candace half-giggly, half-jittery; she began to feel cross-eyed as she tried to adjust her focus in the way he described. Bettina still had her hand in Candace's; Candace was glad of her touch; her string was now held firm, she was earthed.

Then she saw it: it materialised in front of her eyes just a fraction before the same gasp of pleasure escaped from Bettina's lips.

'You cannot photograph it,' said Gervase, still in English for all their benefit. 'It's an image which has no reflection. Because it's not made of light, but only of deeper degrees of shadow. So the only place you can see it is here, and in this darkness.'

342

It was a kind of face; a pair of eyes and a pair of lips; above all a smile; a smile dreaming to itself in space.

'*Acheiropoieton*: made with no hands,' said Gervase. 'A relic so rare I do not think it can be found anywhere else but here. It is the true likeness of a soul in paradise, caught permanently as an impression in the air, in the same way as you see matter dance in the rays of the sun.'

'Did you notice something familiar about her?' Bettina whispered to Candace when they were back at last in their funny gimcrack bed with its dipping support.

'The seraphic smile?'

'Yes.'

'It's his most beautiful piece so far. So ethereal. Visible and invisible. There and not there. Like and not like. Present and not present.'

'If there were eleven thousand of them,' Candace said thickly, through waves of tiredness, 'there's no reason not to have turned up another, I suppose.'

'*Eh già, vero.*'

'Goo . . . night, Bettina.'

'Sleep well, darling Candace.'

'You too.'

'You're glad you came?'

'Ye . . .'

They were both drifting now, coasting through another kind of dark.

Candace Parris was stiff when she got back home, from a bad night trying not to roll her bulk against the childlike slightness of Bettina asleep, and from having sat on the runway in the crowded plane while some passenger whose bag was on board remembered to catch the flight . . . and then she'd taken the crowded tube from the airport and, in the interests of health and beauty, carried her bag the ten-minute walk to her door from the station. But she was still happy, she was still drifting, still laughing; she went to the kitchen and found some washed salad left over in the fridge which hadn't browned too badly, a couple of small tomatoes and a jar of mayonnaise lite. Then she brought down the urn standing on the floor in her wardrobe and took some of Tom's dust and ashes and sprinkled them like pepper on the mayonnaise; she loaded her fork and bit carefully, reverently, expecting a tart, metal pungency, something like semen but dry. The flavour was elusive, so she took another two dressed and seasoned leaves, but found that they tasted no different.

Fay Weldon

BIG WOMEN

An extract from a TV drama in four parts
on the rise and fall of feminism, 1971–1996
and the House of Medusa

Big Women is a fictional account of the lives of four
feminists, Layla, Stephanie, Nancy and Alice, who set out to
change the world and succeed – but at considerable cost to
themselves. The story runs from the seventies through to the
present day. The personal became the political, the political
personal, and the attempt to live according to principle is not
achieved without sacrifice. Indeed it can be fatal.

The story so far: The four women start a co-operative
publishing house – Medusa. Stephanie leaves her husband
Hamish and her two sons, Roy and Rafe. Her place is taken
by Daffy. One of the weaker sisters, Zoe, has taken her own
life. The funeral service becomes an inquest. Layla comes late,
delayed in bed as she is by the apparently irresistible Hamish.
How not to fall in love with men seems at times to be the
most difficult problem of all.

From Part II: *A Nest of Randy Vipers* ...

GOLDERS GREEN CREMATORIUM, 1979

Early, misty, autumnal, beautiful. The first service of the day.
We don't know who's died. A small knot of people begin to
gather outside one of the many chapels: Johnny (just come
out as gay) there with his camera and his new boyfriend
Richard; Alice, the tiny feminist academic, with her good luck
charms; conscientious Stephie, uncomfortable with her two
sons and their stepmother Daffy; Nancy the accountant with

345

her two New Zealand friends, Brian and Beverley; Woman we know from Reclaim the Night and Black Women Demand Wages for Housework. Noticeably absent one Zoe Fairfax, the good if unwilling wife to Bullivant and mother of Saffron, and the impetuous Layla, whose funds keep Medusa afloat. Everyone is upset. This is an untimely death.

JOHNNY: This light's terrific, but it's beginning to go. Where's the fucking hearse?

RICHARD: Late for her own funeral.

JOHNNY: It isn't funny –

NANCY: I hate suicides. So selfish. What about her poor children?

Rafe and Roland, Stephie's boys, have found sticks and are slashing at flowers. They seem thoroughly disturbed. Daffy makes moves to stop them.

DAFFY: Stop that at once – remember where you are.

STEPHIE: Leave them alone. They're boys. They can't help it.

DAFFY: They could be fed oestrogen.

STEPHIE: It's not hormones, it's culture and conditioning make boys behave like boys, and girls behave like girls.

DAFFY: I just don't believe that.

STEPHIE: Studies prove it.

DAFFY: Little girls flirt with their fathers, little boys bang about with sticks. That's that.

STEPHIE: Only because of parental expectation.

DAFFY: Don't let's quarrel. We're all upset.

Roland stops slashing, but only to observe.

ROLAND (*loud and clear*): If it's a suicide, why isn't she being buried in unconsecrated ground?

People hear and shuffle. Faces all around are distraught and distressed. Elsewhere –

ALICE: All these male priests dressing up as women. Earth to earth's all right, but ashes to ashes is dire.

She's talking to MARY, a hard-smoking, lean, shrewd journalist.

MARY: You're into reincarnation, I suppose.

ALICE: Makes sense.

MARY: No it doesn't. Who decides, tell me that? If you're

going to come back as a cow or a horse or a tree-frog? Well?
Is there some committee up there? Or is it a one-person
decision?

ALICE: You've been drinking. It isn't even ten o'clock.

MARY: Wouldn't you – this could be any of us. And where's
Layla? Is she too grand to turn up? God, I hate this kind of
occasion.

Well, at least it isn't Layla who's died.

THE PRIMROSE HILL BEDROOM

*In the rumpled bed a naked Hamish, Rafe and Roland's
father, Daffy's lover, leans on one elbow above none
other than a naked Layla. He strokes her neck, she
succumbs; she seems mesmerised. She makes an effort.*

LAYLA: Not now. I can't be late.

HAMISH: Who's more important, the living or the dead?

LAYLA: The living.

HAMISH: Who do you love?

LAYLA: You.

HAMISH: Who do you want?

LAYLA: You.

HAMISH: What is the proper place for a woman?

LAYLA: Underneath a man. Only kidding. I crossed my
fingers.

HAMISH: I don't think you did.

He moves his body to cover hers.

HAMISH: Owned, controlled, confined. Women will
never find their freedom. They like sex too much.

*Layla suffers, but submits; missionary seems to be
enough.*

LAYLA: I do not take this seriously, Hamish. Don't think
I do.

HAMISH: I hadn't noticed you staying away. Say oh, oh,
oh.

LAYLA (*sincere*): Oh, oh, oh.

HAMISH: What price liberation now?

347

Layla, post-orgasmic, remembering her political stance.
LAYLA: Bloody men. We'll be late for the funeral.

THE CREMATORIUM. DAY

The hearse turns into the crematorium. A big black Rolls, followed by others. The coffin's taken out. Bull and Saffron, in black, follow it into the chapel. So it's poor Zoe who has died, and by her own hand. Last time we saw Zoe, her husband Bull was burning her manuscript page by page; a work on sociology Layla and Stephanie at Medusa had in principle accepted for publication. But this was Zoe's only copy. And it was through Stephie's folly that Bull so much as knew it existed.

The Mourners fall in behind. Organ music plays. The duty Chaplain takes the service. We hear snatches of his sermon; the snuffles and sobs of the mourners.
CHAPLAIN: . . . to mark the passing of our beloved sister, Zoe Fairfax, dutiful wife to – (*he glances at his notes*) – Bulliver, and mother of – uh – Saffron and Sampson . . . Zoe dedicated her life to her family, and was a joy to all who knew her . . . kind, generous, bearing her illness, the scourge of depression, with fortitude and courage – What can we say of such a woman, an example to all who knew her, who turned her back on the whims and fancies of the new world, but that her price was above rubies.
Et cetera. Layla and Hamish enter, late. Reproachful faces turn to look at them. Roland and Rafe wave at their father; Stephie, remembering she's their mother, leans across to slap their hands down. Layla and Hamish take their places behind Stephie and Daffy, who are both furious. Daffy hisses over Layla's shoulder –
DAFFY: You said you'd stop seeing him.
LAYLA: For God's sake, Daffy, this is a funeral.
STEPHIE: It's the total lack of judgement –
DAFFY: It isn't fair on the boys – I don't care about me –

Hamish looks smug. Women fighting over him. They realise that's just what they're doing, and subside. Rafe and Roland slip across to the adjacent row, by way of generalised protest. The hymn starts –

> Lord of all hopefulness,
> Lord of all joy,
> Whose trust ever childlike,
> No care could destroy . . .

Curtains begin to slink apart: the hymn continues, desultorily, the coffin jerks, but at first fails to move –
CHAPLAIN: We are conceived in sin, and born to sin . . . The wonder and the gift is His forgiveness through the miracle of Jesus Christ our Lord . . .
He stops: offended. Johnny has used his flash as the coffin finally slides in.
CHAPLAIN: I'm sorry . . . could you refrain . . .
LAYLA (*loudly, from the back*): But you're writing a book, aren't you, Johnny? Death in the Age of Transition. Everything's OK if you're writing a book.
She's coming forward now, to address the congregation. A stir of alarm and interest. Saffron comes forward.
LAYLA (*to the chaplain*): You, Sir, are giving our sister, Zoe, now burning to a crisp, a truly rotten send-off. She deserves better than this. Zoe the bright star. Zoe head-in-air, killing herself to prove the point. Shall we speak for her?
Bull is on his feet, marshalling his children and the cortege party. He means them to leave, and at once. Saffron lingers.
LAYLA: Oh yes, go, Bull: get out before you hear what you don't want to hear. You must be feeling guilty: you stifled her to death, you and the patriarchy you represent. Why did you bring the kids anyway? Funerals are no place for children.
Saffron looks longingly back.
SAFFRON: I'm not a child.
A point she will continue to make through Part III. Bull drags her forcibly out.

LAYLA: OK. Of Zoe's friends here assembled: who has anything real to say about her death?

Some others in the congregation leave, offended. The Chaplain is alarmed but concludes his best plan is to let those who remain do their own thing. Stephie comes forward.

STEPHIE: They say Zoe was depressed. Of course she was depressed. She was married to Bull Fairfax, and trying to write a book, and be a wife and mother, and it was all too much. Her husband discouraged and diminished her; she had a brain but it was trapped in a female body. She took an overdose of sleeping pills and alcohol, but it was patriarchy mixed the draught, not Zoe.

Daffy's turn to come forward.

DAFFY: Zoe was my friend. She was kind, good, clever and brave. But she was always guilty, she always thought she ought to be somewhere else. Bull made her feel bad because she believed there was something more to life than just handing it on to the next generation. And now she hasn't even got a life of her own. What am I going to do without her?

LAYLA: Thank you, Daffy, you get more likeable by the day. That's what happens if you live with Stephie, who is our feminist conscience incarnate.

Layla smiles at Stephie, making peace. Stephie manages a smile back. Hamish's turn to get to his feet: he beckons Rafe and Ronald; they follow him out –

HAMISH: This is no place for males.

DAFFY (*to the boys*): Don't you dare go with your father –

STEPHIE (*to Daffy*): Let them go –

The boys go, unmoved one way or another by female instruction: since Daffy and Stephie usually say the opposite, they do as they think fit.

CHAPLAIN: Please, this is a chapel of rest, not a women's liberation meeting.

LAYLA: Really? You could have fooled me.

CHAPLAIN: You are being inconsiderate. There is another service waiting to come in.

350

The next group of mourners is indeed waiting outside.
Someone rattles the chapel door. Useless.

NANCY is on her feet.
NANCY: Zoe died because she was in a hopeless double
bind. How could she leave her husband without leaving her
children too? She had a degree, a doctorate, but still she
couldn't earn enough to keep herself, let alone them too.
Women's wages are a third of men's. Back home in New
Zealand at least she'd have a claim on the matrimonial house:
here, if she walks out, she gets nothing. Why does everything
go so slowly? Sometimes I think we'll all die before anything
changes. I'm sorry, I'm upset.
LAYLA: So are we all. Johnny, say something.
JOHNNY: Who, me? A mere man. But I can see this much.
Zoe was born bright, pretty, happy and female. So what went
wrong? That's the problem you women have to solve.
LAYLA: Thank you for your condescension, Johnny. How
fortunate we are to have your support.
A young woman, Janice, speaks from the back of the chapel:
a quiet, pretty, mousy girl.
JANICE: I don't know what you're going on about. I was
having an affair with Bull and Zoe found out. It was nothing
to do with writing books, or being a wife or mother. It was
all my fault. I want to die too. Why can't you leave her in
peace?
JANICE runs from the chapel. Eyes follow her.
LAYLA: Alice?
ALICE speaks in her small voice to a hushed chapel.
ALICE: Zoe died because she was weak: because by virtue of
her gender and her own nature she was prevented from
taking her proper part in society. Everywhere men divide us
and render us powerless. But Zoe died because we failed her
as well. We grieve for her, and our own shortcomings.
LAYLA: Thank you, Alice. That's about it. Lukewarm coffee
and biscuits round at Artemis. Let's go.
She smiles politely at the Chaplain.
LAYLA: Thank you for your courtesy.

351

All file out, righteousness raising them above the ordinary, ruthlessly brushing past the other more conventional mourners as they in their turn enter.

Martin Turner

SNOW

for Peter and Irina Scorer

I. PEREDELKINO

Literature is still the art of the lonely.
To this completely ordinary dacha
came the stream of Nobel mail.
Now the gaunt man is gone from his potato beds.

Writers' houses seem bare. He wrote
standing up, seeing only the newspapers
he sharpened his pencils over.
From the upright desk the words are flown.

In the village church a miraculous icon
once walked up the Aegean to Athos.
Outside tarmac laid for a First Lady
is modestly cased in ice.

The tomb, a family plot; the stone displays
the drooping Arab stallion lines.
Above the growl of passing goods trains rises
the tumult of finches in *ribina* bushes.

II. ABOUT THESE POEMS

After Boris Pasternak, *My Sister Life* (1922)

I will pound them on pavements
with glass and sun,

353

and in winter let their sound
invade the damp corners of ceilings.

The attic room will recite them
to the window with a bow,
so that bad luck and ill omens
leapfrog away up into the roof.

Beginnings and endings will not lie smothered
in month-long drifts of snow.
I will still remember
all the frond-play of sunlight.

Blinking like a jackdaw, Christmas's
short, bright dawn will sharpen for us
– my love and me – things
we had never dreamed of.

Then I'll call from the window, shading
my eyes and protected by a scarf,
to the children in the yard below:
'What century is it outside now?

Who cleared a pathway to the door
of this snow-fast cave
while I was smoking with Lord Byron
and enjoying a drink with Edgar Allan Poe?'

I have been a familiar in the infernal
armoury of Daryal[1]
and with a Lermontov-like[2] shudder
steeped lips and life in Vermouth.[3]

III.

Nature is both wife and widow
to the old man in the witness-box

who never remembers anything.
One day in summer he fell into
a lifelong bed so naturally
he was not swamped by possession.

Preferring beauty raw he ministered
to all women in the one he kissed
with his whole life until
they both fell under the weight.
Later, through deep hours they heard
hooves approaching like rain.

It took a prodigious, almost animal
innocence not to see inessentials.
He was as close, breath for breath,
as a missing twin. Now, he weeps
with joy at all the colours
his heart attack reveals.

Tradition reprieves from self-consciousness.
Creativity is God's school.
Give him veins of prunus in the thin sky,
blossoms staunch on cake-piping of frost
and a flowering shrub visible only
to a blind man at night.

1. A narrow gorge in the Caucasus.
2. Russian romantic poet (1814–41) and dedicatee of *My Sister Life*.
   The Caucasus mountains were a frequent setting for Lermontov's
   poems.
3. Wormwood.

Francis Wheen

THIRSTING FOR A WORSTING

SPRING STREET, EAST LONDON, on a roasting morning in June.

A white-haired black man was calmly butting his head against the red-brick wall outside the tatty PricePopper supermarket. A small crowd gathered to watch. Blood dribbled in slow motion through the tight curls and down the weary forehead. No one flinched.

In the hardware shop across the road, a plumber was buying a plastic S-bend and discussing football. 'England aren't a bad side,' he announced, 'but it's a fart to a fuck they'll blow it in the semi-finals.'

In the front bedroom of 83 Spring Street, obscured by net curtains from the prying eyes of passengers on the top deck of the Number 6 bus, Stanton Harcourt – or Stan, as he preferred to be known in this postal district – was masturbating over the March issue of *Aerobics* magazine.

Outside his front door, maddened by the heat, two young college students were arguing loudly, ostentatiously.

'You're crew brew.'

'?'

'Cruising for a bruising.'

'?'

'You know what I mean. Strolling for a rolling. Lolloping for a walloping.'

'But I –'

'If you don't write that essay, pal, you're germinating for a terminating.'

The tumult and preening were ignored by passers-by. You could kill someone here and not be witnessed. Not only could: did. Two weeks ago, at twilight, a boy had his throat cut on Stanton Harcourt's doorstep. Not until two days later did some busybody think to report the crime. The police did their routine – nothing to worry about, ma'am, just a murder inquiry – but the file remained open. It'll be open at the end of the next millennium. The guy had clearly been heading for a spreading.

How did Stanton Harcourt cope with a corpse blocking his egress for two days? Easy: he stepped over it.

Sometimes, on idle mornings, Stan took his breakfast in the local café, Mary's.

'Hear about Gladys, Mary?' an old thing asked one morning.

'Whabouter?'

Stan was alert, his forkful of sausage suspended half-way to his mouth.

'She got shot.'

'Ah.'

'In the foot.'

'Nasty,' Mary observed, solemn as a High Court judge. 'It's always worse in the foot.'

A donkey-faced dosser was lurking at the bus-stop as Stanton Harcourt arrived to begin his vigil, later that morning.

'Catechism,' the oldster muttered, blowing his ammonia-scented breath over Stan's cheek.

Silence, except for the roar of car-engines.

'Catechism,' the ancient mariner repeated. 'Unusual word.'

Stan nodded agreement.

'Do you know how to spell it?'

'C-A-T-E-C-H-I-S-M,' Stan said helpfully.

'That's right. Beautiful word. Beautiful idea.'

The man with a donkey's face ambled onward, up Spring Street.

Angling for a mangling, Stanton Harcourt skipped on to the bus clad in a pair of white-flannel shorts. He lurched along the top deck to the front seats, enduring insults and raillery from the upper-circle audience. 'Fun boy!' a pockmarked skinhead called out. 'Get those fun-boy legs moving! Sloping for a groping, are we?' Blessed art thou when men revile thee. Nobody likes us and we don't care.

In the seats behind him, two middle-managers in cheap suits were striving rather too hard to be businesslike. He caught odd phrases from their conversation – 'matching vectors . . . upscale . . . downside . . . efficiency matrix . . . bugger up the interpersonals . . .' It meant nothing to him; it probably meant nothing to them.

At the forward end of the first floor he could see the driver's head through a glass, darkly; a periscope in reverse. As the bus laboured eastwards, out of London proper into pre-suburban limbo, the first-floor crowd dispersed. By the time he reached his stop, among the flyovers and industrial estates, Stan was the only passenger. He vaulted down the staircase, and off.

He crossed a urine-scented underpass and a graffiti-spattered footbridge before reaching his place of work, half-way down the High Street. A fading sign, in some forgotten 1970s typeface, announced its function: Social Services Neighbourhood Office.

Stanton Harcourt was a receptionist. His days passed in a busy blur of telephone messages, instant coffee and random badinage with the strange, inarticulate creatures who wandered in off the street. There were sad cases, hard cases and nutcases; some wanted money or a new flat, but others were merely after an occasional dose of human company, an audience for their rambling recollections. Most of his colleagues resented the intrusion of the general public into their neat and orderly world of filing cabinets, memos and case meetings. Stan loved it. He was, he now realised, good at not buggering up the interpersonals.

One of the regular visitors, known only as Jack, was a shrivelled old codger in his early seventies who always wore a grubby fawn raincoat and a tweed cap, regardless of the season. A major stroke a few years earlier had left him paralysed in his left arm and almost incoherent in his speech. Most days, just in time for elevenses, he would call in for a chipped mug of Gold Blend and fifteen minutes of slurred observations about – well, who could tell what he was on about? No one else in the front office could be bothered to listen to Jack's ravings, but Stan was one of those rare specimens who enjoy having their patience taxed.

Or perhaps he was just nosy: having always regarded himself as a bit of a weirdo, Stan had a limitless appetite for the odd and the damaged, his kindred spirits. That, after all, was why he lived in Spring Street. Friends sometimes urged him to move to a better borough – somewhere 'up-and-coming' – but he scorned this estate-agency jargon as a euphemism for pasting a thick layer of make-up on a wizened face. He preferred to stay where he was, down among the scars and bruises of a decaying metropolis.

Toot Baldon, one of the more boisterous and ambitious social workers, swaggered up to Stan's desk at the end of the afternoon. 'I'm heading your way,' he drawled. 'Fancy a lift? I'll be going in half an hour.'

To kill time, Stan went for a lager in the pub round the corner, the Duke of Devonshire. Did Toot fancy him? Had his white shorts awakened hidden desires? Although Stan himself was tediously, irretrievably heterosexual, he still hoped to find a gay gene lurking in his libido – if only because he felt slightly ashamed, as a wilful non-conformist, to have anything in common with the Archbishop of Canterbury or the Prince of Wales. Why, only the other day he had found an old newspaper photograph of Princess Diana in a leotard, and had been as reliably stimulated as even Prince Charles must once have been, years ago, when he saw that same vision made flesh.

Stan tried to banish this uncomfortable daydream by returning to the more urgent question: should he flirt with Toot? But at that moment he was distracted by the sight of a familiar figure entering the pub, limping heavily. It was Jack. He was accompanied – led, really – by his wife, a scrawny, thin-lipped biddy who placed him without ceremony in a corner seat and disappeared to the bar to fetch half a pint of Guinness. When she returned, she sat drinking in silence. Jack had nothing. He watched her balefully as she sipped the froth from her beer-mug. She had several more, each time buying herself one and ignoring her husband, obviously relishing his discomfort.

Feeling a pleasant shiver of curiosity, Stan downed the tepid dregs of his own pint and returned to the office in search of transport.

Toot drove an ageing 2CV, which had been sweltering in the staff car-park for at least eight hours.

'It's as hot as a show-jumper's crotch in here,' Stan said, easing himself painfully into the passenger seat. 'You ought to get an electric fan – you can plug them into the cigar lighter.'

The old wreck didn't have a cigar lighter. Nor did it have a stereo aerial, nor even a windscreen wiper. It had two bullet-holes in the bonnet, put there a week ago by a jumbo dumbo in shell-suit and trainers who disapproved of Toot's choice of parking place in Wirral Lane, where he lived. And its soft-top was embellished with a number of interesting stab wounds, some of them the handiwork of jumbo's colleagues. 'Driving for a kniving,' Stan commented, instinctively, as he inspected the damage.

Still, Toot never much liked cigars.

As they drove along the steaming dual carriageway that led to the city proper, Stan felt a warm drowsiness spreading through his limbs. The beer? The sun? Whatever, he ought to make some sort of conversation, if only to repay Toot's unprecedented generosity. Besides, he still hadn't decided whether he dared risk a seduction. He needed to stall for a bit, before Toot could start chatting him up.

'I just nipped into the Duke,' he said. 'Saw Jack in there.'

A look of puzzlement flickered across Toot's face before he clocked the name. 'Oh, your chatty chum,' he sneered. 'Not exactly a bundle of laughs, is he? I don't think I've ever seen him smile.'

Stan bristled. 'He's had a hard life. This is a rough town. He was forced to take early retirement because of his stroke, you know.'

'What did he do before that?'

'Not sure. Something in a garage, I think – panel-beating, that sort of thing.'

'Well, I wish he'd fix my rust-bucket. It needs a damn good thrashing. Begging for it.'

Stan gazed out at the high-rise flats, their windows glinting in the evening sun. 'Tracking for a smacking,' he murmured.

When they reached Spring Street, Stan hauled himself awkwardly out of the passenger seat, suddenly regretting his impulsive choice of white-flannel shorts. He was surprised to discover that Toot's unthinking contempt for Jack had killed any desire, however hypothetical, to invite him in. He would spend the evening in satisfying solitude. You never know, there might even be some women's gymnastics on the TV later on. There often was at this time of year.

'Thanks, Toot,' he called through the open car-window. 'I know it sounds greedy, but could you do me another favour? I think a duty social worker ought to go and visit Jack at home. Just to see how he lives, case the joint. He lives in a council house behind the pub. Number 23. With his wife.'

What did he hope to learn? Nothing, probably. It was just that old inquisitive impulse.

Toot breezed into the office after lunch the next day. 'Well, Stan old boy. You certainly have some interesting friends.'

He had been to chateau Jack that morning. The wife – Peggy – greeted him as if unexpected visits from officialdom were always a pleasure. She served him tea and digestive biscuits in their spotless kitchen, babbling cheerfully about the latest royal divorce, the shocking price of milk and the joys of an English summer. Jack remained silent throughout. Poor old bugger, Toot thought; he knows his place.

As Toot was leaving, he happened to glance into the sitting room, where he was puzzled to notice several irregular brown stains on the walls. When he asked about them, merely to make conversation, the old woman went immediately to a cupboard by the sofa and pulled out an ancient cricket bat.

'I chastise him with this,' she announced proudly.

Toot stared at her thin, liver-spotted fingers, and then at the sturdy weapon she brandished. She was unperturbed. 'I hope it doesn't shock you,' she continued. 'Before he had his stroke, you see, this cricket bat was used on me. By him, for thirty-odd years of our marriage. Now it's my turn.'

Stan laughed uncontrollably for a full minute after hearing Toot's recitation. 'So what happens now?' he inquired, still choking slightly, as the fit began to subside. 'It's not really any of our business, I suppose. You can't deny the old bugger was asking for it – straining for a caning, searching for a birching, clamouring for a hammering. And he got it. Honours even, I'd say. Match drawn.'

'It's happened already,' Toot replied coldly. 'We have to follow procedures. I've taken out an emergency place-of-safety order. Jack will be transferred to an old people's home this afternoon.'

'And Peggy?'

'Oh, I think she can look after herself. Perhaps she'll start dropping in here. I've told her that you can always be relied on for a friendly chinwag, a cup of coffee and a biscuit. She's rather partial to biscuits. Now, if you don't mind, I've got other business to attend to.'

After Toot's abrupt departure, Stan gazed out of the window for several minutes in a trance. He tried to imagine the sepia-stained torture-chamber only a few hundred yards away, but all he could think of was the cricket bat. He pictured a tall, middle-aged Jack striding out to open the innings, handsome in white flannels and club cap, on a suburban sports ground. His wife would be in the pavilion, brewing an urn of tea and laying out the sandwiches while she chatted to the other wives about the shocking price of milk and the joys of an English summer.

And, every minute or so, she would hear the distant but resonant whack of leather on willow.

Stevie White

BLIND SOLOMON

Extract from a novel in progress

I FINISHED AND came out and washed my hands. The old-timer black man was still there, bare-backed and bent over the sink and shaving; scraping the naked and terrifying blade across the back of his head. Then he put down the razor and stroked his wet pate all over with those big flat hands.

Then I thought, Eh? What an idiot: the wash-basin he was standing at – right in the middle – was the only one that didn't have a wall-mirror in front of it. It was smashed and missing; only shards remaining at the four corners under screw-heads. Why'd he chosen that one, the dickhead? I pulled a frown and watched him for a while. Noticed the eyes waving about uncontrolled as if he was fitting and I twigged he was blind. 'Course. God, get a brain, Frank.

I dried my hands under the machine then went back to lean against the tiles, watching the old blind black guy who was wiping his baby-smooth crown now with a handkerchief. Who did he look like – someone off the telly, a much older Montel Williams only without the body. No body. I wondered first why he was shaving in a public toilet, why he was alone, why he didn't have a guide-dog or something and I guessed either he'd just arrived in the capital and was freshening up before staying with friends (which seemed on the improbable side of unlikely), or he was homeless. He was probably homeless.

My idle thoughts wandered to the messages in the cubicle and I considered how many blind benders there were in the world and if they left messages to one another in the toilets, too, in braille, or if they scratched out some other kind of tactile cuneiform on the –

'What you spyin' at, soldier-boy?'

Shit, it was him. He'd suddenly growled at me in a raspy American accent, Southern it sounded, and I didn't know whether to be embarrassed or confused. So I was scared instead and, unmanned, I started to creep out through the turnstile which stiffened deliberately to tease me, and its extraordinary rattle made much of my departure, the bastard thing. Some madness possessed me and I scrambled for cover like I was under fire until I'd got back outside on the Paddington concourse. Immediately I was ashamed of myself. Not for staring at a harmless old guy, but for hoofing it in such inexcusable panic from an amazing blind man who could see behind him. I composed myself sharpish and moved a long distance away to watch the Gents exit until he came out.

When he did, he was wrapped in a coat and trussed up with string to keep out the cold. On his head was a funny baby's bonnet and he looked cosy enough. And he toddled about in the most incredible manner. He obviously couldn't see a thing cos he made a beeline for the wall of the Croissant Shop, yet he stopped short before he walked into it, reached out and touched and followed it to the corner then off into the vast desert of space that was the station.

Look, Ma, no stick. There weren't a lot of people around but he breezed through the middle of what there was, never stepping out of the way but never walking into anyone either. He'd slow down as if he felt the prickle of a body approaching and let them walk around him. 'Course, people could tell he was blind by those strange, big, yearning eyes that would lean out of his head as if trying to see upward at some impossible angle. Trying to see something no one had ever thought of looking at before. Hang on, don't let him get away!

Out on the dark street I lost some of my sighted advantage but I followed him at a distance, and curious. I was thinking, this is just the sort of diversion I could do with every night, to fill my lonely nocturnal hours. Bit of excitement. He went through Craven Hill down to Bayswater Road and crossed at a pelican when the tone sounded. All the time walking behind him I couldn't believe he was heading for my neck of the woods. 'Course, he might have been gonna keep on the move all night for all I knew, until we reached Notting Hill Gate when he popped into the McDonald's there that'd just opened – how did he know that? – and took the weight off in a corner alone and without a purchase.

I went to the counter and considered what to do. *Soldier-boy?* Christ, he *did* say that, didn't he? The girl asked if she could help me and I told her I was still making up my mind and I pretended to look at the price boards. Blind guy. Why did he say that? Soldier-boy. He says it to everyone. Bound to. Wonder if he has any money. How easy it'd be to roll a blind guy and . . . No, I couldn't do that, I wanted to know a few things first. I wanted to talk to the guy, but how to approach him? Definitely take him a coffee or something, but what would I say?

I dry-ran a few exchanges and they were all disastrous: 'I'm sorry for staring at you earlier. Didn't mean to be rude, I was just curious.' '*That was you? Whaddaya mean by trailing me here? Do you want me to call for the Po-lice?*' 'No, don't! I don't mean anything by it. I just got you a coffee to apologise.' '*You stalking me, boy?*' 'No!' '*You gay? Is that it?*'

God, was it worth it? Just mug the fucker and have done with it. Hang on, why don't I distract him from thinking I'm a stranger. Pretending to *be* someone until I'd warmed him up and cooled him down struck me as a sound plan. I'd be a member of staff, that was perfect, and I was thrilled with my idea. I bought two hot coffees, got plenty of sugar, and took the drinks to the guy's table which I got the impression was trying to be as tucked-away as a table can get in McDonald's; and that isn't very.

The guy had taken off his gloves but he was still trussed up with string like a pork joint and had his bonnet on. I sat down and said, 'You know, sir, we don't usually allow customers to just sit without eating or drinking anything.'

'That a fact?' he asked coolly with breath that crackled and

366

smelled like the doorway of a dry-cleaner's. Even though he was facing me, he didn't convince me his eyes were looking at mine. The accent was definitely American, though.

'That a fact?' he said.

'Yeah. Usually,' I emphasised.

'And what *is* your post here, young feller?'

'I'm the manager,' I said. 'Frank.'

'Well now, Frank, if I was to drink one of them two coffees you got there, I guess there wouldn't be a problem no more, right?'

I said nothing while I stared at him under a frown.

'Why do you say I've got two coffees?' I eventually managed to say.

'I can spy 'em, cain't I?' he said. 'Or d'you know different?'

To say that this wasn't a turn I'd been worried the conversation might take isn't to say I wasn't worried when it did. Only that it was more bizarre and out of control than my limited imagination could ever have cooked up.

'No, you can smell it, can't you? God, *I* can smell it.'

'You can smell there's two?' he said in mock sincerity. 'That's good.'

I looked at the two cups and decided no. I probably couldn't do that.

'Well now,' he said. 'We've seen it, we've smelled it, we've felt it and maybe heard it, too. How about we taste it now, since you fetched one of these for me?'

I shoved a cup at him and he ran his finger over the table to find it then took the lid off and blew steams of coffee up his nose.

'*Are* you blind?' I dared to ask him.

'Only in two o' my eyes.'

What was that? A joke? He didn't even smile.

'So why did you say I had two coffees? A guess?'

'Why did I say you got two coffees?' the blind guy analysed. 'I knew you had two coffees. 'Cos if there was one or if there was three or if there was none at all, then I wouldn't of said there was two. Now, level with me, Frank,' he said. 'You ain't no McDonald's manager, right?'

'Aren't I?'

His head shook, 'Uh-uh.'

'Who am I, then?'

'You're the guy who never saw a blind man shaving before an' you tailed him to see what else he could do.'

I always find in stressful moments there's some particular thing I'm looking at that burns itself into my thoughts. I was examining the little hairs on his wrists trying to be curly when he said that. Then I moved to the guy's pink finger-nails on long, black fingers. He wore no rings, no bracelets. No watch.

'Now,' he said. 'Are you the soldier-boy spied at me in the john or ain't you?'

There. He said it again. 'Why do you keep calling me soldier-boy?' I said.

The eyes waved at me again but I didn't wave back. They scanned and swayed over and around me, but never quite hit.

''Cos there's death around you, son. And sadness. You seen your share, Frank, sure as shit, and you caused some of it. Doctor or soldier, take your pick. Soldier's my guess.'

I sat back and soaked up the shock as the energy and rationality blew out of me like the flesh had torn off my bones. He knows I've killed. Who is this guy? I must know him from somewhere; he must know me. Is he talking about Biddy, too? I fixed my eyes on him and stared and stared till they watered but Christ, I didn't know this guy from Adam and he didn't know me. I would've believed it was Haldane dressed and blacked up. But it isn't. Oh, Jesus. Who the fuck was this guy?

'Are you bullshitting me? There's *death* around me? What's that supposed to mean, where is it, how can you see it?'

The guy sipped his coffee calmly.

'You gonna split now?' the blind man said.

'Am I fuck. Do you expect me to?'

'Don't bother me none whatcha do, Frank. Only, y'tell that sorta shit to a lotta candy asses an' hell, they skedaddle forty ways to Sunday. Can't handle the truth, some folks.'

'You mean you do this a lot? God, it's not the truth they

can't handle, mate, it's 'cos you know stuff without them telling you. That is weird. That is *fucking* weird.'

I laughed. One of those nervous, excited hoots. God, I could have been sitting here like a thousand times before, spinning out a Big Mac and getting stared at by some snotty, sauce-faced brat. But instead I've run into Uri frigging Geller. And Christ. I didn't even have any friends to tell about it! No. I didn't believe it. I'd never believed this stuff.

'You smelled the coffee, didn't you? And I bet you can smell me or something, that's how you knew it was me in the bog.'

'That's right, son. In the john I smelled you was a blue ticket soldier-boy, huh?'

Oh. Fuck. Maybe not. 'What's *blue ticket*?' I said.

'You got blue ticketed, didn'tcha? Discharged without honour, Frank.'

Oh God. Oh God. I *do* believe in spooks, I *do* believe in spooks! It just couldn't be happening. No, sir. This reminded me of the day we saw the *Make room for God this Christmas* poster and Biddy thought maybe God was just an ordinary wee feller. Christ, I might believe she was right and the heavenly geezer was sitting right in front of me – if this wasn't some cruel scam. But it probably was.

I watched him feel carefully for his coffee and sip it and I knew that if I wanted to know anything about him, well then I'd have to ask him. So I did so, unashamedly, and he told me he'd been born and raised in Kentucky and that his name was Solomon. Suleiman, I called him sometimes affectionately. Suleiman the Magnificent.

Solomon's voice was worth listening to. It had a Lee Marvin growl in its texture, but sometimes a wheeze for punctuation, and often his face would show what it took his mouth a moment longer to find words for. Kentucky: famous for coal mines, tobacco farms and bourbon whisky stills. All highly inflammatory stuff and no good for the health in its production if not in its consumption.

He told me lots of things. He told me that when he was young he'd dug coal in the towns of Jackson, Wayland and

Hazard high up in the Cumberland Mountains where the Kentucky river is born. That working with those coal-diggers'd showed him how the hipp'potamiss ain't the only animal who sweats blood. About the first time he was taken to Louisville age twelve when Swaps won the Kentucky Derby the first Saturday of May, and how afterwards he went there every year until he lost the use of his eyes. About sitting out of doors at home in Lexington listening, when listening was all he had left, to the blackbirds in the evening and the nightjars catching bugs on the wing and singing 'Chuck-Will's-widow! Chuck-Will's-widow!' About his rebirth from Southern Baptism to Hinduism and the pilgrimage he made to the holy city of Benares, blind and helplessly crowd-squeezed, in the shallows of the Ganges where he hoped his sins would be washed away and perhaps his sight restored. This he told me and more, and the whole time his cloudy eyes twinkled at something inside of him but he never smiled.

He said it all, though, in his Kentucky blackman's accent and I felt proud – not caring if I grinned – that I'd had the fortune to meet such a magical character, stranded and run out of money months ago on his way home from India, at Christmas time in London West Eleven so ordinary, ordinarily, but not today. I actually forgot my troubles for the first time in . . . well, I don't know. Don't know when I was last untroubled but it was a good feeling to be reminded of.

Stephen Knight

A NIGHT OUT

for Katy

An archaeologist
could reconstruct
the evening, stage

by stage, from this –
a crumpled towel

drying on the floor;
a nebula of talc;
and, in the sink,

the tiniest amount
of powdered hair.

*

Left then right foot
up, against the basin,
you shave your legs.

The razor's buzzing
pesters the house.

The water's running.
On its shelf, our wild
asparagus fern drops

star-shaped blossoms
small as crumbs.

*

371

Suds and flowers brush
the taps, the overflow,
your polished skin.

You ease your body
under with a sigh.

The occasional
plop of the soap
opens your eyes.

Curlicues of steam.
Bubbles popping.

*

Late (as usual!)
you rub a porthole
on the mirror: peer.

The towel falls
around your ankles.

Mascara. Blusher.
Wristwatch. Clothes.
One last look. Yes.

In a moment
you'll be gone.

Karl Miller

AUTOBIOGRAPHICAL INTENTS

AUTOBIOGRAPHY HAS BECOME an issue in contemporary
writing. Books which call themselves autobiographical, and
which abound in the first person singular, may well be rated
uncontroversial, though here, too, there can be challenges:
the critic Robert McCrum, himself an autobiographer,
referred recently to 'the now-notorious genre of confessional
autobiography'. But the issue I have in mind arises elsewhere,
and it takes two forms. It arises where there is uncertainty as
to whether or not a given book is to be seen as autobiography, and when a book which is supposed to be about
something, something out there in the world, can also appear
to be a book about its own author. The second sort of book
may be considered covert or disguised autobiography. It may
also, on current form, be considered a lad's book, though, in
a sense expounded by some feminist critics, such writing
might also be considered women's work.

The first of these two forms can't be thought to have made
its appearance only the other day. It is ancient, though
currently controversial. Seamus Deane's admired novel of
recent date, *Reading in the Dark*, is said to have been made
over into a novel at a lateish point – whether for family
reasons or for tactical, publisher's reasons, or for quite
separate authorial reasons. It is a story of betrayal and
mistake, set within the ambience of the Northern Irish
Republican tradition and of Deane's Derry background. It is
also said that when the novel was placed on the Booker Prize
short-list, the judges discussed whether it was a memoir

rather than a novel. My own view is that it fully deserved consideration for a fiction award, and not because it couldn't be true. There would be no way for an unbriefed reader of the novel to be sure that it's robustly autobiographical. It's clear that the novelist knows what he's talking about – but then we expect that of novelists. Novelists don't write out of ignorance. The knowledge in question, however, is one that makes all fiction in some sense autobiographical. I believe myself that impersonality is a bogus claim in literature, and that the kind of demarcation dispute which may have loomed among the Booker judges is likely to prove futile, and is best pre-empted by amnesty, by an act of toleration.

Seamus Deane is not always tolerant of the personal, I might add. Whatever its presence in his novel may amount to, he was willing to condemn Conor Cruise O'Brien's book on Burke as 'disguised autobiography'. The difference of genre might be deemed to make all the difference here. But why should it make *all* the difference? Why, if he gets his facts right, should O'Brien not write about O'Brien in writing about Burke?

Another recent novel, *Never Mind*, by Edward St Aubyn, has in it the sort of suffering boy who is often found to speak for the author of the fiction in which he figures, or to narrate it on the author's behalf. The events of the novel show an atrocious cruelty, an atrocious snobbery. So striking are the events that the outsider mentioned earlier, the unbriefed reader, might wonder whether or not there are family matters here. But the outsider can only guess. Both novels are capable of inspiring the thought that they can hardly be invented – in the sense implied by Isaac Babel when he said that he invented nothing, that all his stories, one way and another, had happened. But neither of the novels is an unmediated piece of 'real life'. They are art, in other words, whether or not they are also autobiography, and it's as well to admit that there is fiction of which this can be claimed only with difficulty, fiction which is brought down by an entanglement with the concerns and demands, ostensibly divorced from the novel in question, of the writer's private life.

The second aspect of this issue of the autobiographical has come to prominence lately as a result of the publication of a group of non-fictional works where a subject not ostensibly the author is treated autobiographically – and in some cases complicitly and fellow-sufferingly – and where there's an affinity to certain types of fiction. One is Nick Hornby's football book, *Fever Pitch*, in which he traces the course of his long obsession with Arsenal Football Club. Hornby has a hard-earned grasp of the game, but the governing tendency of his book is that of a confessional self-portrait. Others are by Blake Morrison and Andrew O'Hagan. Morrison is the author of two books – the first about his father, the second about the murder by two ten-year-old Liverpool boys of the two-year-old James Bulger – in which a confessional element also features. The witnesses at the trial of the two boys falter and fall silent, and Morrison remembers doing the same when he was young: 'I, too, used to dry up and die.' O'Hagan's book is about Britain's disappeared, and about major and minor atrocity and misdemeanour: he too bullied a boy in Ayrshire when he was young. All three writers have been saddled with the idea of laddishness, and the O'Hagan and Morrison's James Bulger book have been seen as marked by autobiographical self-implication or intrusion and by 'me-tooism' – I too have erred or suffered. The 'worst thing' about Morrison's book, one journalist wrote, is that it is less about the three boys than it is 'about Morrison'.

There are two fallacies here. One is that most of these books are laddish, as distinct from being accounts by lads or ex-lads of behaviour which lads go in for. The second is that there is something atrocious about writing a book about atrocity which is also a book about yourself. Atrocity is hard to discuss without going wrong, without occasioning valid objections: but one way of discussing it is to describe its effect on yourself.

Lads imply lasses, and autobiography implies fiction. It seems to me that both halves of this issue of the autobiographical have a good deal to do with what we think of the history of the novel, and of the involvement in that history of questions of gender. Margaret Anne Doody's treatise on the subject, *The True History of the Novel*, is a help here. It attacks the idea of the 'rise' of the novel in the English eighteenth century, the idea of the novel as an Enlightenment thing and a bourgeois thing, and a male thing, an idea which Ian Watt did much to promote, and which has sometimes been collapsed into the working assumption that, in line with its inception, the novel is, or should be, male and rational and realistic. But there were novels long before those examined by Watt, insists Doody. There were novels in the ancient world. And at various times prior to the eighteenth century they were called romantic and stigmatised as female. Doody's book breaks down, as etymology does, the distinction between novel and romance, and does well to remind us that the novel has many characters and many attributes, some of them at odds with one another. Novels are rational and they are emotional. They are realistic and they are romantic. They are written by men and they are written by women. Rational women write them, and so do irrational men. And it can be hard to tell whether a man or a woman has written some unidentified passage of fiction (or indeed non-fiction). The stigma which asserts that novels are the worse for being read and written by women survived the arrival in the world of female novelists of the greatest importance, and it is still current. Embodied in the stigma is this notion of boundary-crossing autobiography or of disguised or intruded autobiography, as a worst thing – as dirt, in the anthropological sense of 'matter out of place'.

Women are autobiographical and emotional, and they have polluted the literary form which they helped to revive and reinvent for the modern world. They have done this by allowing it to show their feelings, to be a vehicle for their avowals and candours. So one story runs, and it is a story for which, in varying degrees, these lads have been made to suffer. Their lads' writings have been condemned by critics with a horror of autobiographical intrusion, who have in effect aligned them with the sort of writing that women have been condemned for producing. Some feminists have argued that it is good for women writers to show their feelings, say who they are, say where they are coming from. This is represented as women's work, though one might want to add that it can be men's work too. In pursuing these arguments, the writers in question are making a virtue of an old reproach, and an attack on the old desideratum of male impersonality and rationality. The old reproach is that women, not men, do it – show their feelings, let them get in the way. Naomi Wolf pointed out not long ago that a double standard has applied here: 'Male writers from Norman Mailer to Edmund White write at great length about their lives, but no one ever says that men's personal experience is a suspect source.' Well, they do say it, and they have been saying it a lot lately, as we have seen: but they have been more inclined to say it about women's personal experience.

It isn't that it can never be right to complain of autobiographical intrusion in contexts not expressly autobiographical. But it is wrong to complain that, in such contexts, autobiography is necessarily intrusive. Where, in general, would we be without it? Something has to have happened to someone for something to be written, though they may not want to say straight out what it was. It can be easier, and less truthful, to try to exclude yourself from an account you are giving than to bring yourself in, and fairness is a more appropriate goal in literature than objectivity or impersonality is. In and out of place, in and out of fiction and of non-fiction, autobiography, with its standing invitation to egotists and amateurs, can go wrong. But so can other genres, even the most august, and the personal accounts currently in vogue and in contention are no advertisement for failure.

Geoff Dyer's *Out of Sheer Rage – In the Shadow of D. H. Lawrence*, published in the spring of 1997, is a personal account which succeeds. At first sight, it seems about to be a meditation on Lawrence, that most personal of impersonalists. But then you notice on the jacket that Geoff's eyes have been inset into the writer's famous bearded face. *Sheer Rage* proves to be a book about them both – 'intermittently' about Lawrence, *passim* about Dyer. The opening pages take you aback with the harpingness of their self-preoccupation. Should Geoff do this, or that? Write his novel, or his book about Lawrence? How best may he contradict himself? But the book soon settles down – which may be more than its author is ever likely to do.

It settles down as a comedy of wanderings and uncertainties which displays Geoff Dyer – a likeable, vexed fellow who hates children, like W. C. Fields, and their parents, and who hates novels, or the way they are now, and who may be only one Geoff Dyer, or a Dyer slivered in dualistic sub-division, for is there not an epigraph here from Barthes which reads: 'It must all be considered as though spoken by a character in a novel'? This is not the only autobiography targeted by the Barthes epigraph, which hints here that we may be about to read a novel. *Sheer Rage* is nevertheless a book which has in it a real man other than its author. Lawrence is 'not like me', the author conveys. But he is like Geoff Dyer too. Each of them is both cross and comic. A benign me-tooism may be glimpsed, which does not efface the other man. Intimately present is the Lawrence of his letters and notes, of his poetry and travel writings, of the snaps that exist of him, the feats of the furious handyman, rather than the Lawrence of the novels, which, apart from *The Rainbow*, Geoff refrained from rereading for his study. So it's not so much a novel as a tribute in kind to a Lawrence on the trot, the fleeting, footloose, note-taking Lawrence. A nomadic book about a nomadic writer.

He peers into his album of Lawrence photographs – sees the bony wrist, the Schiele wrist, of the sick writer (his own wrist is 'thin'), notes his having to wrap up even in the Sicilian sun, mentions his habit of referring to his bronchials, of not mentioning his tuberculosis. Dyer does what you might think difficult – visits the places where Lawrence lived and raises his ghost, while being interesting about what these places are like now. It crossed my mind to wonder how he could afford all these global trips in the footsteps of the master. But then he didn't always go on them, being a changer of his mind. The book ends with bravura accounts of his depressions and hypochondria. Like Geoff Dyer, I travelled to New Mexico in search of Lawrence's shack and grave, and I also found myself able to trade symptoms with him as I rose to the story of his hypochondria – who said that autobiography cuts you off from other people, from your kind? He writes in a way which might suggest that hypochondria – a devotion to symptoms – is modern. Italo Svevo, Woody Allen, also cause you to think this. Something of the sort must be as old as ailing is. And yet Geoff Dyer's book leaves you with the feeling that it's a condition which has come to be associated with autobiographers, but which you might hesitate to attribute to the ailing prince of depressive autobiographers, Boswell.

Lawrence at one point beautifully evoked the landscape he remembered from the years he spent in Nottingham's Walker Street. Dyer takes a dim view, which is also a brilliant one, of the view of the industrial skyscape which he discovered there:

The pavement was grey with cold, the sky was pavement grey. It would have come as no surprise to find that in the local dialect there was a single expression for 'it's getting light' and 'it's getting dark'. If the sky was supposed to serve as a conduit for light then it was no longer working. It turned up on time each day but there was never anything doing. Skies have their history too, remember, and this one was still recovering from the bruising it took in the last century.

This is followed by a riff on beautiful views commanded by ideal places in which to write: 'What they all had in common, these ideal places for working, was that I never got any work done in them.'

As it happens, I am writing this in a place with a beautiful view. I am looking down at an Ionian cove, with a beach where, when there is rain, a stream runs out to sea, through olive groves, beside trees where oranges and lemons hang, as Lawrence might have seen it, like lights. Friends say that this may be where Nausicaa and her women were laundering and playing when Odysseus walked naked out of the foam – a horrendous, and then, after a wash, a god-like spectacle. The site of her father Alcinous' palace may be round the next headland, and Ithaca is just over the horizon. This may or may not be a claim acceptable to scholars specialising in the locations and historicity of the Homeric epics, which are not usually felt to be full of personal impressions based on first-hand observation. But as I sat there watching the waves, I basked in the possibility that even Homer nods by letting in real life, in the shape of something that someone had once witnessed on the ground. The *Odyssey* is both epic and romance, and both epic and romance have been defined in terms of a distance from the domestic realities, the very places, the very laundry-baskets, of the past. But I don't mind telling you that I carried out a close inspection of that beach.

Lachlan Mackinnon

STAYING WITH FRIENDS

The lawn of marital unhappiness,
the big house and the ha-ha,

the scary stabled horse
I knew could kill me with a kick,

would have been grist
to any gossip-columnist,

given the fame
that lapped them all,

but we were children,
lost among the bewildering

tall grasses, quarrels, poppies
and adult silences.

Elegy

(For Caroline Fraser)

                                    Yesterday
I lit a candle for you in the vast
cathedral darkness.
                                        Light,
drained of radiance, changes into space.
A tree stretches but can't get out of it.
Each limb points at its vanishing-point.
                                        Space,
since you died, widened. We are smaller,
more apart in the grey light of 11.30 a.m.
It turns lonely on earth.

Ian Hamilton

INTERVIEWED BY GREGORY LESTAGE

Ian Hamilton (b. 1938) was educated at Keble College, Oxford, where he started a literary magazine and was president of the Oxford University Poetry Society. His publications include biographies of Robert Lowell and J. D. Salinger, three studies of poetry, *The Modern Poet* (1968), *A Poetry Chronicle* (1973), and *Walking Possession* (1994), and two collections of poetry, *The Visit* (1970) and *Fifty Poems* (1988). He is perhaps best known as the editor of the *Review* (1962–72) and the *New Review* (1974–9). He was also Poetry and Fiction editor at the *Times Literary Supplement* (1965–73), and Lecturer in Poetry at Hull University (1972–3). After nearly forty years in poetry, he is one of the genre's few living paladins.

GL: Your criticism is often in the context of shifts and developments in poetic traditions: the retrenchment in 'Englishness' since Auden and with The Movement, the penetration from America of Confessional Poetry in the 1960s. What has happened since the 1960s?

IH: In general, I think there is this continual process of action and reaction throughout the development of poetry. Al Alvarez examined this [in his essay, 'Beyond the Gentility Principle'] with the notion of 'negative feedback'. Eliot wrote about it a lot. You expect poetry of any given epoch to be in a quarrelsome relationship with the epoch that preceded it.

I think I could have probably predicted – and perhaps even did – the Martian phenomenon that came after the kind of stuff I was encouraging in the *Review* and the *New Review*.

383

When I was arguing, as a reviewer and critic, for Lowell and company, I was arguing for a kind of poetry of intense personal experience, a kind of lyric poetry based in individual experience. This excluded the fanciful, the inventive, the narrative. It excluded lots of things, in fact. It got narrower and narrower and narrower in its focus; too narrow in the end. Of poets like Auden and Wallace Stevens, we would have said, 'Oh, they're *thinking* poets; they're *inventing* poets; they're poets who make up things. They're not poets who write out of the sort of visceral intensities we're concerned with.' So, you could have predicted that the next thing would be a resurgence of Auden and Stevens, and I think that Martianism comes out of that. Then you might have predicted the resurgence of narrative or political poetry. The gulf between the idea of poetry as intensely personal and the idea of poetry as a political instrument had become vast. Political poetry had been taken over by the Liverpool Poets or Pop poets or Beat poets. They're the people who wrote sloganeering verse about Vietnam and other hot issues. That wasn't the kind of thing we did. If we were to write about Vietnam, it would have to do with going into a field and picking a flower that would somehow faintly remind us of a look or a gesture that distantly might hint at a war in Southeast Asia. But the poem would be *about* walking in the field. We were very against overtly political poetry. So, you could have predicted that there would have been a sort of coming together of this political role for poetry and non-Pop poetry. You'd get someone like Heaney, for example, who's training is in what you might call 'mainstream', or 'traditional', poetry, but you have a political location and situation in Ireland.

GL: You have written that Heaney was a pivotal figure in shifting poetry from the residual confessioneering left over from the sixties to a resurgence of the impersonal, or antipersonal. He reintroduced 'bardic anonymity', which allows him to address deeply-felt cultural and intensely political issues, such as the mythic and the Troubles, with all of the power and none of the whinging.

384

IH: Exactly. You can't say that he's introverted, self-obsessed, subjective, or narrow because he's got The Subject. And having The Subject gives him the confidence to 'put on the airs', as it were. I don't mean that unkindly at all. Having put on the poetic airs, he can speak in an authoritative poetic voice. I think that one of the legacies of The Movement, which destroyed the poet's bardic self-confidence, was to rob the poet of a sense of his own possible centrality and authoritativeness. Overwhelmingly, their message was that *the poet mustn't take himself too seriously.* So then you've got me and my peers, who were prepared to take our 'selves' seriously, but were not prepared to promote or to send those seriously-perceived 'selves' out into the world to comment authoritatively about things that had nothing to do with us, i.e. society, politics, etc. It always seemed slightly bogus to us to assume authority over issues in those realms. Some authority was ceded as a result of The Movement enterprise because it said, 'you can't write with authority'; 'you can't write like Auden'. In the thirties, Auden had this marvellous authority in writing about 'necessary murder' and about Spain. You simply couldn't have written that way about Vietnam.

GL: In the early seventies, you mediated a symposium in the *Review* entitled 'The State of Poetry', taking measure of poetry and poets of that time. What and who would be the key issues and players in such a symposium today?

IH: I'm a bit out of touch really, but what I see around I don't feel greatly in sympathy with, I must say. I am not sure that those poets who are considered popular now should be proposed as poets to be admired. I don't even know that I could define this period at all. I do feel that poetry's become more of a rag bag – more inclusive, more shapeless, more chatty, more discursive, more of a receptacle for amusing observations. I think that poetry should begin with the kind of intensity and focus and craftsmanship that insists on every line being perfect. Most of what is out there today isn't really poetry. Is the 'New Gen' really about poetry? It might be a form of writing that is engaging and sharp and entertaining, but it is not poetry. It's important to make distinctions: every line doesn't count, every word hasn't been chosen carefully, it doesn't have any structure; there's no reason why this line is broken and that line is not. What we see today is more what poetry *is not* than what it *is*. This is what I am continually struck by. You call this poetry? I think it's something, but I don't think it's poetry.

GL: Your critical persona is detached, avoids camps and schools, and stands back and considers issues of poetry in and out of their own contexts, each with their own strengths and weaknesses. It's a kind of criticism of equilibria. However, one senses a set of standards for poetry.

IH: I think the idea that poetry is still hard to do – that there are some rules – is very important. You can play around with the rules, but you don't just throw it all out. I think that this tendency has to be resisted, particularly in an age of informality. There has to be a way of insisting on form, or directing the attention towards form without finding oneself in that 'why isn't it rhyming, why isn't it scanning?' position. Everything must be ventured in poetry and criticism from an informed position. I think that the reason I liked a book like Lowell's *Life Studies* was that the whole of that tradition could be heard at the back of this seemingly free verse. There is the essential noise of iambic pentameter running under it all. It sounded relaxed, like talk or prose, but you could always hear the rules he was breaking. You could always see the structures he was departing from. I heard and saw it less in Berryman. I always thought there was something slightly bogus about Berryman, I must say.

GL: In your essay, 'Songs Among the Ruins' (1965), you favour the controlled, balanced rage of Plath to the total breakdown of Berryman. You suggest that she exhibits a kind of 'poetic responsibility' in saying that hers is 'the only kind of moral choice that we can now insist on from our poets – the choice of life against death, of the human rather than the brutal, of the reflecting imagination rather than the engulfing nightmare'. In an essay on 'Roy Fuller' (1968), you praised his self-deprecating, but self-aware, sobriety and emotional responsibility as against the mania of much of the period's confessional poetry: 'Guarding against this kind of breakdown is the critic's minimal, but solemn, mission.' This is certainly consistent with the things you've been saying today. From the standpoint of 1997, what is the poet's and the critic's 'mission'?

IH: I think that poetry, increasingly, must define itself, must ask repeatedly 'What is this thing called poetry that makes it a distinct form?' The drift of poetry has been to make itself like other things in order to win audiences or to keep itself alive. So, when you put poems on the Underground, or hold mass poetry 'performances' or 'slams', you're trying to make it like something else, you're trying to make it palatable – effectively making it less than it is, it seems to me. Difficult, complex poetry has become a minority art. There are still things in the best poems that cannot be found in any other form of literary expression. And it's those things which are to do with the shapes and sounds of true poetry. They are to do with concentration and a strange combination of intense feeling and icily controlled craftsmanship. These are the kinds of things that excite me in poems – when I find them. I couldn't get this excitement from a novel or movie or a pop song; it wouldn't be the kind of excitement unique to poetry. I think that it is treasonable for people writing poems and writing about poetry today, in their anxiety to promote what *they* call 'poetry', to lose sight of what poetry ideally is and can be and must be if it is to be worth promoting at all. The drift is that you'll end up promoting and developing something that isn't poetry at all.

GL: As an anthologist and magazine editor, you are conscious of the significance of your function in the formation and preservation of the poetic tradition. In *The Oxford Companion to Twentieth-Century Poetry* (1996), for instance, you state: 'It isn't true that "if it's good it will survive"; someone, somewhere has to keep saying that it's good.' Can you elaborate on this?

IH: I believe what I wrote. This is why one would do

anthologies or edit poetry magazines. Because cultural memories are short, they need to be jogged. As an editor or anthologist, you can both shape the future and protect the past. Best of all, your work can show where the links are, where the continuities are between the past and future.

GL: In the preface to *Poems Since 1900*, you declared that 'anthologies . . . should either be representative or personal'. Are today's anthologies and anthologists fulfilling their responsibilities to poetry?

IH: Today, I think that many anthologies are published chiefly to woo an audience, which they do by finding the lowest common denominator. They sell short the idea that poetry can be and should be difficult and complex. To be able to translate the difficulty and complexity into something meaningful, you must have read other poetry. This allows you to see the merits because you can hear the echoes of and references to other poems. In other words, most poems of the past and most poems of the immediate past have been written by people who have read a lot of poetry – they've got a lot of poetry in their heads. Today, I think many poems are being written by people who have no poetry in their heads. They don't know where their work came from. Maybe they spin off from the Pop scene, maybe they spin off from journalism, maybe they spin off from television, but they don't emerge from or have the support of the poetic tradition. Of this they are largely ignorant. And so you get bad readers. Bad writers produce bad readers. They don't know where they are when you present them with a poem by Hardy or Frost. They're not prepared for the immediate sense of difficulty or strangeness because they have no background in poetry. If it doesn't hit them in the face or make them laugh, it has no value to them. This is the lowest common denominator.

Those who publish anthologies today are worried about making their audiences 'comfortable'. That's the depressing thing about poetry readings, too. Everybody has to throw in a poem that makes people laugh so that everyone can relax and cough and shift around in their seat. So, every hack on the circuit will know that you have to have a poem that makes people laugh. There is something odious about this, about the fact that you have to say, 'OK, I'll read something a little lighter now', and they all perk up, and you throw them out some piece of doggerel, and they all laugh, and then you get back to the grim business of zapping them with your serious subject matter.

GL: You have not been afraid of producing an anthology based on personal taste. You did so with *Poems Since 1900* and inform the reader of that fact in the preface. You choose poems within the tradition that you supported when you were editor of the *Review*. You like poetry of 'intelligent lyricism', poetry that is short, 'concrete' and has 'a purchase on matter'.

IH: The people who have read that book – and there aren't that many – usually like it quite a lot because the poems in it aren't at all obscure. Also, it follows the lyric tradition through, giving it consistency. It is partisan in terms of the poems and poets chosen, leaving a lot of room for argument. But such arguments are necessary. If someone asked me, 'What should I read?', I would still give them that book.

If you're going to engage in the criticism of poetry, you have to be polemical. You have to give a sense of where you are by expressing what you think things *should* be like, who you think has been neglected in the past, which direction you would like poetry to take. In so doing, there are enemies that should be headed off and destroyed: 'Here come some narrative poets: let's stop them in their tracks. Here come some Pop Liverpool poets: let's stop them.' The defensive posture, I think, came out of some strange sense of duty to the poets of the past.

GL: Let's move on to your own poetry. You have suggested yourself as 'a lyric poet of the "miraculous" persuasion' who 'will never grow up'. What do you mean by this?

IH: It's based on the old idea of inspiration, on the 'miraculous' notion that you are visited by poems. If a poem is not there, you will never find it, no matter how hard you look. If it's not there, you can't invent it, however inventive you're feeling. This is a youthful notion. Were you to be a 'grown-up' poet, you would approach the project like this: 'Well, I must write a poem today, and I will write the following sort of thing: I think I'll write a narrative poem about an interviewer's visit to me. I'll include quotations from his questions and observations about his tape recorder. That will be my task for the day.' That would be a grown-up poetry task. This other, slightly more infantile, view is of being seized by poems, of being involved in a kind of miracle as it occurs; there is nothing you can do about it except to make yourself available to it. The approach, I suppose, is Romantic with a capital 'R'.

GL: Your own poetry tempts the Romantic, but keeps a distance. It is deeply personal without being confessional, always risking attachment. In other words, many of your poems are about you, involving and including you, but there is very little sense of '*moi* poetry'. We sense we are in the *presence* of feeling, not an *audience* to it. You use the second-person singular and first-person plural and almost eschew the first person and the third person. Infrequently, but with great power, you have put the confessions into the mouths of others, as in the first-person mother voice in 'Complaint'. But even she is dissociated from the 'I' of her self.

> *And up the road, the man,*
> *My one man, who touched me everywhere,*
> *Falls to bits under the ground.*
>
> *I am dumpy, obtuse, old and out of it.*
> *At night, I can feel my hands prowl over me,*
> *Lightly probing at my breasts, my knees,*
> *The folds of my belly . . .*

Do you feel this detachment, or are you subtly avoiding what Ian Hamilton the critic dislikes about some sixties confessional poetry?

IH: Lowell had this wonderful idea about heartbreak poetry, which is always treading a tightrope, teetering above sentimentality without falling into it. It dared to get that close.

That's been my aim. The concomitant fear is of sentimentality, of toppling over. If you're on the tightrope, you're more concerned with not falling over than you are of running the risk. Using the second-person singular is a device to get control, to establish a distance, to find a way into this experience that doesn't sound self-pitying and maudlin – all the things it could very easily be if you weren't very, very careful.

GL: Why do you think that you tend to use the iamb and to write the short lyric poem?

IH: Iambs are always in one's head. I think I am constantly breaking it up, or playing around with it, or trying to, but it is the essential metre of English speech. We speak, much more than we realise, in iambic pentameter. I am aware of that as being a tyrannical presence, as well, but I don't think I am able to do much about it. Nor could Shakespeare, so what the hell. Maybe the short lyric has been my thing because the Imagist project was quite important to me. I started reading a lot about it then in Pound's early letters and manifestos. He had a problem with poems having a lot of unnecessary furniture. He felt that the poet should get to the heart of the matter, to the maximum point of intensity, and then get rid of the furniture. You don't need, 'And then he walked across the room and opened the door and slapped her in the face'. You want the slap. That's the poetic bit. The other stuff is the narrative lead-up; it might as well be in a novel. One of the difficulties is that the walking across the room and the opening of the door have to be implied. You must give a sense of setting, past events, likely future events.

GL: In your poems about people, about which there are many, you regularly use the images of hands and hair, but very seldom describe a face or a body. The physicality of your subjects is sensed to be there and near, but it is never portrayed or defined.

IH: There is a kind of blurred effect that you go for, even if you want your particulars to be very concrete. The atmosphere that you're in, especially during periods of heightened emotions, can feel blurred like that. Hands, which are the most sensitive instrument of communication, are a strong image, with a great deal of implied meaning.

GL: The poem 'The Forties' seems like an elegy of your previous life, your version of Larkin's 'At Grass', if you will. Not coincidentally, it is the last poem in *Fifty Poems*. You seem to be resigned to another life, pastured in domesticity:

> At forty-five
> I'm father of the house now and at dusk
> You'll see me take my 'evening stroll'
> Down to the dozing lily pond:
> From our rear deck, one hundred and eleven yards.
> And there I'll pause, half-sober, without pain
> And seem to listen; but no longer 'listen out'.
> And at my back,
> Eight windows, a veranda, the neat plot
> For your (why not?) 'organic greens',
> The trellis that needs fixing, that I'll fix.

Is this the case, can we expect more poetry?

IH: I still do write poems and publish them in magazines and reviews from time to time, and in fact I've just brought out a small pamphlet from a private press. At the time of writing 'The Forties', I was feeling both relief and a sense of imprisonment. I thought that maybe I was going for the quiet life once and for all. It didn't work out. I jumped the gun.

GL: Maybe you can just continue applying versions of this poem to the coming stages in your life.

IH: Yes, at sixty-five, 'that trellis that I never fixed', 'that trellis that *you'll* fix', 'that trellis that I'll pay someone else to fix'.

C. K. Stead

SUFFENIA
THE POET

Cleopatra, Helen and the Mother of God
are some of her roles, but also I think Cassandra
truth-teller, deeply regretful, painfully honest
as she reads her lying verses in a lying-down voice
a neck-scarf hiding her wattles, and that painted-on face
the one, she thinks, that launched a thousand ships
but more likely sank them, smiling in the lectern light
saying over and above the words, 'Believe me! Believe!'

Cathal McCabe

KERKENNA

for Justyna Kołaczkowska

I

An olive tree,
alive with electricity,
buzzes at will, intermittently.

A little grey
lizard picks his way
across the wall then rests, for the day.

A fishing boat
might drift into sight,
its (obtuse) triangular sail a delight.

A wonder, too,
the fronds that you
marvelled at, staked out in the blue,

translucent sea
at our door. Amazingly,
a life is lived on this singly

unexceptional ruse,
this wondrous design whose
modest aims have set me thinking, just as

the enig-
matic oil rig,
a Gatsby-light, has intrigued

us now
for weeks. Somehow
the long-legged raft and crew

have again
eluded our pain-
staking watch, again moved on.

The zoukra's
shrill, tireless verve has
drifted through the open windows

night after
night for over
a month, a light, as it were,

left on for those
out all hours in the close
summer night. A mile away the frenzy grows . . .

Arrayed
in sumptuous red
and gold, the child bride

will by now
have removed, in view
of all, her veil and then two

hand-held nap-
kins (this to the whoop-
ing of the crowd) before being snapped

for posterity
with *everyone* in the family.
A celebration! – So why should I see

only glum
nights to come
with the photograph album?

For these
are lives and this
is place, as surely and unceas-

ingly (or so
we like to think) as O-
magh, Leeds, the life we know.

I raise
my glass and the dying rays
across the sound at Sidi Fredj

all join
in turning the wine
from blood to this semi-precious stone.

1 a.m. and pitch
black. Only the milky glimmer of Sfax
like the edge of an all-night total eclipse.

II

But then there has to be time
in which to do nothing but think. I sit on the crumbling wall
of Borj el Hassar, in the blinding glare
of the afternoon, surveying my temp-
orary home, across from the *zone touristique.* A palm
creaks in the night breeze, a gas lamp
fizzes on the ground beside me,
the flies have yet to stir.
The wind kicks up, and all
my good intentions have drifted out to sea.

III

A weird abundance
of hairdressing establishments
in the two-street capital of the islands

broadcast Khaled
's Algerian rap, assorted
pop, and generally sought to raise the dead.

(By the graveyard,
tho', by the fork in the road
at Ouled Kacem, all to be heard

was the sigh
of the sea, a bird and maybe
the diminishing drone of a scooter gone by.)

A waste
of parched palms and dust
ended here – a rugged ride past

doleful donkeys
tethered to trees,
minds intent on the coming breeze.

The lone rocket
of a mosque, a couple of ragged
coffee bars (no chance of a cognac or Ricard

here), two petrol
pumps, a single school,
a bus stop by the one hotel

no brochure
would accommodate – and, sure
enough, you'd want a bar, a pool, the shore.

Sat at the café
opposite, I began to play
with the images I would take away:

a jasmine flower,
its scent and cheer,
tucked behind an old man's ear;

your hands-
ome hennaed hands
and feet (which now, with hinds-

ight, you would have
darker – and then more involve-
d – not to be soaked or sun-burnt off);

a postcard of our
whitewashed den, far
out on a limb of land, and there we are:

now drifting at sea,
now 'victims of hospitality',
now flat-out beneath the weight of the sky;

or now all
ears in the night, in thrall
to the clear, narcotic muezzin-call.

L'étranger
you read in a day
while I watched the sun on our private bay.

At the wat-
er's edge I suddenly thought
how we, too, had our own, distraught,

398

next-door Salamano,
forever shouting 'Salaud!'
at his dog – that I see now as Perez on a solo

run: poor
Kikou, the flagging figure
in the dust in the Renault's rear-view mirror.

THE HARBOUR

We have taken a house above the harbour
Set between land and a glittering sea.
Its walls keep back the foaming rocks
That snap at the heels of returning boats
(They rarely come back before night)
And glisten all day in the sun.

Each morning we stroll on the quay in the sun,
Exploring the whole of the harbour
(Something we can't do at night):
In smells of diesel, fish and sea
We point to the multi-coloured boats
(Every one scraped and scratched by the rocks

And one or two little more than wrecks
Rusting and resting now in the sun).
Freshly-painted bits of boats
Dry on drums. All over the harbour
Scraps of colour: out of the oily, rainbowed sea,
Lemons and oranges shine in a net.

Come 5 a.m., the end of the night,
Will drift out past the moonlit rocks
Arctic Warrior, Margreta M, Girl Beth, Sparkling Sea,
Karima and *Melita* (a name that belongs in the sun),
The children that dived from the harbour
Wall turned now to gulls that laugh by the boats.

Couples come down to admire the boats
Then walk along the beach before night.
That you should harbour
Thoughts of another! Tell me, is our love on the rocks?
The heart is the fiery disc of the sun
Sinking into a chilly sea.

Now we have turned our backs on the sea,
Having lost sight of the last of the boats,
And now that the day has cooled and the sun
Has gone down behind the waves, and the night
Has come up, we have climbed over rocks
And up to the house, from where we look down on the
   harbour

That rocks to sleep the little boats
Thinking perhaps of the sun on the sea,
In the harbour parked for the night.

Charlotte Mendelson

BLOOD SUGAR

'IS IT BECAUSE of the way I put on my tights?'

The remains of three years together lie scattered around the room: CDs of difficult music, small amusing presents, the skirt she thought he liked. Amid the squalor she'd learnt to love he's ended it, suddenly, gently.

Never speak his name again.

Give her a year and some mouth-to-mouth, they say, and there's every chance she will survive. Anna's always valued certainty; now she'd do anything just to know she'll be all right. She's sadder than she'd ever imagined; too sad to hate him, to write mournful poetry, to keep up appearances. She's too sad to wash.

There is always a Bitchwoman. Look across the dance floor and she's got her hand on his shoulder. Invite her to your party and she'll bring him a present too. He thinks she's lovely; you know that's not the point. She's the one you pray he never runs off with, but never guess he will. Bitchwoman is twice Anna's height and half her width. And now he's hers, according to his thoughtful note. It was the only letter Anna didn't keep. It was the first time she cried on the tube.

Granted, the last six months in London had been misery, and quiet calm had never been Anna's forte. But although Bitchwoman has perfect English self-control and a tragic past, Anna's seen her claws, and hopes that he has felt them. She has an ego like broken glass and tits like soggy cupcakes.

Anna knows a thing or two about tits, and there's no question that hers win. Hands down. Months later she'll joke about him choosing her opposite, but how can she believe in a love he could swap for its antithesis?

It seems to Anna they were happy. Or something similar. In a sunny room above the college kitchens they'd fuck lovingly and then feed each other on apples and pulpy Weetabix, which he claims she'll grow to love as sodden as he does. She almost believes him. During essay crisis nights she drinks blackcurrant tea alone, teases her hair into an electric frizz and forages in the muesli for morsels to boost her blood sugar. She hunts raisins to near extinction. In bed together these become the ultimate love-token. They force them on each other in sticky kisses, refusing to be the one who denies the other, their chins glistening with spit and sugar.

Anna learns her taste from his lips. At times she prefers it to his own.

Two years later, she works in London, he works in Cambridge. Their food life has changed. In his new kitchen, the cooking is suddenly adult. He sautés a morning's pay in scallops. Anna stands in London clothes at his table and chops onions with his flat-mate's breadknife. She knows he has flair. She reads the instructions on the box before making tea. He wants to work in a restaurant kitchen and is learning to bone chickens. Every Saturday, while he sells Finnish pancake mix and twelve types of herring in a failing delicatessen, Anna walks around town, hoping to bump into slight acquaintances she's too proud to visit. She reads recipes in W. H. Smith and novels in wintry college gardens. At the end of his eight-hour shift she retrieves him, almost shyly. If Bitchwoman comes for dinner, Anna makes a special effort, while her heart spits. She always wants to go to bed before he does. She waits in his smell under the icy duvet, and tries not to ache. They no longer tongue raisins into each other's mouths.

Once again, food in bed becomes a solitary pleasure. As a

child Anna took provisions upstairs for sleepless summer evenings. With orange segments staining her pillowcase, she read worryingly adult novels and dreamed of being fat and happy in a room filled with jelly. Yet as she looks at her own eight-year-old thighs, she realises that she will not do. For the next eleven years Anna vows each night to eat only carrots, or toast, or vitamins – whatever it will take to lose the curves she senses building slowly in the dark. Failing that, she wants someone to confirm that the side of her breast as she lies on her back, or the scoop of her hip as she lies on her side, really are as perfect as they feel to her guilty palm.

Now Anna reads cookery books before she sleeps, graphic descriptions of Provençal markets and outrageous ancient menus. She cannot imagine how Edwardian honeymooners found room for eleven courses including trifle, but knows she'd like to try. After work she cooks what she knows. In a file she keeps recipes for a possible future: how to make a bloody Mary, bouillabaisse, breakfast for forty, yoghurt. She doesn't buy biscuits and the butter is very old, but she knows she'll never be concave. She can now eat a chocolate without doing penance, but still likes her body much better in the dark.

She never got round to asking him what he thought of the curve of her breast. Maybe she'll make up her own mind about it now.

Anna goes swimming. She waits for the person she thinks she fancies from last time. Without her lenses, she can't see enough to be sure. He's been there in different shorts (or is it two similar looking people?) several weeks in a row. She's almost sure she's sold him a ticket at the theatre where she works. Now the pool is empty. Should she be doing Breaststroke when he appears? She does a few lengths, but her neck gets stiff and the froggy legs aren't very attractive, and her face is unflatteringly submerged in the water. Crawl? She feels Amazonian and sexy but goes red and starts panting after one length. She is afraid it's too focused and unapproachable, and knows she won't hear or see him with the splashing and the great gasps for air. Backstroke? It's elegant and rather St Tropez, but she's terrified of splitting her head open on the edge and sinking bloodily to the bottom. She can't help crossing the pool diagonally every length, and her breasts, while splendidly round and buoyant, are definitely the most prominent thing in the water. She feels as if she's attached to a pair of lifebuoys.

So she decides on Butterfly, which seems to combine forwards-looking with athleticism and dolphin-like grace. Her legs and arms entirely fail to co-ordinate, she swallows three pints of chlorinated water and emerges bright red with half her hair sticking Coco-the-Clown-like out of her cap – face to face with the man, who has just come down the steps with a tall brown girlfriend in bikini and waterproof mascara. She pulls herself up and out of the pool, scraping her knee on the anti-slip mat, and in a studied, elegant gesture she pulls off her cap to reveal tumbling locks of raven hair, but gets it tangled in her expensive goggles and is forced to march to the changing rooms with hair and goggles and cap flapping in a lump on her neck.

Anna, who hates parties, goes to a party. In a tall house in Kilburn belonging to someone's boyfriend, she tries to radiate happy independence. Everyone is pretending they're still students, while emphasising how far they've come. Once she could kiss his navel, choke with laughing, be utterly happy on an ordinary night. Now this is the pinnacle of her week, the best thing she can have. She walks through a room full of lawyers flashing their intellects, and goes in search of food, but it's not that sort of party. She leans against a door frame, and watches to see how her work-mates manage. When one calls to her, Anna walks slowly over, makes a few jokes, doesn't try too hard. She is introduced to a slightly famous musician, and doesn't even flatter him. Leaving early, she tells herself she could get a cat.

The musician rings her at work and asks her out. Anna is so shocked she drops her coffee in the till. For their first date he books dinner at a new restaurant, and tells her to meet him just inside. She only half remembers him from the party. As she looks in through the huge low window, her heart, tense with possibilities, slowly subsides. The man before her is dark and compact: the sort of looks she'd always thought she'd like. His eyebrows are fascinatingly huge. She notices he's wearing the same suit, and obviously knows how to use it. Anna knows she should be flattered. He will be part of her cure: glamorous, foreign, divorced. He is everything That Boy was not.

They sit in a row of couples, none of whom look as good as the staff. The air is thick with libido and ego. Anna wishes everyone would just wear discreet labels giving income bracket and sexual expertise, and leave it at that. The menu features soup cappuccinos and chunks of offal she'd assumed were illegal. They talk of the party, their jobs, the restaurant. She thinks Why don't I fancy you? and Why aren't you trying to seduce me? His mother is an Indian science teacher in Bristol, he hasn't mentioned the divorce, he'll be thirty-nine in April. He is fairly interesting, perfectly amiable, and seems happy to know nothing about Anna, which she finds faintly insulting. After queuing for the loo behind a girl with two agents and a pager, Anna knows she doesn't even want him for his money. She lets him pay, and declines a £15 ashtray as a souvenir. As they leave, she accidentally sets off her rape alarm; the irony is too obvious to mention.

Now Anna stands in the supermarket stroking an aubergine. Her mind is elsewhere. She can't remember if they're supposed to be aphrodisiac, or just can't help the way they look. She doesn't even know if she wants to turn him on, and in less than two hours he's coming to dinner. It seemed a good idea at the time; she'll pay him back, and he might get round to kissing her. Strange to want a kiss and not the person, but after two more dates, and the avidity of her over-excited work-mates, she's had enough. Besides, she can't face another awkward evening wondering if he'll seize his chance as she gets into her taxi.

Novice cooks with limited experience shouldn't offer to feed men with unknown appetites. Thank God she doesn't fancy him, or she'd be lying on the bathroom floor tranquillising herself with Night Nurse and wishing she'd gone for a full body wax. Once again she curses Safeways. Any other supermarket, and she could smudge the edges of something ready-made and claim it for her own, or knock up an insouciant yet manly salad with rocket and wind-dried venison. As it is, her options are limited to frozen cod goujons, scrag end and an enormous range of toilet fresheners. Resolutely, Anna replaces the aubergine, turns, turns back. Ratatouille is a vegetable, she tells herself. I still need meat.

She toys with the thought of roasting peppers and draping them over some chicken. If it's true that all you really need is good ingredients, it might just work. Then she remembers last night's experiment with rollmops and char-grilled carrots. You don't want him, she reminds herself, you just want him to want you. Casual yet sexy, like Debbie Harry – if the food's a disaster you can laugh carelessly and next time he'll bring his toasted sandwich maker and dedicate his next five songs to you.

After ten minutes at the ice-cream section, wishing there was something in the sexual hinterland between Häagen-Dazs and Mini-Milks, she has a burst of conviction. Picking up her basket she hurries to the steaks (braising recommended), the potatoes (baking only) and the Sara Lee Apple Danishes. Yet as she stands in line behind a very tall man buying fourteen loaves of Economy white sliced and a small packet of cress seeds, she lowers her choices to the splotched vinyl and marches swiftly to the nearest exit, heart thumping, where a tiny old woman wrestles her tartan trolley through the automatic doors.

Half an hour later, Anna sits in the cinema eating popcorn, dazed with exhilaration and fear. In an hour he'll knock, and then . . .

She knows she has to end it, prays he doesn't first. That Boy can be her excuse. She fervently hopes that he isn't the reason. On the screen two teenagers exchange chewing-gum and fall in love.

A year later, Anna still goes swimming and to Safeways. But now she too knows a thing or two about antitheses. She's had opposites neither of them had dreamt of. They're a field she is making her own. She's beginning to learn how brave she can be, how much she doesn't know. She's done foreign, she's done famous, she's done very very hairy, and now she's doing something else again. And loving it.

BIOGRAPHICAL NOTES

Julian Barnes was born in Leicester in 1946. He is the author of seven novels, among them *Metroland*, *Flaubert's Parrot* and *A History of the World in Ten and a Half Chapters*, and a collection of essays, *Letters from London*. He is the first Englishman to have won both the Prix Medicis and the Prix Fémina, and in 1988 he was made a Chevalier de l'Ordre des Arts et des Lettres. His work has been translated into more than thirty languages.

Jonathan Coe was born in Birmingham in 1961. He is the author of five novels, *The Accidental Woman*, *A Touch of Love*, *The Dwarves of Death*, *What a Carve Up!* (winner of the John Llewellyn Rhys prize and the Prix du Meilleur Livre Étranger) and *The House of Sleep*. He is currently working on a biography of the British experimental novelist, B. S. Johnson.

Wendy Cope was a London primary school teacher for fourteen years, before becoming a freelance writer. Her collections of poems, *Making Cocoa for Kingsley Amis* (1986) and *Serious Concerns* (1992), both reached the bestseller lists. She has won a Cholmondeley Award and the American Academy of Arts and Letters Michael Braude Award, and is a Fellow of the Royal Society of Literature. She lives in Winchester.

Louis de Bernières was born in 1954, and is now a full-time writer. He is the author of *The War of Don Emmanuel's Nether Parts* (Commonwealth Writers Prize for best first novel, 1991), *Señor Vivo and the Coca Lord* (Commonwealth Writers Prize, Eurasia Region, 1992), *The Troublesome Offspring of Cardinal Guzman* and *Captain Corelli's Mandolin* (Commonwealth Writers Prize, 1995).

Michael Dibdin was born in 1947 and attended universities in England and Canada. He spent four years in Italy where he taught at the University of Perugia, and currently lives in Seattle. He is the author of eleven novels, including *Così Fan Tutti*, *The Dying of the Light*, *Dead Lagoon*, *Dark Spectre* and *Ratking*, which won the Crime Writers Association Gold Dagger Award.

Lucy Ellmann was born in Evanston, Illinois, and came to England in the 1970s as a teenager. Her first novel, *Sweet Desserts*, won the Guardian Fiction Prize and was followed by *Varying Degrees of Hopelessness*. She now lives in Hampshire. Her new novel, *Man or Mango*, will be published by Headline in 1998.

Penelope Fitzgerald won the Booker Prize with her third novel, *Offshore*, which was based on her experience of living with her three children on a barge on the Thames. Two later books, *The Beginning of Spring* and *The Gate of Angels*, were also shortlisted for the Booker Prize. Her most recent book was *The Blue Flower*. In 1996 she was awarded the Heywood Hill Prize for her achievement as a writer.

Ian Hamilton was born in 1938, and lives in London. In the spring of 1998 he is to publish two new books: *A Gift Imprisoned: The Poetic Life of Mathew Arnold*, and *The Trouble with Money*, a collection of new and recent essays.

Georgina Hammick has published two collections of short stories, *People for Lunch* and *Spoilt*, and edited *The Virago*

Book of Love and Loss. Her first novel, *The Arizona Game*, appeared in 1996. She lives in Wiltshire.

Michael Hofmann was born in Freiburg in 1957 and lives in London and Gainesville, Florida. He has published three books of poems; a fourth, *Approximately Nowhere*, is due later this year, along with a book of essays. Among his numerous translations are novels by Franz Kafka, Wolfgang Koeppen and Joseph Roth.

Ted Hughes was born in Yorkshire in 1930 and educated at Cambridge. His publications include *The Hawk in the Rain*, *Lupercal*, *Wodwo*, *Crow*, *Gaudete* and *Winter Pollen*. His *New and Selected Poems 1957–1994* and his *Collected Animal Poems* (4 volumes) appeared in 1995. He has also written extensively for children. He was appointed Poet Laureate in 1984.

Philip Kerr was born in Edinburgh in 1956, and lives in London with his wife and two sons. He is the author of eight novels, and the editor of two anthologies. His most recent novel, *Esau*, is now available as a Vintage paperback. In 1993 he was selected as one of the Best of Young British Novelists.

Matthew Kneale was born in London in 1960. He travelled extensively while at university and, on completing his degree, he spent a year in Tokyo, supporting himself by teaching English. His novels include *Whore Banquets* (Somerset Maugham Prize, 1987) and *Sweet Thames* (John Llewellyn Rhys/Mail on Sunday Prize, 1993). He lives in Oxford.

Stephen Knight was born in 1960. His collections are *Flowering Limbs*, *Dream City Cinema* (both shortlisted for the T. S. Eliot Prize) and *The Sandfields Baudelaire*, a pamphlet of poems about his home town, Swansea. His reviews appear in the *Times Literary Supplement* and *Poetry Wales*.

Hermione Lee is Professor of English Literature at the University of York, and is well known as a critic, broadcaster and reviewer. From 1982 to 1986 she presented Channel 4's first book programme, *Book Four*, and is currently a presenter for BBC Radio Three's *Night Waves*. She has written books on Elizabeth Bowen, Willa Cather and Philip Roth, has edited the work of Stevie Smith, Woolf, Bowen, Kipling and Trollope and has compiled two anthologies of women's short stories, *The Secret Self 1* and 2. Her biography of Virginia Woolf was published by Chatto & Windus in 1996.

Gregory LeStage grew up near Boston, Massachusetts and has an M. Phil. in English from Oxford. After three years of working in finance, he returned to Oxford to pursue a D. Phil. on the British short story and to teach 20th-century literature. His current research includes examining the roles of editors and periodicals in the development of modern fiction. He has compiled two indexes on British fiction and criticism between the wars. Publications include numerous reviews in *The Times Higher Education Supplement* and *The Times Literary Supplement*, as well as journal articles on the subject of poetry. He is president of the Oxford University Poetry Society, has published some poems, and edits the little magazine, *The Reader*.

Kathy Lette achieved succès de scandale as a teenager with the novel, *Puberty Blues*, now a major motion picture. After several years as a newspaper columnist in Sydney and New York and as a television sitcom writer for Columbia Pictures in Los Angeles, her novels, *Girls Night Out* (1988), *The Llama Parlour* (1991), *Foetal Attraction* (1993) and *Mad Cows* (1996), became international bestsellers. Her plays include *Grommits, Wet Dreams, Perfect Mismatch* and *I'm So Happy For You I Really Am*. Recently she has presented *Behind the Headlines* (BBC TV), *01* (ITV), *Envy* (Channel 4) and *Devil's Advocate* (BBC Radio 4).

Andrea Levy was born in England to Jamaican parents. She lives in London. Her first novel, *Every Light in the House Burnin'*, was published in 1994. Her second novel, *Never Far from Nowhere* (1996) was on the long list for the 1996 Orange Prize. She has given many readings and her work has also been broadcast on Radio 4. She was a judge on the Saga Prize and the 1997 Orange Prize for Women's Fiction. She is currently working on her third novel.

Earl Lovelace was born in Trinidad in 1935 and studied at Johns Hopkins University where he has also been Visiting Novelist. He has published plays, poems, short stories, novels, including *While Gods Are Falling* (1965, winner of the BP Independence Award), *The Schoolmaster* (1968), *The Dragon Can't Dance* (1979, which he adapted as a play), *The Wine of Astonishment* (1979) and *A Brief Conversation* (1988, a book of short stories). His most recent novel, *Salt*, appeared in 1996 and won the 1997 Commonwealth Writers Prize. He is currently Visiting Professor at Wellesley College, Boston.

Cathal McCabe was born in Newry, Northern Ireland, in 1963 and grew up in Warrenpoint. Educated at St Colman's College, Newry, and at the Universities of York and Oxford, he taught for many years at the University of Łódź, in Poland. *A Letter from Łódź* appeared from Correspondances des Arts, Łódź, in 1996. He now lives in Warsaw.

Ian McEwan was born in 1948 and is the author of *First Love Last Rites*, *In Between the Sheets*, *The Cement Garden*, *The Comfort of Strangers*, *The Child in Time*, *The Innocent*, *Black Dogs* and *Enduring Love*. Most of his novels have been filmed. He has also written several television plays, including *Solid Geometry* and *The Imitation Game*, the libretto for Michael Berkeley's oratorio, *Or Shall We Die?* and a children's book, *The Daydreamer*. He lives in Oxford.

Lachlan Mackinnon was born in 1956 and educated at

Charterhouse and Christ Church, Oxford. He has written two collections of poems, *Monterey Cypress* (1988) and *The Coast of Bohemia* (1991), two critical studies, *Eliot, Auden, Lowell: Aspects of the Baudelairean Inheritance* (1983) and *Shakespeare the Aesthete* (1988), and a biography, *The Lives of Elsa Triolet* (1992). He reviews regularly for the *Times Literary Supplement* and the *Independent*. In 1987 he received an Eric Gregory Award for poetry.

Patrick Marber was born in London in 1964 and was educated at Wadham College, Oxford. He has written two plays, *Dealer's Choice* and *Closer*, both originally premièred at the Royal National Theatre and directed by the author in 1995 and 1997 respectively. He has also written extensively for television and radio.

Charlotte Mendelson was born in 1972 and grew up in Oxford. 'Blood Sugar' is her first published fiction and she is currently working on a novel. She also reviews for the *Times Literary Supplement*.

Karl Miller was born in Midlothian in 1931 and educated at the Royal High School of Edinburgh and at Downing College, Cambridge. In 1979 he founded the *London Review of Books* and edited it for several years. Before that, he was literary editor of the *Spectator* and the *New Statesman* and editor of the *Listener*. From 1974 to 1992 he was Lord Northcliffe Professor of Modern English Literature at University College, London. His books include *Cockburn's Millennium, Doubles, Authors* and a memoir of his adolescence.

Paul Muldoon's most recent collection of poems was *The Annals of Chile*, which won the 1994 T. S. Eliot Prize. A new collection, *Hay*, is due in 1998.

Bernard O'Donoghue was born in Cullen, Co. Cork, in 1945 and still spends part of every year there. In 1962 he moved to Manchester, and since 1965 he has lived in Oxford where he teaches Medieval English and Linguistics at Wadham College. He has published books on medieval English poetry and on Seamus Heaney, and his three principal volumes of poetry are *Poaching Rights* (Gallery, 1987); *The Weakness* (Chatto & Windus, 1991); and *Gunpowder* (Chatto & Windus, 1995) which won the Whitbread Poetry Prize.

Oliver Reynolds was born in 1957 in Cardiff, where he grew up. After studying drama at the University of Hull, he worked as a playwright. His first book of poetry, *Skevington's Daughter*, was published in 1985; two more followed, *The Player Queen's Wife* (1987) and *The Oslo Tram* (1991). He now lives and works in London.

Ben Rice was born in Devon in 1972 and grew up there. He studied English at Newcastle University and Wadham College, Oxford. He has won several awards for poetry and radio drama including, most recently, first prize in the Cardiff International Poetry Competition for 1997. He holds the 1997 Harper-Wood studentship for English Poetry and Literature from St John's College, Cambridge. He lives in London and is working on a collection of poetry, a book of short stories and a film script.

Kirsty Seymour-Ure was born in Canterbury in 1965, lived and worked until recently in London as a freelance editor and has just moved to the rural Marche region of Italy. Her poems and short stories have been published in a variety of magazines and anthologies. She was a winner in the first two London Short Story competitions and won an Ian St James Award in 1995. She is currently working on a collection of short stories.

Nicholas Shakespeare was born in Worcester in 1957, brought up in the Far East and South America and educated at Cambridge. His work for television includes *The Evelyn Waugh Trilogy* and several documentaries set in Peru. From 1988 to 1991 he was Literary Editor of the *Daily* and *Sunday*

Telegraph. He has written three novels, *The Vision of Elena Silves* (1989, winner of the Somerset Maugham Award), *The High Flyer* (1993) and *The Dancer Upstairs*, which has been translated into twelve languages. In 1993 he was nominated as one of Granta's Best of Young British Novelists. He is currently writing the biography of Bruce Chatwin.

Matthew Singh-Toor was born near Leicester in 1967 and now lives in Brixton. He is currently writing a screenplay and a collection of short stories, works as a freelance subtitler and is completing a Ph.D. at the University of East Anglia. One of his short stories appeared in *New Writing 3*.

C. K. Stead (b. 1932) lives mainly in New Zealand and has published nine books of poetry, seven of fiction and four of criticism, including *Letters and Journals of Katherine Mansfield* and *The Faber Book of South Pacific Stories*. Three of his novels, including *The Death of the Body*, have recently been reissued; *Straw into Gold: New and Selected Poems* appeared in the UK and New Zealand in 1997. He was appointed CBE in 1985.

Frances Stonor Saunders read English at St Anne's College, Oxford, before living in Rome for two years, where she worked at *Associated Press* and *Newsweek*, struggled with the newsroom rule that 'less is more' and failed conspicuously to excel. She also worked for the Pier Paolo Pasolini Foundation, co-editing *Pasolini: A Future Life*. Returning to England, she produced arts documentaries, including the four-part series, *Hidden Hands: A Different History of Modernism* for Channel 4. She is currently writing a history of the CIA's involvement in culture during the Cold War (to be published by Granta Books later this year).

Peter Straughan was born in 1968 in the north-east of England. After working as a professional musician and an actor, he took a first-class degree in Literature at Newcastle University. At this time he also formed his first theatre company and began to write plays. His work, including *Rat, Lorca, A Rhyme for Orange* and *18–12*, has been produced in London and New York. He is currently working on his first collection of short stories.

Adam Thorpe was born in Paris in 1956. He has published two volumes of poetry, *Mornings in the Baltic* (1988) and *Meeting Montaigne* (1990), and two novels, *Ulverton* (1992) and *Still* (1995). He has written three plays for BBC Radio and his first stage play, *Couch Grass and Ribbon*, was performed in 1996. His third novel, *Pieces of Light*, is to be published later this year, and he is currently working on a new poetry collection.

Martin Turner has worked as an educational psychologist for twenty years and as head of psychology at the Dyslexia Institute since 1991. Following his analysis, in *Sponsored Reading Failure* (1990), of declining reading standards among British seven-year-olds, his critique has come to be reflected in public policy. His poetry collection, *Trespasses*, was published by Faber in 1992. Translations, with his wife and others, of the work of the modern Persian poets, Forugh Farrokhzad and Sohrab Sepehri, including a prize-winning version of the latter's *Water's Footfall*, appeared between 1986 and 1992.

Marina Warner is a novelist, historian and critic. Her most recent fictions are *Indigo* (1992) and the collection of short stories, *The Mermaids in the Basement*. Her non-fiction includes *Alone of All Her Sex, Monuments and Maidens* and *From the Beast to the Blonde*, and in 1994 she gave the BBC Reith Lectures on the theme, *Managing Monsters: Six Myths of Our Time*.

Fay Weldon is one of Britain's most influential and prolific writers and has published 20 novels, five collections of short stories, children's books, biography, magazine serials and countless plays for TV, radio and the theatre as well as adaptions of classic novel for the theatre. Her novels, short stories and plays – substantially about the affairs of women and their fraught and frequently frustrating relationships with men – are bestsellers in eleven languages. Perhaps her best-known novels are *The Life and Loves of a She-Devil* and *The Cloning of Joanna May*. Her most recent novel, *Worst Fears*, is published in paperback by HarperCollins

Francis Wheen is a columnist for the *Guardian, Esquire* and *Private Eye*, and a regular broadcaster on BBC Radio 4. His books include *Tom Driberg: His Life and Indiscretions* (shortlisted for the Whitbread Biography Prize) and *The Chatto Book of Cats*. He is working on a life of Karl Marx and lives in Essex.

Stevie White was born in Yorkshire in 1966. After some involvement in the family's building construction firm, Stevie graduated in computing from Lancaster University. Before his first novel, *Boy Cuddle*, was published by Penguin in 1993, he worked as a cycle courier, guitarist and singer in live bands and as a karate instructor. He now develops financial software for the Dodge Group in Surrey. His most recent novel, *Blind Solomon*, is as yet unpublished.

Susan Wicks was born in Kent in 1947 and studied French at the Universities of Hull and Sussex where she wrote a D.Phil. thesis on the fiction of André Gide. She has lived in France, Ireland and the United States. She has published three collections of poems, a short prose memoir, *Driving My Father*, and a novel, *The Key*. She was one of the Poetry Society's 'New Generation Poets' in 1994. Her most recent collection of poems, *The Clever Daughter*, was a Poetry Book Society Choice and shortlisted for the T. S. Eliot and Forward Prizes.